LECTURE AND NOTE-TAKING GUIDE

To Accompany CALCULUS CONCEPTS
2016-2017

Sherry Biggers | Randy Davidson | Jennifer Hanna |
Judith McKnew

CENGAGE
Learning·

Australia • Brazil • Japan • Korea • Mexico • Singapore • Spain • United Kingdom • United States

LECTURE AND NOTE-TAKING GUIDE: To
Accompany CALCULUS CONCEPTS
2016-2017

Sherry Biggers | Randy Davidson | Jennifer Hanna |
Judith McKnew

Custom Project Manager:
Louis Schwartz

Manufacturing & Inventory Coordinator:
Spring Stevens

Premedia Content Project Manager:
Chris Doughman

Intellectual Property Project Manager:
Brian Methe

For product information and technology assistance, contact us at
Cengage Learning Customer & Sales Support, 1-800-354-9706

For permission to use material from this text or product,
submit all requests online at **cengage.com/permissions**
Further permissions questions can be emailed to
permissionrequest@cengage.com

ISBN: 978-1-337-05505-5

Cengage Learning
20 Channel Center Street
Boston, MA 02210
USA

Cengage Learning is a leading provider of customized learning solutions with
office locations around the globe, including Singapore, the United Kingdom,
Australia, Mexico, Brazil, and Japan. Locate your local office at:
www.international.cengage.com/region.

Cengage Learning products are represented in Canada by Nelson Education, Ltd.

For your lifelong learning solutions, visit **www.cengage.com/custom.**

Visit our corporate website at **www.cengage.com.**

Lecture & Note-taking Guide to Accompany Calculus Concepts
An Informal Approach to the Mathematics of Change 5e

Chapter 1   **Ingredients of Change: Functions and Limits**
    1.1   Functions: Four Representations   1
    1.2   Function Behavior and End Behavior Limits   11
    1.3   Limits and Continuity   15
    1.4   Linear Functions and Models   20
    1.5   Exponential Functions and Models   29
    1.6   Models in Finance   36
    1.7   Constructed Functions   43
    1.8   Logarithmic Functions and Models   51
    1.9   Quadratic Functions and Models   57
    1.10   Logistic Functions and Models   63
    1.11   Cubic Functions and Models   69

Chapter 2   **Describing Change: Rates**
    2.1   Measures of Change over an Interval   77
    2.2   Measures of Change at a Point - Graphical   82
    2.3   Rates of Change – Notation and Interpretation   87
    2.4   Rates of Change – Numerical Limits and Nonexistence   92
    2.5   Rates of Change Defined over Intervals   98
    2.6   Rate of Change Graphs   104

Chapter 3   **Determining Change: Derivatives**
    3.1   Simple Rate-of-Change Formulas   115
    3.2   Exponential, Logarithmic, and Cyclic Rate-of-Change Formulas   122
    3.3   Rates of Change for Functions That Can Be Composed   125
    3.4   Rates of Change for Composite Functions   129
    3.5   Rates of Change for Functions That Can Be Multiplied   136
    3.6   Rates of Change of Product Functions   142

Chapter 4   **Analyzing Change: Applications of Derivatives**
    4.1   Linearization and Estimates   146
    4.2   Relative Extreme Points   150
    4.3   Absolute Extreme Points   158
    4.4   Inflection Points and Second Derivatives   163
    4.5   Marginal Analysis   172

Chapter 5   **Accumulating Change: Limits of Sums and the Definite Integral**
    5.1   An Introduction to Rates of Change   179
    5.2   Limits of Sums and the Definite Integral   186
    5.3   Accumulation Functions   193
    5.4   The Fundamental Theorem   200
    5.5   Antiderivative Formulas for Exponential and Natural Log Functions   207
    5.6   The Definite Integral - Algebraically   212
    5.7   Differences of Accumulated Change   218
    5.8   Average Value and Average Rate of Change   223

Chapter 6   **Analyzing Accumulated Change: Integrals in Action**
    6.1   Perpetual Accumulation and Improper Integrals   228
    6.2   Streams in Business   234
    6.3   Calculus in Economics: Demand and Elasticity   242
    6.4   Calculus in Economics: Supply and Equilibrium   250
    6.5   Calculus in Probability (Part 1)   258
    6.6   Calculus in Probability (Part 2)   265

Chapter 7   **Multivariable Change: Models, Graphs, Rates**
    7.1   Multivariable Functions and Contour Graphs   272
    7.2   Cross-Sectional Models and Rates of Change   279
    7.3   Partial Rates of Change   285
    7.4   Compensating for Change   292

Chapter 8   **Analyzing Multivariable Change: Optimization**
    8.1   Extreme Points and Saddle Points   300
    8.2   Multivariable Optimization   304
    8.3   Optimization under a Constraint   313

Calculator Reference

Section 1.1
Enter a function into the equation editor
Evaluate the output value for the function entered in Y1
Re-evaluating a function
Using the equation solver to solve an equation
Finding a second solution
Graphing on a specific domain
Using a graph and the intersect function to solve an equation (an alternate method)

Section 1.4
Entering data
Graphing a scatter plot of the data
Finding and storing a linear function to model data
Aligning data
Trouble-shooting: Restoring a missing column on the list screen

Section 1.5
Finding, storing, and viewing an exponential function

Section 1.6
Using the solver to find the doubling time of an investment
Using the table to find the doubling time of an investment

Section 1.7
Evaluating a function constructed using function composition
Swapping input and output data

Section 1.8
Finding, storing, and viewing a logarithmic function

Section 1.9
Finding, storing, and viewing a quadratic function

Section 1.10
Finding, storing, and viewing a logistic function

Section 1.11
Finding, storing, and viewing a cubic function

Section 2.4
Numerically estimating a rate of change

Section 3.1
Evaluating the derivative function at a point

Section 4.2
Finding relative maximum and relative minimum points
Using critical points as an alternate method for finding relative maximum and relative
minimum points

Section 4.4
Finding both coordinates of an inflection point

Section 6.5
Finding probabilities using the normal probability density function

Section 7.1
Evaluating a multivariable function
Solving a multivariable function to find the value of one of the input variables

Section 7.3
Evaluating a partial derivative at a point

Section 7.4
Evaluating a derivative at a point

Section 8.3
Solving a system of linear equations using matrices

Section 8.3
Determining the nature of the solution to the Lagrange system

Section 1.1: Functions - Four Representations

A **relation** is a rule that links one input value (x) to an output value (y). If any particular input value corresponds to more than one output, the relation is not a function.

A **function** is a rule that assigns <u>exactly</u> <u>one</u> output value (y) to each input value (x). An input value can be referred to as a member of the function's domain; an output value can be referred to as a member of the function's range. **Function notation** $f(x)$ is used to describe a function with input variable x and output $f(x)$.

A function can be represented **numerically** (*in table form*), **algebraically** (*as an equation*), **verbally** (*a description*), or **graphically**.

The **Vertical Line Test** can be used to determine whether a relation satisfies the definition of a function. If there is a vertical line that crosses the graph of a relation in two or more places, then the graph does not represent a function.

Example 1: (CC5e pp. 11-12)

Determine whether each of the following graphs of a relation is also a function. If the relation is not a function, explain why not. (The horizontal axis is the input axis.)

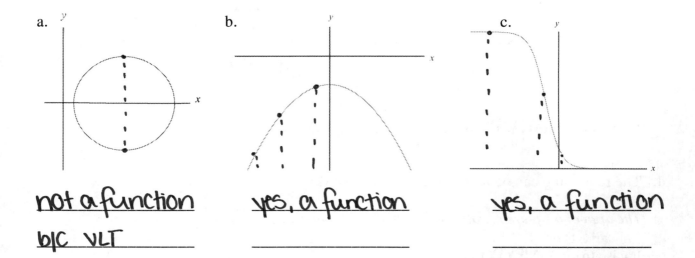

a.   b.   c.

not a function   yes, a function   yes, a function

b/c VLT   _____   _____

Example 2: (CC5e pp. 3-4)

Determine whether the following functions are represented *numerically, algebraically, verbally, or graphically.*

a. The function *g* can be represented by either of the tables shown below.

It has a(n) __numerically__ representation.

t	g(t)
2	18
3	54
4	156
5	435

t	2	3	4	5
g(t)	18	54	156	435

b. The function *g* can be represented by the graph shown below.

It has a(n) __graphically__ representation.

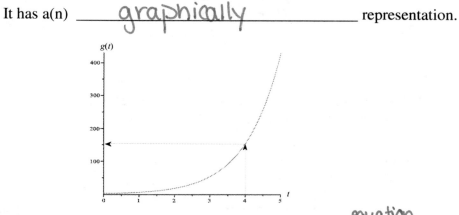

c. The function *g* can be represented as $g(t) = 3e^t - 2t$. *equation*

It has a(n) __algebraically__ representation.

d. The function *g* can be represented by the statement:

The area of a square equals the length of a side squared.

It has a(n) __verbally__ representation.

e. The resident population of the United States between 1900 and 2000 can be modeled as $g(t) = 80(1.013^t)$ million people where *t* is the number of years since the end of 1900.

equation

The function *g* has a(n) __algebraically__ representation.

Example 3: (CC5e pp. 5-6)

$p(t) = 80(1.013^t)$ million people gives the US population, where t is the number of years since the end of 1900, between the years 1900 and 2000.

a. Explain why p is a function. *for each input (year), there is exactly one output (population)*

b. Identify the notation, unit of measure, and description for the input and output.

	Input	**Output**
Notation (variable)	t	$p(t)$ *← function notation*
Unit of measure	years	million people
Description	# of years since the end of 1900	US population

An **input/output** diagram is a drawing that uses a box and arrows to identify the notation representing the input, output, and rule for a particular function.

a function can be thought of as a factory

c. Draw an input/output diagram for p.

d. The ordered pair $(0, 80)$ lies on the graph of $p(t)$. Rewrite the ordered pair using *function notation*.

$p(0) = 80$

applies in general

n this las, all lata is assumed to reference the end of the year

> A **sentence of interpretation** for an ordered pair uses ordinary conversational language to answer the questions *when?*, *what?*, and *how much?*
>> *When?* refers to the input value and does not necessarily involve time.
>> *What?* refers to the output description for the function.
>> *How much?* refers to the output value.

e.   Write a sentence of interpretation for part *d*.

when: In 1900 (at the end of 1900),

what: the US population

how much: was 80 million people.

> Given a function, when an input value is given, the output value is found by evaluating the function at the specified input value.
>
> When an output value is given, the function is used to write an equation which is **solved** to find the necessary input value or values.

Example 4: (CC5e p. 4, p. 6)

Consider the function: $g(t) = 3e^t - 2t$. The input variable to the function is t and the output variable is g.

a.   Find the corresponding output value for an input of 4, using your calculator. In other words, evaluate $g(4)$. Round the answer to 3 decimal places.

$$g(4) = 155.794$$

Using a TI-83/84 calculator, check that the calculator is set to FLOAT and TURN PLOTS OFF:

- **MODE**
  If FLOAT isn't highlighted, hit ▼ (down arrow) **ENTER** to change the mode to FLOAT

- **Y=**
  If Plot1, Plot 2, or Plot 3 is highlighted, hit ▲ (up arrow) on the name of the plot you want to turn off and hit **ENTER**. Repeat if needed.

```
NORMAL  SCI   ENG
FLOAT  0123456789
RADIAN   DEGREE
FUNC  PAR  POL  SEQ
CONNECTED    DOT
SEQUENTIAL   SIMUL
REAL   a+bi   re^θi
FULL   HORIZ   G-T
SET CLOCK 01/02/16 11:16PM
```

```
Plot1 Plot2 Plot3
\Y1=█
\Y2=
\Y3=
\Y4=
\Y5=
\Y6=
\Y7=
```

Enter a function into the equation editor:

- **Y=** (located directly under the calculator screen) opens the equation editor

- Enter the right side of the function equation into Y1 using **2ND LN** [e^x] for e and **X,T,θ,n** for x

- **2ND MODE** [QUIT] returns to the home screen

```
Plot1 Plot2 Plot3
\Y1■3e^(X)-2X
\Y2=
\Y3=
\Y4=
\Y5=
\Y6=
\Y7=
```

```
Plot1 Plot2 Plot3
\Y1■3e^X-2X

\Y2=
\Y3=
\Y4=
\Y5=
```

vars → y-vars → function

Evaluate the output value for the function entered in Y1:

- **VARS ▶** (right arrow) obtains the VARS Y-VARS options

- **ENTER** or **1** chooses **1: Function**

- **ENTER** or **1** chooses **1: Y1**

- **(4)** indicates the input value to be evaluated

- **ENTER** evaluates g at $t = 4$

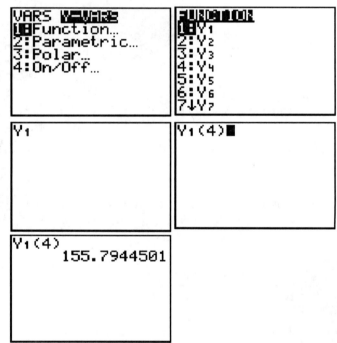

```
VARS  Y-VARS
1■Function...
2:Parametric...
3:Polar...
4:On/Off...
```

```
FUNCTION
1■Y1
2:Y2
3:Y3
4:Y4
5:Y5
6:Y6
7↓Y7
```

```
Y1
```

```
Y1(4)■
```

```
Y1(4)
        155.7944501
```

b. Find $g(9)$. Round the answer to 3 decimal places.

$$g(9) = 24291.252$$

Re-evaluating a function:

- **2ND ENTER [ENTRY]** copies a previous command (that has not yet been deleted)
- Use ◀ to move the cursor over the 4 then change 4 to **9**
- **ENTER** re-evaluates the function

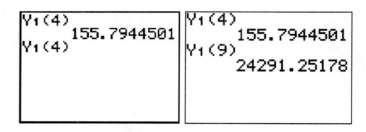

c. Find all input values corresponding to an output of 10. In other words, solve the equation $3e^t - 2t = 10$.

$$g(t) = 10 \qquad 0 = 10 - g(t)$$

need clarification

Using the equation solver to solve an equation: *not fool proof*

- **MATH:SOLVER**   (0: Solver or B: Solver) returns the solver

- ▲ (up arrow) returns the **EQUATION SOLVER** screen

- Complete the equation to be solved so that it reads $0 = Y_1 - 10$

- ▼ (down arrow) returns a new screen

- Position the cursor on the $X =$ line (shown as $X = 0$ in the screenshot to the right)

- **ALPHA ENTER [SOLVE]** returns a solution to the equation

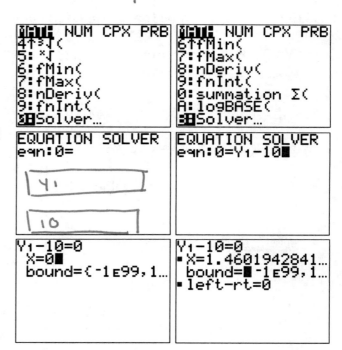

For an equation with only one solution, any value in the domain of the function will return the solution. For an equation with multiple solutions, the solver returns the solution that is closest to the initial x-value provided by the user.

Finding a second solution:

- Use ▲ to return to the $X =$ line and type a different x-value, such as **-2**
- **ALPHA ENTER** returns a second solution

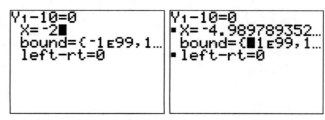

d. Sketch a graph of $g(t) = 3e^t - 2t$ on $-20 \le t \le 5$.

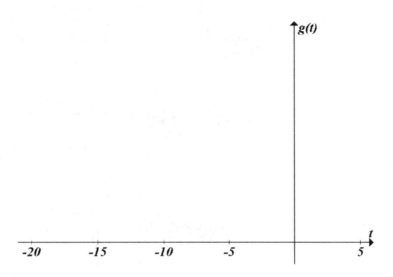

Graphing on a specific domain:

- Set the **WINDOW** (x-values only):
  Xmin = **-20** and Xmax = **5**

- **ZOOM 0** (0:ZoomFit)

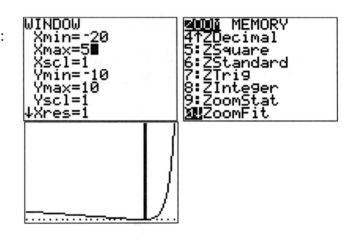

Example 5:

Consider $f(x) = \dfrac{15}{1 + 2e^{-0.5x}}$ on the interval $-10 \le x \le 10$. Solve for the input value that corresponds to output value $f(x) = 10$.

$f(x) = 10$

$-10 \le x \le 10$

$x = 2.773$

2nd trace
intersect   enter
             enter
             enter

7

Using a graph and the intersect function to solve an equation (an alternate method):

- In the Y= list, enter $f(x)$ in Y1 and the output value in Y2

- **WINDOW**

- Xmin=**-10** and Xmax=**10**

- **ZOOM 0** [ZoomFit] returns the graph

- **2ND TRACE 5** [intersect]

- Place the cursor on one of the functions and hit **ENTER**

- Place the cursor on the other function and hit **ENTER**

- Use the ▶ to move the cursor to the intersection point and hit **ENTER**

- **2ND MODE** [QUIT] to return to the home screen

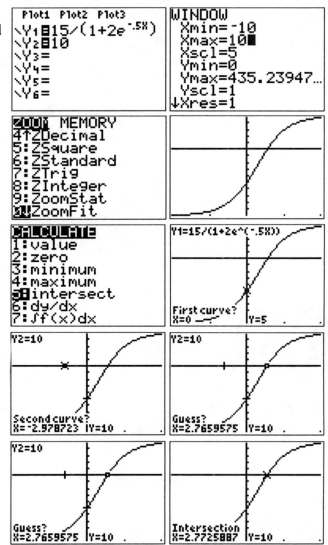

Example 6: (CC5e pp. 5-6)

$p(t) = 80(1.013^t)$ million people gives the US population, where t is the number of years since the end of 1900, between the years 1900 and 2000.

2nd window → table set
indpnt → ask

a. Calculate the values of $p(t)$ for the given values of t. Report the answers correct to three decimal places.

2nd graph

1. calc evaluate using Y.

2. table

t years since 1900	0	20	40	60	80	100
$p(t)$ million people	80	103.581	134.112	173.643	224.826	291.095

b. Use p to calculate the U.S. population at the end of 1945. Include units with the answer.

$t = 45$

$p(45) = 143.059$ million people

c. Write the answer to part b using *function notation*.

$P(45) = 143.059$

d. Write a sentence of interpretation for parts b and c.

In 1945, the US population was 143.059 million people.

e. Sketch a graph of p on the interval $0 \le t \le 100$. Note the variable and unit of measure on each axis.

xmin   xmax

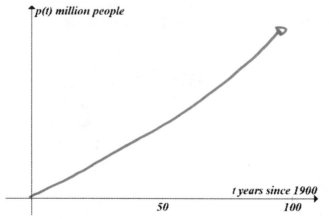

trace

f. According to the function p, in what year did the U.S. population reached 250,000,000 people?

$p(t) = 250$ $t = 88.217$ years after the end of 1900

1989

Example 7: (CC5e p. 10, Activity 17)

Consider the function $t(n) = 15e^{0.5n} - 5n^2$. If an input value is given, find its corresponding output value. If an output value is given, find its corresponding input value(s). Round answers to three decimal places.

a. $n = 3$ vars-function-$Y_1(3)$ $n(3) =$ _22.225_

b. $n = 0.2$ " $n(0.2) =$ _16.378_

c. $t(n) = 200$ $Y_2 = 200$ $n =$ _6.679_

   2nd calc - intersect - enter 3

Example 8: (CC5e p. 10, Activity 25)

Consider the function $t(n) = \dfrac{15}{1 + 2e^{-0.5n}}$. If an input value is given, find its corresponding output value. If an output value is given, find its corresponding input value(s). Round answers to three decimal places.

a. $n = -2.5$ vars function $Y_1(-2.5)$ $t(-2.5) =$ _1.980_

b. $t(n) = 7.5$ $Y_2 = 7.5$ $n =$ _1.386_

c. $t(n) = 1.8$ $Y_2 = 1.8$ $n =$ _-2.599_

   change window

Example 9: (CC5e p. 10, Activity 31)

Consider the function $g(x) = 4x^2 + 32x - 13$. If an input value is given, find its corresponding output value. If an output value is given, find its corresponding input value(s). Round answers to three decimal places.

a. $x = -3$ -73 $g(-3) =$ _____

b. $g(x) = 247$ $x =$ _____ or _____

   -13   5

Section 1.2: Function Behavior and End Behavior Limits

The **direction** of a function is described as:
Increasing if output values increase as input values increase,
Decreasing if output values decrease as input values increase, and
Constant if output values remain the same as input values increase.

The **curvature** of a function is described as **concave up** on an interval where the graph appears as a portion of an arc that opens upward. The curvature of a function is described as **concave down** on an interval where the graph appears as a portion of an arc opening downward. A line has no concavity.

Any point on a continuous function where the concavity changes is called an **inflection point**.

Example 1:

Identify each function as *increasing, decreasing, or constant* on the given interval.

Identify each function as *concave up or concave down* on the given interval.

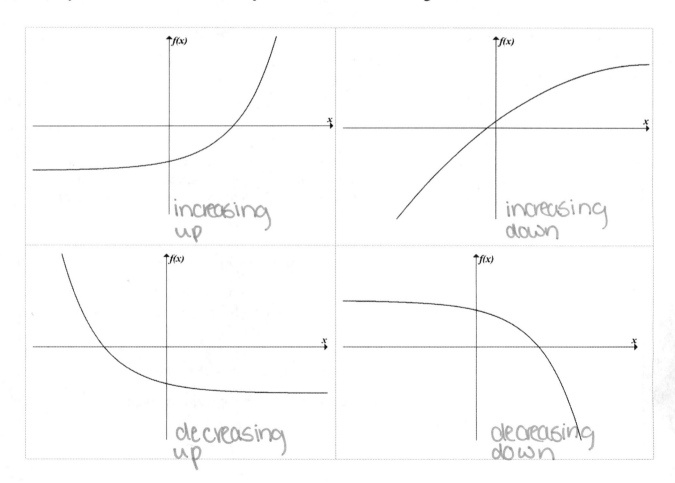

increasing
up

increasing
down

decreasing
up

decreasing
down

Example 2: (CC5e p. 15)

The figure shows the graph of function w that models the number of 20- to 24-year-olds employed full time for years between 2001 and 2008.

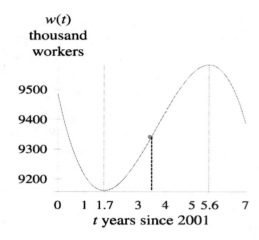

a. State the interval(s) on which w is increasing.

$$1.7 < t < 5.6$$

b. State the interval(s) on which w is decreasing.

$$0 < t < 1.7 \text{ and } 5.6 < t < 7$$

c. State the interval(s) on which w is concave up.

$$0 < t < 3.5$$

d. State the interval(s) on which w is concave down.

$$3.5 < t < 7$$

e. At what input value does w have an inflection point?

$$3.5$$

The **end behavior** of a function describes output values of a function as input values either increase or decrease without bound. It can be estimated by evaluating the function at increasingly large or decreasingly small input values. This process is called **numerical estimation**.

The notation $\lim\limits_{x \to \pm\infty} f(x) = L$ indicates that the output values of a function f have a **limiting value** of L as x increases or decreases without bound. When a function has a limiting value of L, the line with equation $y = L$ is called a **horizontal asymptote**.

The notations $\lim\limits_{x \to \pm\infty} f(x) = \infty$ and $\lim\limits_{x \to \pm\infty} f(x) = -\infty$ indicate that the output values of a function f do not have a limiting value, but instead increase or decrease indefinitely as x increases or decreases without bound.

Example 3: (CC5e p. 18)

The number of credit card holders in the United States can be modeled as

$$C(t) = \frac{29}{1+18e^{-0.43t}} + 158 \text{ million credit card}$$

holders where t is the number of years since 2000, $0 \le t \le 15$.

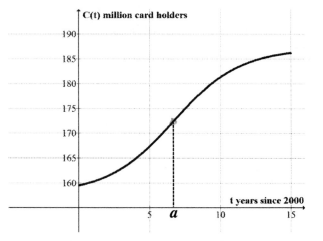
C(t) million card holders
t years since 2000

a. Describe the behavior of C over the intervals $0 < t < a$ and $a < t < 10$ using the terms increasing or decreasing and concave up or concave down.

0 < t < a
→ increasing
→ concave up

a < t < 10
→ increasing
→ concave down

b. How does the behavior of C change at the point with input $t = a$?

changes concavity : inflection point

c. What is the mathematical name for the point with input $t = a$?

inflection

d. Complete the tables, stopping when the end behavior can be estimated. *Show rounding to three decimal places in the table.*

★ be sure to highlight outputs

$t \to \infty$	$C(t)$
10	181.308
30	186.999
90	187
270	187
810	187

$t \to -\infty$	$C(t)$
−40	158
−80	158
−120	158

e. Using *limit notation*, describe the end behavior of C as t increases without bound and as t decreases without bound.

$$\lim_{t \to \infty} C(t) = 187 \qquad \lim_{t \to -\infty} C(t) = 158$$

f. Write the equations for the two horizontal asymptotes of C and draw them on the graph.

$$y = 187 \qquad y = 158$$

13

Example 4:

Using *limit notation*, describe the end behavior of each function as *x* decreases without bound and as *x* increases without bound. How many horizontal asymptotes does each function have?

cubic

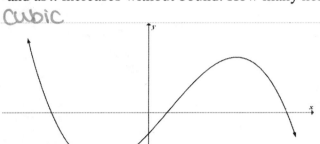

$$\lim_{x \to -\infty} f(x) = \underline{\infty} \; ; \quad \lim_{x \to \infty} f(x) = \underline{-\infty}$$

Number of horizontal asymptotes: 0

exponential

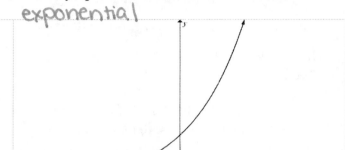

$$\lim_{x \to -\infty} f(x) = \underline{0} \; ; \quad \lim_{x \to \infty} f(x) = \underline{\infty}$$

Number of horizontal asymptotes: 1, y=0

quadratic

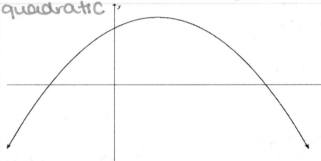

$$\lim_{x \to -\infty} f(x) = \underline{-\infty} \; ; \quad \lim_{x \to \infty} f(x) = \underline{-\infty}$$

Number of horizontal asymptotes: 0

logarithmic

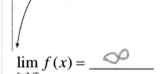

$$\lim_{x \to \infty} f(x) = \underline{\infty}$$

Number of horizontal asymptotes: 0

logistic

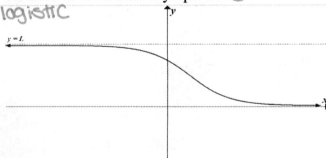

$$\lim_{x \to -\infty} f(x) = \underline{L} \; ; \quad \lim_{x \to \infty} f(x) = \underline{0}$$

Number of horizontal asymptotes: 2,

y=L   y=0

linear

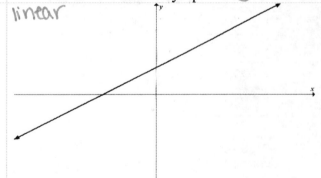

$$\lim_{x \to -\infty} f(x) = \underline{-\infty} \; ; \quad \lim_{x \to \infty} f(x) = \underline{\infty}$$

Number of horizontal asymptotes: 0

14

Section 1.3: Limits and Continuity

HA $\lim\limits_{x \to \pm\infty} = C$

y = C

For function f defined on an interval containing a constant c (except possibly at c itself), if $f(x)$ approaches the number L_1 as x approaches c from the left, then the **left-hand limit** of f is L_1 and is written $\lim\limits_{x \to c^-} f(x) = L_1$.

Similarly, if $f(x)$ approaches the number L_2 as x approaches c from the right, then the **right-hand limit** of f is L_2 and is written $\lim\limits_{x \to c^+} f(x) = L_2$.

The **limit** of f as x approaches c **exists** if and only if $\lim\limits_{x \to c^-} f(x) = \lim\limits_{x \to c^+} f(x) = L$. It is written $\lim\limits_{x \to c} f(x) = L$. Otherwise, the limit of f as x approaches c does not exist.

If $\lim\limits_{x \to c^-} f(x) = \infty \; or -\infty$ or $\lim\limits_{x \to c^+} f(x) = \infty \; or -\infty$, then the graph of f has a **vertical asymptote** at $x = c$.

$\lim\limits_{x \to c^{\pm}} = \pm \infty$ *V.A*

Example 1:

Use the graph of $f(x) = \begin{cases} x^2 - 4x + 1 \; for \; x \neq 1 \\ 3 \; for \; x = 1 \end{cases}$

shown to the right to find the following.

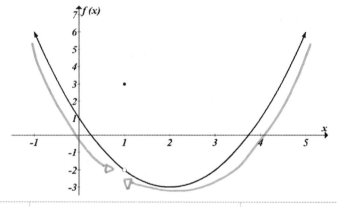

a. $f(1) = 3$

b. $\lim\limits_{x \to 1^-} f(x) = -2$

c. $\lim\limits_{x \to 1^+} f(x) = -2$

d. $\lim\limits_{x \to 1} f(x) = -2$

$x \to 1^-$	$f(x)$
0.9	-1.79
0.99	-1.9799
0.999	-1.99799
0.9999	-1.99979999

$x \to 1^+$	$f(x)$
1.1	-2.19
1.01	-2.0199
1.001	-2.001999
1.0001	-2.00019999

Example 2: (CC5e pp. 23, 26)

Use the graph of f shown to the right to find the following.

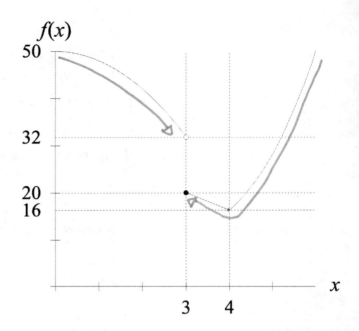

a. $f(3) = $ __20__ $\lim_{x \to 3^-} f(x) = $ __32__

$\lim_{x \to 3^+} f(x) = $ __20__ $\lim_{x \to 3} f(x) = $ __does not exist__

b. $f(4) = $ __16__ $\lim_{x \to 4^-} f(x) = $ __16__

$\lim_{x \to 4^+} f(x) = $ __16__ $\lim_{x \to 4} f(x) = $ __16__ yes

Example 3:

Use the graph of g shown to the right to find the following.

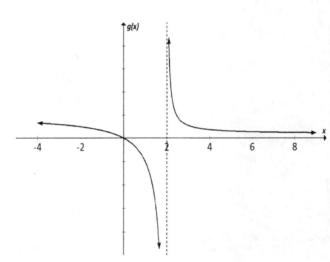

a. $g(2) = $ __undefined__ $\lim_{x \to 2^-} g(x) = $ __$-\infty$__

$\lim_{x \to 2^+} g(x) = $ __∞__ $\lim_{x \to 2} g(x) = $ __does not exist__

b. The graph shows a vertical asymptote. Write its equation.

$x = 2$

A function f is **continuous at input c** if and only if the following three conditions are satisfied:

    (1) $f(c)$ exists ✓

and (2) $\lim_{x \to c} f(x)$ exists ✓

and (3) $\lim_{x \to c} f(x) = f(c)$ ✓

$$\lim_{x \to c^-} f(x) \neq \lim_{x \to c^+} f(x) \qquad \lim_{x \to c} f(x)$$

A function f is **continuous on an open interval** if all three conditions are met for every input value in the interval.

A function is continuous everywhere if it meets all three conditions for every possible input value. Such a function is called a **continuous function**.

Example 4:

a. Answer the following questions about function f in example 1 to determine whether f is continuous at $x = 1$.

Does $f(1)$ exist? $= 3$	Does $\lim_{x \to 1} f(x)$ exist? $= -2$	Does $\lim_{x \to 1} f(x) = f(1)$? $3 \neq -2$
yes	yes	no

Is f is continuous at $x = 1$? no

Why or why not? b/c condition #3 is violated,

$$\lim_{x \to c} f(x) \neq f(c)$$

b. Answer the following questions about function f in example 2 to determine whether f is continuous at $x = 3$.

Does $f(3)$ exist? $= 20$	Does $\lim_{x \to 3} f(x)$ exist?	
yes	no	

Is f is continuous at $x = 3$? no

Why or why not? b/c condition #2 is violated, $\lim_{x \to c} f(x)$ does not exist

c. Answer the following questions about function f in example 2 to determine whether f is continuous at $x = 4$.

Does $f(4)$ exist? =16 yes	Does $\lim_{x \to 4} f(x)$ exist? = 16 yes	Does $\lim_{x \to 4} f(x) = f(4)$? yes
Is f is continuous at $x = 4$? yes Why or why not? b/c all conditions are met		

d. Answer the following questions about function g in example 3 to determine whether g is continuous at $x = 2$.

Does $g(2)$ exist? no, undefined	
Is g continuous at $x = 2$? not continuous Why or why not? b/c condition #1 is violated	

Example 5: (CC5e p. 30, Activities 5 and 6)

Graphically estimate the values for the function f.

a. $f(6) = $ __-1__ $\lim_{x \to 6^-} f(x) = $ __-∞__

$\lim_{x \to 6^+} f(x) = $ __-1__ $\lim_{x \to 6} f(x) = $ __does not exist__

Explain why f is not continuous at $x = 6$.
condition #2 $\lim_{x \to 6} f(x)$ DNE

b. $f(0) = $ __undefined__ $\lim_{x \to 0^-} f(x) = $ __-1__

$\lim_{x \to 0^+} f(x) = $ __-1__ $\lim_{x \to 0} f(x) = $ __-1__

Explain why f is not continuous at $x = 0$.
condition #1 $f(0)$ is undefined

Limits – Algebraically (Optional)

Limit Rules
- The limit of a **constant** is that constant.
- The limit of a **sum** is the sum of the limits.
- The limit of a **constant times a function** is the constant times the limit of the function.
- If f is a **polynomial function** and c is a real number, then $\lim_{x \to c} f(x) = f(c)$.
- The limit of a **product** is the product of the limits.
- The limit of a **quotient** is the quotient of the limits.
- If f is a **rational** function and c is a valid input of f, then $\lim_{x \to c} f(x) = f(c)$.
- If the numerator and denominator of a rational function share a common factor, then the new function obtained by algebraically **cancelling** the common factor has all limits identical to the original function.

Example 6:

Algebraically determine $\lim\limits_{x \to 0} \dfrac{(5+x)^2 - 5^2}{x}$

Example 7: (CC5e p. 29)

Given $d(x) = \begin{cases} x^2 + 2 & for\ x < 4 \\ -3x + 2 & for\ x \geq 4 \end{cases}$

Use the definition of a continuous function to determine whether d is continuous at $x = 4$.

Example 8: (CC5e p. 29)

Given $f(x) = \begin{cases} x^2 + 2 & for\ x < 4 \\ -3x + 30 & for\ x \geq 4 \end{cases}$

Use the definition of a continuous function to determine whether f is continuous at $x = 4$.

Section 1.4: Linear Functions and Models

A **completely defined model** is a statement that describes the relationship between an output variable and an input variable in context. It includes the following:
- an equation
- an output description, with units
- an input description, with units
- an input data range to describe the interval of data used to find the model

Extrapolation refers to the use of a model to predict an output value for an input value that is *outside* the input data range used to obtain the model.

Interpolation refers to the use of a model to predict an output value for an input value that is *within* the input data range used to obtain the model.

A **Linear Function** has an equation of the form $f(x) = ax + b$. Its graph is a **line,** with **slope** a. It has a **y-intercept,** or **initial value,** $f(0) = b$.

A linear function has a constant slope and therefore has a **constant rate of change**.

A sentence of **interpretation** for the **slope of a line** uses ordinary conversational language to answer the questions:
What? refers to the output description for the function
Increased(es) or Decreased(es)?
By how much? refers to the slope, including slope units
When? refers to the domain of the function

incr. a is pos.
decr. a is neg.

Example 1: (CC5e p. 36)

The linear function $r(t)$, giving the resale value of a car t years after it is purchased, is represented graphically in the figure to the right.

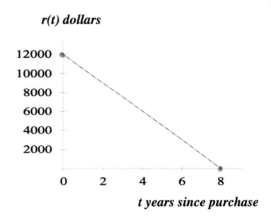

r(t) dollars

t years since purchase

a. Write a sentence of interpretation for the **initial value**.

$t=0 \quad \$12000$

when the car was first purchased its value was $12,000.

b. Write a sentence of interpretation for the point at which the output is 0.

$t=8 \quad \$0$

Eight years after purchase the car has no value.

c. Find the **slope** of the line and write a sentence of interpretation.

$(0,12000) \quad (8,0)$

$$\frac{y_2-y_1}{x_2-x_1} = a$$

$$\frac{0-12000}{8-0} = -1500$$

The car's resale value decreased by $1500 per year on an 8 year period since it was first purchased.

d. Write an equation for $r(t)$.

$$r(t) = -1500t + 12000$$

e. Write a completely defined linear model for $r(t)$.

$r(t) = -1500t + 12000$ dollars gives the value of a car t years after purchase, $0 \le t \le 8$.

Since a linear function has constant rate of change, a linear function should be considered in modeling a set of data that displays constant (or nearly constant) **first differences**. **First differences** are found by subtracting the output values between successive **evenly spaced** input values. For successive data points (x_1, y_1) *and* (x_2, y_2), the first difference is $y_2 - y_1$.

Example 2: (CC5e p. 39-40)

Retail sales in kilowatt-hours (kWh) of electricity to commercial consumers are shown in both the table and scatter plot.

Stat >edit

Year	Retail Sales, in Quadrillion kWh
2003	1.20
2004	1.23
2005	1.27
2006	1.30
2007	1.33
2008	1.35

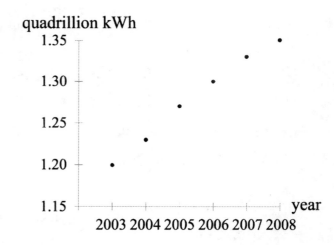

a. View a scatter plot of the data.

Entering data:
Enter the data from the table
into lists L1 and L2.

- **STAT** returns options for editing data in lists L1 and L2.
- **1** (or **ENTER**) chooses **1: Edit** enabling data entry/editing

- If there is data in L1 or L2, use the arrows to move the cursor to L1 and then hit **CLEAR ENTER** to clear the list.

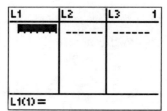

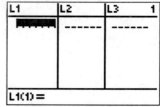

- **2003** enters 2003 as the first input in L1
- **ENTER** (or ▾) moves the cursor to enter **2004 2005 2006 2007 2008**
- ▶ moves the cursor to L2 where output values are entered
- **1.2 1.23 1.27 1.3 1.33 1.35**

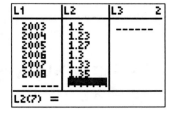

2ⁿᵈ > Stat Plot > ON   L₁ + L₂   Zoom:9

Graphing a scatter plot of the data:

- Use **2ND Y=** [STAT PLOT] **ENTER** to verify that **1: Plot1** is set up as shown in the near right screen
  - **Plot1** is **On**
  - A scatter plot is shown
  - **Xlist = L1** (2nd **1**) and **Ylist = L2** (2nd **2**)
  - The large Mark is selected
  - Make any necessary changes by placing the cursor over the item you wish to select and hit **ENTER**. The selected item should them be highlighted.

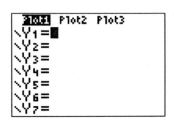

- **Y=** to verify that the Y list is empty (or that any equations are turned off) and Plot1 is turned on.

Note: Plot1 can be turned off and on by placing the cursor on Plot1 and hitting **ENTER**. If there are equations in the Y= list that should not be graphed with the scatter plot, turn the equations off by placing the cursor on each corresponding = and hit **ENTER** to turn off each equation.

- **ZOOM 9** [ZOOMSTAT] to view the scatter plot.

Stat > Calc > 4: Lin Reg

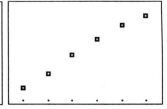

b. Calculate first differences in the data and discuss the amount of concavity suggested by the scatter plot. Verify that it is reasonable to use a linear function to model the data.

Year	2003	2004	2005	2006	2007	2008
Retail Sales, in Quadrillion kWh	1.20	1.23	1.27	1.30	1.33	1.35
First differences		1.23-1.20 = 0.03	1.27-1.23 .04	1.3-1.27 .03	1.33-1.3 .03	1.35-1.33 .02

c. Find a linear function $r(t)$ that best fits the data. View the graph of the linear function and the scatter plot at the same time on your calculator. Write a completely defined linear model. Round coefficients to three decimal places.

$r(t) = 0.031t - 60.604$ quadrillion kwh. gives the retail sales of electricity to commercial customers in year t, $2003 \leq t \leq 2008$.

Finding and storing a linear function to model data:

- **STAT** ▶ [CALC] ▼ to 4 [LinReg] **ENTER** returns LinReg(ax+b) on the Home Screen.
- **VARS** ▶ [Y-VARS] **1** or **ENTER** [Function] **1** or **ENTER** [Y1] selects Y1 as the storage position for the equation.
- **ENTER**
  The equation form as well as the values for the parameters appear on the Home Screen and are pasted into Y1.
- **Y=** to verify the unrounded model is stored in Y1.
- **ZOOM 9** [ZOOMSTAT] shows the graph of the function with the scatter plot.

OR

For TI calculators with Stat Wizard ON:

- **STAT** ▶ [CALC] ▼ to 4 [LinReg] **ENTER** returns the LinReg(ax+b) Stat Wizard screen.
- Xlist: **2ⁿᵈ 1** [L1]
  Ylist: **2ⁿᵈ 2** [L2]
  Store ReqEQ:
- **VARS** ▶ [Y-VARS] **1** or **ENTER** [Function] **1** or **ENTER** [Y1] selects Y1 as the storage position for the equation.
  Put the cursor on Calculate and hit **ENTER.** The equation form as well as the values for the parameters appear on the Home Screen and are pasted into Y1.

Vars > func > Y₁
⟹ Store Reg Eq : Y₁

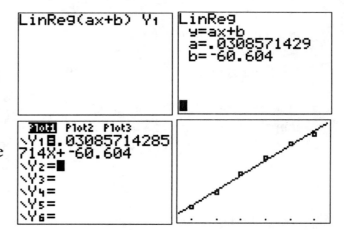

- **Y=** to verify the unrounded model is stored in Y1.
- **ZOOM 9** [ZOOMSTAT] shows the graph of the function with the scatter plot.

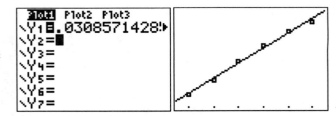

Note: Although equations are generally reported to three decimal places, it's important to use all of the digits found by the calculator when working with the model to reduce the possibility of round-off error as a result of intermediate rounding. The unrounded equation should always be stored in the Y= list whenever a regression equation is found.

d. Write a sentence of interpretation for the slope of the linear model. 0.031

Retail sales of electricity to commercial customers increased by 0.031 quadrillion kwh. per year between 2003 and 2008.

e. According to the model (the unrounded function in Y1), what were retail sales of electricity to commercial customers in 2002? Include units with the answer. Does this use *interpolation or extrapolation?* vars>function> Y_1

$Y_1(2002) = 1.172$ quadrillion kwh.

extrapolation

f. According to the model, what were retail sales of electricity to commercial customers in 2005? Include units with the answer. Does this use *interpolation or extrapolation?*

$Y_1(2005) = 1.265$ quadrillion kwh.

interpolation

g. According to the model, in what year did retail sales first exceed 1.4 quadrillion kWh?

math> solver > $Y_1 - 1.4$ > Alpha>enter

$Y_1(t) = 1.4$

$t = 2009.389$ 2010

h. **Align the data** in the table so that *t* is the number of years since 2000. Find a linear function to model the aligned data (paste it into Y2). Write a completely defined linear model for the aligned data. stat>edit > $L_1 - 2000$

stat > calc > 4: LinReg > Y_2

$r_2(t) = .031t + 1.110$ quad. kwh. gives the retail sales of electricity to commercial customers t years since 2000, $3 \le t \le 8$.

25

Aligning data:

- **STAT ENTER** to edit L1
- Highlight **L1**
- Complete the equation to read
  L1= 2ⁿᵈ 1 [L1] – 2000
- **ENTER**

- **STAT ▶ [CALC] ▼** to 4
  [LinReg(ax+b)] **VARS ▶**
  [Y-VARS] **ENTER** [Function]
  2 [Y2] to find a linear function and
  paste it in Y2.

- **Y=** to verify both functions are stored
  in Y1 and Y2

OR

- **STAT ▶ [CALC] ▼** to 4
  [LinReg(ax+b)]
- Xlist: **2ⁿᵈ 1** [L1]
  Ylist: **2ⁿᵈ 2** [L2]
  Store ReqEQ:
  VARS ▶ [Y-VARS] **ENTER**
  [Function] **2** [Y2]
  Cursor on Calculate and hit **ENTER**
  to find a linear function and paste it
  in Y2.
- **Y=** to verify both functions are stored
  in Y1 and Y2

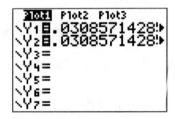

i. Compare the *linear function* in part *h* to the linear function in part *c*. Compare the *input description* and *input data range* for the models in parts *h* and *c*.

t year
2003-2008
3-8
6 years
since
2000

slopes are the same, y-intercepts are different,
input description and input data range are
different

j. According to the model in part *h* (the unrounded function in Y2), what were retail sales of electricity to commercial customers in 2002? Is this the same result as in part *e*?

$Y_2(2) = 1.172$ quad. kwh.

same

26

Example 3: (CC5e p. 45, Activity 25)

The table shows the number of people in North America who use email as a part of their jobs.

Year	Business Email Users, in millions
L₁ -2005	
2005 0	125.2
2006 1	128.7
2007 2	132.4
2008 3	136.0
2009 4	139.8
2010 5	143.6

a. Find a function to model the number of business email users, aligning the data to the number of years since 2005. Write a completely defined model.

$$f(x) = 3.683x + 125.076$$

gives the number of people in North America who use email as a part of their jobs, $2005 \leq x \leq 2010$.

x years since 2005

b. What is the **constant rate of change** of the number of North American business email users indicated by the model? Include units with the answer.

(0, 125.2)
(5, 143.6)

slope: 3.683 # of email users (million people)

$$\frac{y_2 - y_1}{x_2 - y_1} = 3.683$$

million users per year

c. Use the (unrounded) model to estimate the number of North American business email users in 2013.

154.54 million people
.639

d. Is the estimate in part c found by *interpolation or extrapolation*?

extrapolation

Example 4: (CC5e p. 43, Activity 15)

The figure shows a linear function f used to model industrial carbon dioxide emissions.

a. Estimate the slope of the graph.

$(0, 1725)$

$(4, 1850)$

$\dfrac{1850 - 1725}{4 - 0}$

$= 31.25$ million metric tons per year

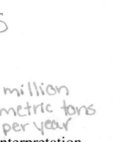

b. Report the slope in a sentence of interpretation.

The industrial carbon dioxide emissions increased by 31.25 million metric tons per year ~~since it was first recorded.~~ between 2004 to 2008

c. Are emissions increasing, decreasing, or constant? How is this reflected in the value of the slope?

increasing
positive slope

Trouble-shooting: Restoring a missing column on the list screen

If delete **DEL**, rather than **CLEAR**, is selected to remove data from one of the lists, the entire list will be deleted.

If the lists are <u>incomplete</u> (*as in the near right screen shot*), restore all lists:

- **STAT**

- **5** selects **5: SetUpEditor**

- **ENTER**

- **STAT ENTER** shows the complete set of lists

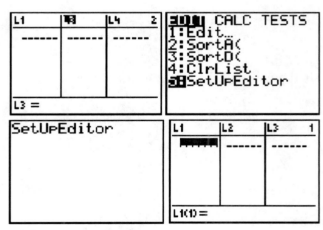

Section 1.5: Exponential Functions and Models

An **exponential** function has an equation of the form $f(x) = ab^x$, with **initial value** a and a **constant multiplier** b.

[handwritten: $\underset{=}{}$ ↑y-int.]

Percentage change between two points of a function $f(x)$ is calculated as

[handwritten left margin: new-old / old]

$$\frac{f(x_2) - f(x_1)}{f(x_1)} \cdot 100\%$$ where $(x_1, f(x_1))$ and $(x_2, f(x_2))$ are two points on the function.

An exponential function has a **constant percentage change**. The **constant percentage change** over one unit input is equal to $(b-1) \cdot 100\%$.

[handwritten right margin: linear func. has constant rate of change →slope]

The graph of an exponential function $f(x) = ab^x$ has **one concavity**, determined by the sign of a:

- for $a > 0$, f is concave up
- for $a < 0$, f is concave down

The graph of an exponential function $f(x) = ab^x$ has a **horizontal asymptote** at $y = 0$. The values of b and a determine the end behavior of f, as x increases without bound:

- for $0 < b < 1$, $\lim\limits_{x \to \infty} f(x) = 0$

- for $b > 1$, $\begin{cases} \text{if } a > 0, \text{ then } \lim\limits_{x \to \infty} f(x) = \infty \\ \text{if } a < 0, \text{ then } \lim\limits_{x \to \infty} f(x) = -\infty \end{cases}$

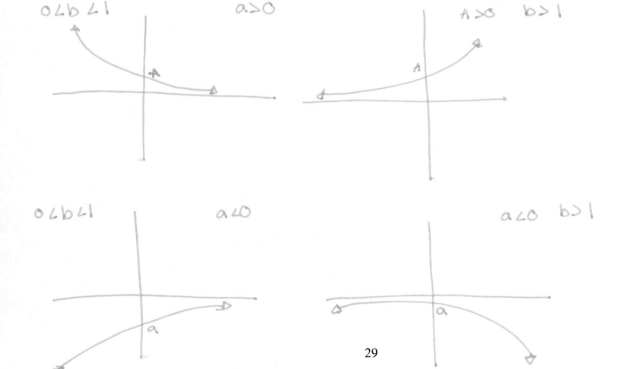

Example 1:

a. Label each of the following graphs as either *increasing* or *decreasing* and as either *concave up* or *concave down*. Complete the limit statements that describe the end behavior.

b. Find the following for the function $f(x) = 3(2^x)$.

 - a = 3   b = 2   (Note that $b > 1$.)

 - percentage change = $(2-1) \cdot 100 = 100\%$

 - Does graph I or graph II look like the graph of $f(x) = 3(2^x)$? I
    $a>0 \quad b>1$

 This is an example of **exponential growth**.

c. Find the following for the function $f(x) = 3(0.35^x)$.

 - a = 3   b = .35   (Note that $0 < b < 1$.)

 - percentage change = $(.35-1) \cdot 100 = -65\%$

 - Does graph I or graph II look like the graph of $f(x) = 3(0.35^x)$? II
    $a>0 \quad\quad 0<b<1$

 This is an example of **exponential decay**.

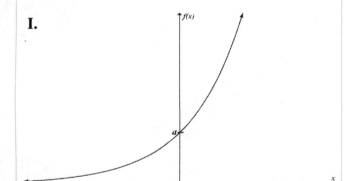

I.

Increasing or decreasing?

Concave up or concave down?

$\lim\limits_{x \to -\infty} f(x) =$ ___0___ ; $\lim\limits_{x \to \infty} f(x) =$ ___∞___

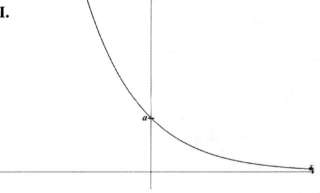

II.

Increasing or decreasing?

Concave up or concave down?

$\lim\limits_{x \to -\infty} f(x) =$ ___∞___ ; $\lim\limits_{x \to \infty} f(x) =$ ___0___

Example 2: (CC5e p. 49)

Apple introduced the iPod in 2001. iPod sales were 7.68 million units in 2006 and increased approximately 9.1% each year between 2006 and 2008.

a. Why is an exponential model appropriate to describe iPod sales between 2006 and 2008?

constant percent change

b. Find an exponential model of the form $f(x) = ab^x$ for iPod sales between 2006 and 2008. Align the input data to the number of years since 2006. (*Aligned input is generally necessary for exponential models.*)

- $a = 7.68$ $b = 1.091$ $(b-1) \cdot 100 = 9.1$

  initial value $(x-1)100 - 9.1 = 0$

                                                       $x = 1.091$

- model: $f(x) = 7.68(1.091)^x$ *million units gives the yearly sale of iPods x years after 2006, our data is from $0 \le x \le 2$.*

c. Use the model to estimate iPod sales in 2010.

$S(4) = 7.68(1.091^4) = 10.881$ *million iPods*

d. Was *interpolation or extrapolation* used to answer part *c*? Explain.

extrapolation, b/c outside range

Example 3: (CC5e p. 54)

According to the Social Security Advisory Board, the number of workers per beneficiary of the Social Security program was 3.3 in 1996 and is projected to decline by 1.45% each year through 2030.

a. Find a model for the number of workers per beneficiary from 1996 through 2030.

$$f(x) = 3.3 \left(.986^x \right)$$ workers per beneficiary of SS program gives # of workers per beneficiary of SS x years since 1996, $0 \le x \le 34$.

$(x-1)\cdot 100 = -1.45$
$(x-1)100 + 1.45 = 0$
$x = \dfrac{}{.986}$

b. What does the model predict that the number of workers per beneficiary will be in 2030?

$$f(34) = 2.043 \text{ workers per beneficiary}$$

Example 4: (CC5e p. 51)

Over the past 30 years, wind power has been harnessed by wind turbines to produce a low-cost, green alternative for electricity generation. The table gives the cumulative capacity in thousand megawatts (MW) for wind power worldwide.

Year	1990	1991	1992	1993	1994	1995	1996	1997	1998
Wind Power thousand MW	1.9	2.2	2.6	3.2	4	5	6	8	10
Year	1999	2000	2001	2002	2003	2004	2005	2006	2007
Wind Power thousand MW	13	18	24	31	40	47	59	75	94

a. Verify that the figure to the right shows a scatter plot of the data.

b. How does the end behavior and suggested concavity of the scatter plot indicate that an exponential function is appropriate for the wind power capacity data?

- end behavior

as x gets bigger, output values increase

x→0 output values are close to 0

- concavity up

c. Align the data so that $x = 0$ in 1990 and find an exponential function to model the data in the table. Write a completely defined model. $L_1 - 1990$ Stat>calc< 0 Exp Reg

$f(x) = 1.608 (1.271^x)$ gives the cumulative capacity in thousand megawatts (MW) for wind power worldwide x years after 1990, data from $0 \le x \le 17$.

Finding, storing, and viewing an exponential function:

- With the data in L1 and L2, **STAT** ▸ [CALC] ▾ to 0 [ExpReg] **ENTER** returns ExpReg on the Home Screen. **VARS** ▸ [Y-VARS] **1** [Function] **1** [Y1] returns Y1 **ENTER** finds and stores the function

  OR

  STAT ▸ [CALC] ▾ to 0 [ExpReg] **ENTER** returns the ExpReg Screen
  Xlist: **2nd 1** [L1]
  Ylist: **2nd 2** [L2]
  Store RegEQ: **VARS** ▸ [Y-VARS] **1** [Function] **1** [Y1]
  Move cursor to Calculate and hit **ENTER**

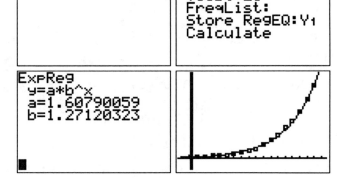

- **Y=** to verify the unrounded model is stored in Y1.

- View the function and the scatter plot at the same time: **ZOOM 9** [ZoomStat]

d. What is the percentage change for the exponential function?

$(b-1) \cdot 100$

$(1.271 - 1) \cdot 100 = 27.1\%$ change

Between 1990 and 2001 world wide wind capacity increased each year by 27.1%

Since an exponential function has constant percentage change, an exponential function should be considered in modeling a set of data that displays constant (or nearly constant) **percentage change.** For successive evenly spaced data points (x_1, y_1) *and* (x_2, y_2),

percentage change is calculated by $\dfrac{y_2 - y_1}{y_1} \cdot 100\%$.

Example 5: (CC5e p. 49)

The data in the table represent the estimated population of northern Canadian cod over a specific range.

Decades (since 1963)	0	1	2	3	4
Population (billions)	1.72	0.63	0.24	0.085	0.032
Percentage Change	$\dfrac{0.63-1.72}{1.72} \cdot 100$ $= -63.372$	-61.905	-64.583	-62.353	

a. Do the percentage changes appear to be nearly constant?

yes

b. Discuss the end behavior and concavity of the scatter plot.

$\lim_{x \to -\infty} f(x) = \infty$ $\lim_{x \to \infty} f(x) = 0$ concave up

c. Write a completely defined model for the data.

$f(x) = 1.722(.369^x)$ gives the pop. of North. Canadian Cod over a specific region x decades since 1963, our data $0 \le x \le 4$.

d. Find the percentage change of the exponential model.

$(.369 - 1) \cdot 100 = -63.1\%$ change

Between 1968 and 1960 the population of Northern Canadian Cod decreased each year by 63.1%.
   decade
          (over a specific region)

34

Example 6: (CC5e p. 55, Activity 21)

The data in the table gives the percentage of MySpace users who are a certain age.

Age (years)	17	19	21	23	25	27	29	31	33	35
Female (percent)	9.6	7.8	6.1	5.1	4.3	3.8	2.4	2.1	1.2	1.1

a. Align the input data to the number of years after 17.   Write an exponential model for the female MySpace user data.

$f(x) = 10.420(.885^x)$ gives the % of female myspace users who are (17+x) years of age; data from $0 \le x \le 18$.

b. Use the model found in part a to find the constant percentage change in the percentage of female MySpace users.

-11.5%

c. What percentage of female MySpace users are 18 years old? 20 years old? Are these answers found using extrapolation or interpolation?

18 yrs old : 9.222% int.   Y₁(1)

20 yrs old : 7.223 % int.   Y₁(3)

Section 1.6: Models in Finance

The **future value** of an investment (or a loan) is given by $F(t)$, where t represents the amount of time since the investment was made (or the loan was taken) in years. P represents the **present value** (called the *principal* of an investment, or *face value* of a loan). The decimal form r of the **annual percentage rate (APR)** is called the **nominal rate** of interest.

Simple Interest
- The *simple interest*, I, accumulated after t years at an interest rate r (in decimal form) on a present value of P dollars is calculated as
$$I(t) = Prt \text{ dollars}$$
- The *future value* in t years, is obtained by adding the interest to the present value
$$F_s(t) = P + Prt = P(1 + rt) \text{ dollars}$$

Compound Interest Investments (n times per year)
- *Compounding* of interest occurs when interest is earned (or charged) on previous interest.

- The *future value* in t years of an investment (or loan) with present value of P dollars is calculated as $F_c(t) = P\left(1 + \dfrac{r}{n}\right)^{nt}$ dollars, where n is the number of compoundings per year, nt is the total number of compounding periods in t years and r is the nominal rate of interest (in decimal form).

t is in years   n=1 annually   n=4 quarterly
                 n=2 semianually   n=12 monthly

Continuously Compound Interest Investments
- *Continuous compound interest* occurs when the number of compoundings in a year, n, is allowed to increase without bound.

- When interest is compounded continuously, the *future value* in t years of an investment (or loan) with present value of P dollars is $F_c(t) = Pe^{rt}$ dollars, where r is the nominal rate of interest (in decimal form) compounded continuously.

Example 1:

Suppose $1,000 is invested at 4.2% APR.

a. What is the (future) value of the investment after 19 months, if interest is **compounded quarterly**?

   i.   Choose the appropriate interest formula to use in this situation: *simple interest, compound interest n times per year, or continuously compound interest.*

   ii. Write the formula for $F(t)$, using the given information.

$$F(t) = P\left(1 + \frac{r}{n}\right)^{nt}$$

   - $P = 1000$ $r = .042$ $n = 4$

   - $F(t) = 1000\left(1 + \frac{.042}{4}\right)^{4t}$

   iii. The shaded cells in the table show the months in which interest is calculated when compounding quarterly. To find the value of the investment after 19 months, evaluate the function after _____18_____ months. Find the future value after 19 months.

1	2	3	4	5	6	7	8	9	10	11	12
13	14	15	16	17	18	19	20	21	22	23	24

$$f(t) = f\left(\tfrac{18}{12}\right) = \$1064.68$$

b. What is the (future) value of the investment after 19 months, if interest is **compounded continuously**?

   i.   Choose the appropriate interest formula to use in this situation: *simple interest, compound interest n times per year, or continuously compound interest.*

   ii. Write the formula for $F(t)$, using the given information.

$$f(t) = Pe^{rt}$$

   - $P = 1000$ $r = .042$

   - $F(t) = 1000e^{.042t}$

   iii. Find the value of the investment after 19 months.

$$f(t) = f\left(\tfrac{19}{12}\right) = \$1068.76$$

Example 2:

Suppose $1,000 is invested at 4.2% APR.

a. Find the time it takes the investment to double, if interest is compounded quarterly.

    i. Write an equation to be solved for *t*. math>solver

$$f(t) = 1000\left(1 + \frac{.042}{4}\right)^{4t} = 2000$$

$$t = 16.5899$$

    ii. Solve the above equation using the calculator's Math Solver or the calculator's Table. To interpret the result, consider the months in which compounding occurs. Answer by stating the number of years and months it takes the investment to reach double its present value.

quarterly,
3, 6, 9, 12, 15...

16 years
9 months

.58999 × 12 = 7.079

Logo up to 9

Using the solver to find the doubling time of an investment:

- **Y= 1000 (1 + .042 /4) ^ (4X)** enters the right side of the doubling time equation for the investment into Y1
- **MATH 0 [SOLVER]** OR **MATH B [SOLVER]**accesses the Equation Solver
- Complete the equation to be solved as 0 = **Y1 – 2000**
- Enter a guess for X, the number of years it will take the investment to double (any positive number will work).
- With your cursor in the X = row, hit **ALPHA ENTER** [SOLVE] to solve.
- Don't forget to consider how often interest is compounded before answering the question.

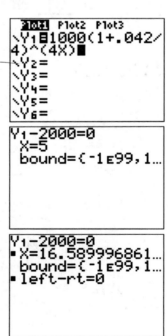

Using the table to find the doubling time of an investment:

- **Y= 1000 (1 + .042 /4) ^ (4X)** enters the right side of the doubling time equation for the investment into Y1

- **2ND WINDOW** [TBLSET] accesses the Table Setup; Use the options as shown in the 2nd screen shot (Note: Δ Tbl = .25 because interest is compounded quarterly)

- **2ND GRAPH** [TABLE]

- Hold down ▾ to scroll down the X column until the value in the Y1 column is at least 2000.

Plot1 Plot2 Plot3
\Y1◼1000(1+.042/
4)^(4X)◼
\Y2=
\Y3=
\Y4=
\Y5=
\Y6=

TABLE SETUP
TblStart=0
▵Tbl=.25
Indpnt: **Auto** Ask
Depend: **Auto** Ask

X	Y1	
0	1000	
.25	1010.5	
.5	1021.1	
.75	1031.8	
1	1042.7	
1.25	1053.6	
1.5	1064.7	

X=0

X	Y1	
15.75	1931	
16	1951.3	
16.25	1971.8	
16.5	1992.5	
16.75	2013.4	
17	2034.6	
17.25	2055.9	

Y1=2013.41498259

b. Find the time it takes the investment to double, if interest is compounded <u>continuously</u>.

i. Write an equation to be solved for *t*. math > solver

$$F(t) = 1000e^{.042t} = 2000$$

$$t = 16.504$$

ii. Solve the equation using the calculator's Math Solver. (The calculator's TABLE is not useful in this case.) Answer in years. Round the answer to three decimal places.

16.504 years

Annual percentage yield (APY) is the percentage change in the value of an investment (or loan) over a one year period. It is used to compare investments or loans.
The decimal form of the APY is called the **effective rate** of interest.

For compounding *n times each year*, $APY = \left(\left(1 + \dfrac{r}{n} \right)^n - 1 \right) \cdot 100\%$.

For compounding *continuously*, $APY = \left(e^r - 1 \right) \cdot 100\%$.

Example 3:

Compare two investments, one offering 4.2% APR compounded quarterly, and another offering 4.15% APR compounded continuously.

a. Find the APY of a $1000 investment with 4.2% APR compounded quarterly.

$$APY = \left(\left(1 + \frac{r}{n}\right)^n - 1\right) \cdot 100\%$$

$$\left[\left(1 + \frac{.042}{4}\right)^4 - 1\right)\right] \cdot 100\% = 4.267\%$$

b. Find the APY of a $1000 investment, with 4.15% APR compounded continuously.

$$APY = \left(e^r - 1\right) \cdot 100\%$$

$$\left[\left(e^{.0415} - 1\right) \cdot 100\%\right] = 4.237\%$$

c. Which is the better investment? A

d. Does the answer to part c change if the principal is $10,000? Why or why not?

No, the principle is not factored into either equations

Example 4: (CC5e p. 60)

An investment at 2.8% APR compounded quarterly has a future value of $5000 payable in five years. Find the present value, the amount that must be invested into this account today to obtain $5000 in 5 years.

a. Write the equation that can be used to solve for P.

$$f(t) = P\left(1 + \frac{r}{n}\right)^{nt}$$

$$5000 = P\left(1 + \frac{.028}{4}\right)^{(4)(5)} = \$4348.91$$

b. Solve the equation using the calculator's Math Solver. Include units with your answer.

$$\$4348.91$$

Example 5: (CC5e p. 61)

Suppose $50,000 is invested at 5% APR. Find the value of the investment after 23 months in various situations. Then find the time it take the investment to double.

Compounding	Formula	Value of t	Future Value	Doubling Time
Annually $F(t) = 50000\left(1 + \frac{.05}{1}\right)^t$ $100,000 = 50000\left(1 + \frac{.05}{1}\right)^t$		12 $t=1$	$62,600	$t = 14.2$ 15 yrs ___ mos
Semiannually $F(t) = 50000\left(1 + \frac{.05}{2}\right)^{2t}$ $100,000 = 50000\left(1 + \frac{.05}{2}\right)^{2t}$		$\frac{18}{12}$	$53,843.53	$t = 14.016$ 14 yrs 6 mos
Quarterly $F(t) = 50000\left(1 + \frac{.05}{4}\right)^{4t}$ $100,000 = 50000\left(1 + \frac{.05}{4}\right)^{4t}$		$\frac{21}{12}$	$54,542.52	$t = 13.949$ 14 yrs ___ mos
Monthly $F(t) = 50000\left(1 + \frac{.05}{12}\right)^{12t}$ $100,000 = 50000\left(1 + \frac{.05}{12}\right)^{12t}$		$\frac{23}{12}$	$55,017.83	$t = 13.892$ 13 yrs 10 mos 11?
Continuously $F(t) = 50000 e^{.05t}$ $100,000 = 50000 e^{.05t}$		$\frac{23}{12}$	$55,028.78	13.863 yrs

(margin notes: 6,12,18, 24... ; 3,6,9,12, 18,21... ; 1,2,3,4... ; 13 yrs 12 months)

Example 6: (CC5e p.59)

A student borrows $1000 at an APR of 4% compounded monthly. What is the future value of the loan if the borrower repays the loan after 1 year? 2 years? 3 years? 4 years? 5 years?

a. Write the formula for $F(t)$, using the given information.

 - $P =$ $r =$ $n =$

 - $F(t) =$

b. Find the future value of the loan at the various times indicated in the table.

Year	0	1	2	3	4	5
Value	$1000					

Example 7: (CC5e p. 61)

Which is better for a borrower, a loan with an APR of 7.2% compounded monthly or a loan with an APY of 7.4%? Compare the effective rates for a one-year loan. Assume all other conditions are equal.

want lower   *APY*

	APR	APY
Loan 1	7.2% compounded monthly	7.442%
Loan 2 → *better*	------------	7.4%

Loan 1: $\left[\left(1+\frac{.072}{12}\right)^{12}-1\right]\cdot 100\% = 7.442\%$

Example 8: (CC5e p. 63)

Consider two investment offers: an APR of 6.9% compounded quarterly (Investment A) or an APR of 6.7% compounded monthly (Investment B).

   a. Determine the better investment by calculating the effective rate (APY) for each.

      • Investment A $APY = \left[\left(1+\frac{.069}{4}\right)^{4}-1\right]\cdot 100\% = 7.081\%$

   better

      • Investment B $APY = \left[\left(1+\frac{.067}{12}\right)^{4}-1\right]\cdot 100\% = 6.910\%$

   b. Compare the time it will take an investment to double for each offer. Which investment doubles more quickly and is therefore the better investment?

$$F(t) = P\left(1+\frac{r}{n}\right)^{nt}$$

      • Investment A

better $t = 10.132$ 10 yrs 3 month $\dfrac{2P}{P} = \dfrac{P\left(1+\frac{r}{n}\right)^{nt}}{P}$

      • Investment B

worse $t = 10.37$ 10 yrs 5 month $2 = \left(1+\frac{r}{n}\right)^{nt}$

$\left(1+\frac{.069}{4}\right)^{4t} - 2$

$\left(1+\frac{.067}{12}\right)^{12t} - 2$

42

Section 1.7:   Constructed Functions

New functions can be formed by combining known functions using **addition, subtraction, multiplication, or division.** A new function can also be formed using **function composition** or by finding the **inverse of a function.**

Terms from Business and Economics:

• **Total Cost =** fixed costs + variable costs, where **fixed costs** are costs that do not depend on the number of units produced and **variable costs** are costs that vary according to the number of units produced. **Cost** (without a modifier) is assumed to be Total Cost unless the context indicates otherwise.

• **Average Cost** $= \dfrac{\text{total cost}}{\text{number of items produced}}$

• **Revenue** $= \left(\dfrac{\text{selling price}}{\text{unit}} \right) \cdot (\text{number of units sold})$

• **Profit** = Revenue − Cost. (Equivalently, Revenue = Profit + Cost.)

• **Break-even point** is the point at which total cost is equal to total revenue, or the point at which profit is zero.

A new model may be created from existing models as long as the input and output units of the functions in the existing models can be combined in such a way that the new function makes sense.

Operation used to form new function:	First check:	Then check:
Addition $(f+g)(x) = f(x) + g(x)$ Subtraction $(f-g)(x) = f(x) - g(x)$	$f(x)$ and $g(x)$ must have identical input descriptions and units for x	If so, then $f(x)$ and $g(x)$ must have identical output units
Multiplication $(f \cdot g)(x) = f(x) \cdot g(x)$ or Division $(f \div g)(x) = \dfrac{f(x)}{g(x)}, g(x) \neq 0$	$f(x)$ and $g(x)$ must have identical input descriptions and units for x	If so, then output units must be compatible
Composition* $(f \circ g)(x) = f(g(x))$	Output description and units of $g(x)$ must be identical to input description and units of $f(x)$	

put g(x) into f(x) (handwritten)

Left margin handwritten notes:
$g(x)$ x = input
$g(x)$ = output
$f \ g(x)$ = input
$f(g(x))$ = output

Function composition is a method of constructing a new function by using the output of one function as the input of a second function.

Example 1: (CC5e p. 66)

The number of student tickets sold for a home basketball game at State University is represented by $S(w)$ tickets when w is the winning percentage of the team. The number of nonstudent tickets sold for the same game is represented by $N(w)$ hundred tickets when the winning percentage of the team is w.

a. Write the input units and description and output units of measure for functions $S(w)$ and $N(w)$.

Function	$S(w)$	$N(w)$
Input units and description	w = winning percentage	w = winning percentage
Output units	S = tickets	N = hundred tickets

b. In order to use **function addition**, the output units of the two functions need to be the same:

$N(w)$ *hundred* tickets could be rewritten as ___100___ $N(w)$ tickets.

c. A new function, T, giving total tickets sold for a home basketball game at State University is modeled as:

$T(w) =$ _$S(w) + 100 N(w)$_ tickets gives the total number of tickets

sold for a home basketball game at State University, when w is _winning_

percentage.

d. Suppose more nonstudent tickets than student tickets are sold for a home basketball game at State University. A new function, D, giving the number by which nonstudent tickets exceeded student tickets sold is:

$D(w) =$ _$100 N(w) - S(w)$_ tickets gives the number by which nonstudent

tickets exceeds student tickets sold, when w is _winning percentage_.

Example 2: (CC5e pp. 67-68)

→exponential

Sales of 12-ounce bottles of sparkling water are modeled as $D(x) = 287.411(0.266^x)$ million bottles when the price is x dollars per bottle.

a. Revenue is a product of _(price per unit) × (# of units)_.

Although only one function, $D(x)$, appears to be defined, a second function that describes the price can be defined as $p(x) = x$.

Write the input units and description and output units of measure for the functions.

Function	$p(x)$	$D(x)$
Input units and description	$x =$ price in dollars per bottle	$x =$ price in dollars per bottle
Output units	$p =$ dollars per bottle	$D =$ million bottles

b. Write a completely defined model for the *revenue* from the sale of 12-ounce bottles of sparkling water.

$R(x) = p(x) \cdot D(x) = 287.411(.266^x)$ million ~~bottles~~ dollars gives the revenue from the sale of 12.oz bottles of sparkling water when the price is x dollars per bottle.

c. Find the revenue if bottles of sparkling water are priced at $2.50 per bottle.

$R(2.5) = \$ 26.221$ million

Example 3: (CC5e pp. 68-69)

The level of contamination in a certain lake is $f(p) = \sqrt{p}$ parts per million when the population of the surrounding community is p people. The population of the surrounding community is modeled as $p(t) = 400t^2 + 2500$ people where t is the number of years since 2000.

a. Write the input and output description and units of measure for functions $f(p)$ and $p(t)$.

Function	$f(p)$	$p(t)$
Input description and units	$p =$ population	$t = $ # of years since 2000
Output description and units	$f =$ contamination level in parts per million	$p =$ population

b. Why do these two functions satisfy the criterion for **composition** of functions?

input description of f(p) = output description of p(t)

c. Which function is used as the input for the new function?

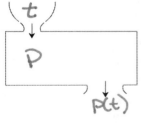

Complete the input output diagrams to demonstrate the composition. Find the new composition function.

d. Write a completely defined model for the new function.

$C(t) = f(p(t)) = \sqrt{400t^2 + 2500}$ parts per million gives the level of contamination in the lake t years after 2000.

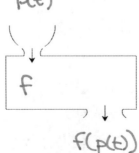

e. Calculate the level of contamination in the lake in 2007.

$$C(7) = \sqrt{400(7^2) + 2500} = 148.661 \text{ ppm.}$$

Evaluating a function constructed using function composition:

- Enter $f(p)$ in Y1 and $p(t)$ in Y2

- Enter $f(p(t))$ in Y3 as **Y1(Y2)**

- Return to the Home Screen
  2nd MODE [Quit]

- **Y3(7) ENTER** evaluates Y1(Y2(7))

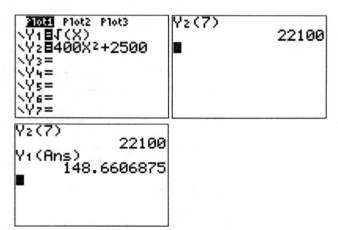

Alternate method: **Use two steps to evaluate a function constructed by composition:**

- Enter $f(p)$ in Y1 and $p(t)$ in Y2 and then return to the Home Screen

- To evaluate $f(p(7))$, first evaluate $p(7)$ by finding **Y2(7)**

- To evaluate f at $p(7)$,
  Y1 (2nd (-) [ANS]) ENTER
  which evaluates Y1 at the previous answer

If the input and output values of a function $f(x)$ are reversed, a new relation is created. If the new relation satisfies the definition of a function, that new relation is called the **inverse function** to $f(x)$.

Example 4: (CC5e p. 70)

Underwater pressure (measured in atm), d feet below the surface is shown in the table below.

Depth below surface, in feet	Surface (0)	33	66	99	132
Underwater pressure, in atm	1	2	3	4	5

a. Verify that $p(d) = 0.030d + 1$ atm (atmospheres) gives the underwater pressure, d feet below the surface of the water, $0 \le d \le 132$.

b. Reverse the input and output data:

Underwater pressure, in atm	1	2	3	4	5
Depth below surface, in feet	Surface (0)	33	66	99	132

c. Find the **inverse** function to the linear function, $p(d)$, and write a completely defined model.

$d(p) =$ 33x -33 ft gives the depth below the surface of the water where p atm is the underwater pressure, $1 \le p \le 5$

Swapping input and output data:

- **STAT ENTER** [Edit…] to view the previously entered data

- With L3 highlighted, complete the equation as L3 = L2 by hitting **2ⁿᵈ 2** [L2]

- **ENTER** copies L2 into L3

- With L2 highlighted, **CLEAR ENTER** clears the data from L2

- With L2 highlighted, complete the equation as L2 = L1 by hitting **2ⁿᵈ 1** [L1]

- **ENTER** copies L1 into L2

- With L1 highlighted, **CLEAR ENTER** clears the data from L1

- With L1 highlighted, complete the equation as L1 = L3 by hitting **2ⁿᵈ 3** [L3]

- **ENTER** copies L3 into L1

- With L3 highlights, **CLEAR ENTER** clears the data from L3

L1	L2	L3	3
0	1	▬	
33	2		
66	3		
99	4		
132	5		
------	------		

L3(1)=

L1	L2	▦	3
0	1	------	
33	2		
66	3		
99	4		
132	5		
------	------		

L3 =L2

L1	L2	L3	3
0	1	▮	
33	2	2	
66	3	3	
99	4	4	
132	5	5	
------	------	------	

L3(1)=1

L1	L2	L3	2
0	▬	1	
33		2	
66		3	
99		4	
132		5	
------	------	------	

L2(1)=

L1	▦	L3	2
0	------	1	
33		2	
66		3	
99		4	
132		5	
------	------		

L2 =L1

L1	L2	L3	2
0	0	1	
33	33	2	
66	66	3	
99	99	4	
132	132	5	
------	------	------	

L2(1)=0

L1	L2	L3	1
▬	0	1	
	33	2	
	66	3	
	99	4	
	132	5	
------	------	------	

L1(1)=

▦	L2	L3	1
------	0	1	
	33	2	
	66	3	
	99	4	
	132	5	
------	------		

L1 =L3

L1	L2	L3	1
▮	0	1	
2	33	2	
3	66	3	
4	99	4	
5	132	5	
------	------	------	

L1(1)=1

L1	L2	L3	3
1	0	▬	
2	33		
3	66		
4	99		
5	132		
------	------		

L3(1)=

A **horizontal line test** can be used to determine graphically whether a function is *one-to-one*. A one-to-one function is a function for which every output value corresponds to exactly one input value.

If a function is one-to-one, then it has an **inverse function**.

If $f(x)$ and $g(x)$ are inverse functions, then $f\big(g(x)\big) = x$ and $g\big(f(x)\big) = x$

Example 5: (CC5e p. 69)

I.

II.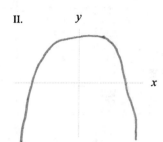

III.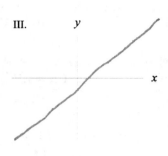

a. Use the horizontal line test to determine which of the functions shown above are one-to-one.

I, III

b. Which of the functions have an inverse function?

I, III

Example 6:

Show that $p(x) = \dfrac{1}{33}x + 1$ and $d(x) = 33x - 33$ are inverse functions.

a. $p(d(x)) =$

b. $d(p(x)) =$

Section 1.8: Logarithmic Functions and Models

A **logarithmic function** has an equation of the form $f(x) = a + b \ln x$, where a and $b \neq 0$ are constants, and input values $x > 0$.

The graph of a logarithmic function $f(x) = a + b \ln x$ is an **inverse** function to an exponential function. It has **one concavity**, determined by the sign of b:

- for $b < 0$, f is concave up
- for $b > 0$, f is concave down

The graph of $f(x) = a + b \ln x$ has a **vertical asymptote** at $x = 0$.

As x increases without bound, output values show an increasingly slow increase or decrease.

- for $b < 0$, $\lim\limits_{x \to \infty} f(x) = -\infty$
- for $b > 0$, $\lim\limits_{x \to \infty} f(x) = \infty$

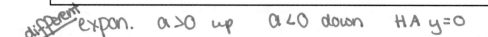 different expon.   a>0 up   a<0 down   HA y=0

Example 1:

a. Label each of the following graphs of $y = a + b\ln(x)$ as either *increasing* or *decreasing* and as either *concave up* or *concave down*. Complete the limit statements that describe the end behavior.

b. Find the following for the function $f(x) = -1 + \ln x$.

- a = -1 b = 1 (Note that $b > 0$.)

- Does graph I or graph II look like the graph of $f(x) = -1 + \ln x$?

    I

c. Find the following for the function $f(x) = 1 - \ln x$.

- a = 1 b = -1 (Note that $b < 0$.)

- Does graph I or graph II look like the graph of $f(x) = 1 - \ln x$?

    II

I.

$b > 0$

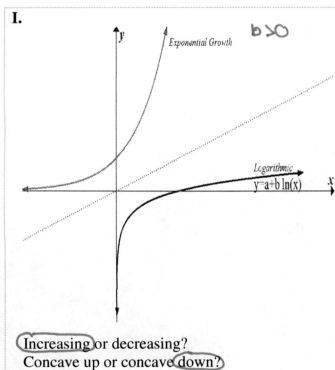

Increasing or decreasing?
Concave up or concave down?
$\lim\limits_{x \to 0^+} f(x) = -\infty$; $\lim\limits_{x \to \infty} f(x) = +\infty$

II.

$b < 0$

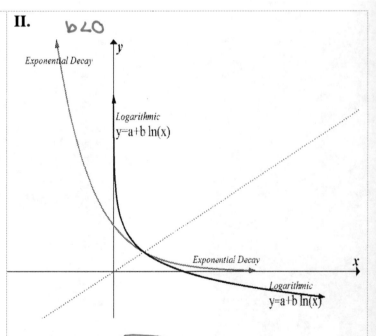

Increasing or decreasing?
Concave up or concave down?
$\lim\limits_{x \to 0^+} f(x) = \infty$; $\lim\limits_{x \to \infty} f(x) = -\infty$

Example 2: (CC5e p. 78)

The outer ear in humans continues to grow throughout life even when other organs have stopped growing. The table shows the average length of the outer ear for men at different ages.

Age, in years	0 (at birth)	20	70
Age + 10	10	30	80
Outer Ear Length, in inches	2.04	2.55	3.07

a. Find a scatter plot for the data given in the table.

b. How does the suggested concavity of the scatter plot indicate that a logarithmic function is appropriate for modeling human male outer ear length?

increasing
concave down

c. **Since 0 cannot be used for input in a logarithmic equation**, the input data must be aligned. Complete the second row of the table.

Stat > Calc > 9: Ln Reg

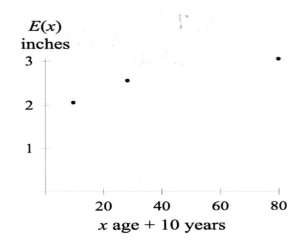

d. Find the logarithmic function to model the aligned data. Is it a good fit? __yes__ (yes/no) Complete the model below, paying attention to the input description.

$E(x) =$ __0.890 + 0.495 ln x__ inches is the average outer ear length for human males, where $x - 10$ is the age in years, $10 \le x \le 80$.

Finding, storing, and viewing a logarithmic function:

- With the aligned data in L1 and L2, **STAT** ▸ [CALC] ▾ to 9 [LnReg] **ENTER** returns LnReg on the Home Screen. **VARS** ▸ [Y-VARS] **1** [Function] **1** [Y1] returns Y₁ **ENTER**

  OR

  Xlist: **2ⁿᵈ 1** [L1]
  Ylist: **2ⁿᵈ 2** [L2]
  Store RegEQ: **VARS** ▸ [Y-VARS] **1** [Function] **1** [Y1]
  Move cursor to Calculate and hit **ENTER**
- Hit **ZOOM 9** [ZoomStat] to view the function and the scatter plot

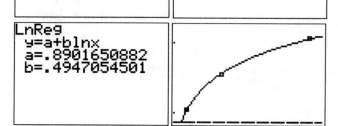

e. Use the (unrounded) model found in part d to find the average outer ear length for 60-year-old men.

$Y_1(60)$

~~annun~~   2.992

Examples 3: (CC5e p. 77, 79)

A pressure altimeter determines altitude in thousand feet by measuring the air pressure in inches of mercury ("inHg" or "Hg").

Air Pressure, in inHg	Altitude, in thousand feet
0.33	100
0.82	80
2.14	60
5.56	40
13.76	20

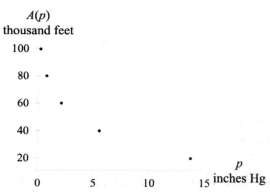

a. Describe the concavity of the scatter plot (no concavity, one concavity, two concavities). What two types of functions might fit the data?

I concavity
    exponential or logarithmic

b. Find the best-fitting exponential function and store it in Y1. Find the best-fitting logarithmic function and store it in Y2. View the graphs of both functions over the scatter plot. Which function fits the data best? Explain why. $0: ExpReg$
$9: Ln Reg$

$$Y_1: Exp(x) = 86.331 (0.894^x)$$

$$Y_2: Ln(x) = 76.174 - 21.331 \ln x$$

c. Write a completely defined logarithmic model for altitude, given air pressure.

$A(p) = 76.174 - 21.331 \ln p$ thousand feet gives the altitude when the air pressure is p inches, $0.33 \le p \le 13.76$.

d. Exchange the input and output data to complete the table. Graph the scatter plot of the inverse function on the axes provided.

exp model

Altitude (thousand feet)	Air Pressure (inches Hg)
100	.33
80	.82
60	2.14
40	5.56
20	13.76

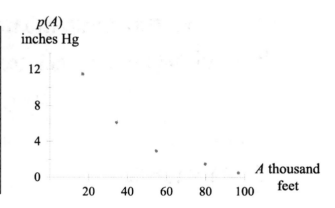

e. Write a completely defined exponential model for air pressure, given altitude. View the graph of the exponential function over the scatter plot and comment on the fit of the exponential function.

$p(A) = 35.541 (.954^A)$ ✓inches Hg gives the Air pressure at an altitude of A thousand ft., $20 \le A \le 100$.

Example 4: (based on CC5e p. 82, Activity 11)

The table gives estimated concentrations in the bloodstream, in micrograms per milliliter (μg / ml), of the drug piroxicam taken in 20 mg doses once a day.

Days	1	3	5	7	9	11	13	15	17
Concentration (μg / ml)	1.5	3.2	4.5	5.5	6.2	6.5	6.9	7.3	7.5

a. What features of the scatter plot indicate that a logarithmic function may be a good fit for the data?

· It has 1 concavity

· slow increasing values

· concave down

b. Write a completely defined logarithmic model for the data.

$f(x) = 1.182 + 2.216 \ln x$ concentration (ug/ml) gives the est. concentrations in the bloodstream of drug piroxicam when taken x days, $1 \le x \le 17$.
       ^
    20 mg doses once a day

c. According to the unrounded logarithmic model, what is the concentration of piroxicam in the bloodstream after 20 days?

$f(20) = 7.821$

The concentration of piroxicam in the blood stream after 20 days is 7.821 ug/ml.

d. According to the unrounded logarithmic model, when will the concentration of piroxicam in the bloodstream reach 8.5 μg / ml ?

$f(x) = 8.5$ $x = 27.166$

The concentration of piroxicam in the blood stream reaches 8.5 ug/ml at 27.166 days.

Section 1.9:   Quadratic Functions and Models

A **quadratic** function has an equation of the form $f(x) = ax^2 + bx + c$, $a \neq 0$, b, and c are constants.

The graph of a quadratic function $f(x) = ax^2 + bx + c$ is a parabola with **one concavity**, determined by the sign of a:

- For $a < 0$, f is concave down, with a **maximum value**, and end behavior
$$\lim_{x \to -\infty} f(x) = -\infty = \lim_{x \to \infty} f(x)$$

- For $a > 0$, f is concave up, with a **minimum value**, and end behavior
$$\lim_{x \to -\infty} f(x) = \infty = \lim_{x \to \infty} f(x)$$

Example 1:

a. Label each of the following graphs as either *concave up* or *concave down*. State the intervals on which the graph is *increasing* or *decreasing*. Mark and label the *absolute maximum* or *absolute minimum* on each graph. Complete the limit statements that describe the end behavior.

b. Identify the graph of $f(x) = -x^2 + 4x + 21$ below.

   $a =$ ___-1___.   (Note $a < 0$.)

c. Identify the graph of $f(x) = x^2 - 4x - 16$ below.

   $a =$ ___1___.   (Note $a > 0$.)

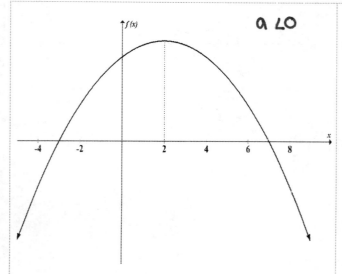

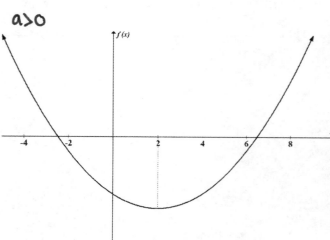

Increasing: ___$(-\infty, 2)$___   Increasing: ___$(2, \infty)$___

Decreasing: ___$(2, \infty)$___   Decreasing: ___$(-\infty, 2)$___

$\lim_{x \to -\infty} f(x) =$ ___$-\infty$___; $\lim_{x \to \infty} f(x) =$ ___$-\infty$___ $\lim_{x \to -\infty} f(x) =$ ___∞___; $\lim_{x \to \infty} f(x) =$ ___∞___

$f(x) =$ ___$-x^2 + 4x + 21$___ $f(x) =$ ___$x^2 - 4x - 16$___

Example 2: (CC5e p. 86)

The percentage of people in the U.S. over age 14 who are asleep at a given time of night is given in the table.

Hours after 9 pm	0	1	2	3	4	5	6	7	8	9	10
Percentage of people asleep	14.0	36.5	64.4	82.2	89.7	93.0	94.4	91.9	85.2	65.1	41.2

a. Verify that the figure to the right shows a scatter plot of the data.

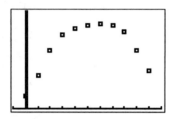

b. How many concavities are suggested by the scatter plot?

  1

c. The scatter plot indicates that the function is concave __down__ over its entire input interval. The function **changes direction** and has an **absolute maximum value** somewhere between _____5_____ and _____7_____ hours after 9 pm.

d. Name two other functions that display a single concavity. Discuss why a quadratic is better than these two functions for modeling the data. In particular, how does the end behavior of a concave down logarithmic function compare to the end behavior of a concave down quadratic function?

  exponential
  logarithmic

e. Write a completely defined **quadratic** model for the data. stat > calc > 5:QuadReg

  $f(x) = -2.731x^2 + 30.376x + 12.589$ gives the percentage of people asleep at x hours after 9pm, $0 \le x \le 10$, in the US over age 14 who are

Finding, storing, and viewing a quadratic function:

- With the data in L1 and L2, **STAT** ▶
  [CALC] ▼ to 5 [QuadReg] **ENTER**
  returns QuadReg on the Home Screen
  VARS ▶ [Y-VARS] **1** [Function]
  1 [Y1] returns Y1 **ENTER**

  OR

  STAT ▶ [CALC] **5** [QuadReg]
  Xlist: **2ⁿᵈ 1** [L1]
  Ylist: **2ⁿᵈ 2** [L2]
  Store RegEQ: **VARS** ▶ [Y-VARS]
  1 [Function] **1** [Y1]
  Move cursor to Calculate and hit
  ENTER

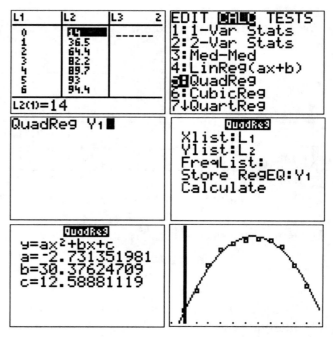

- Hit **ZOOM 9** [ZoomStat] to view the
  function and the scatter plot

Example 3: (CC5e p. 89)

The percentages of U.S. Internet users who will shop online in a particular year, as reported by *eMarketer Daily*, 6/24/2009 are shown in the table below.

Year	2008 ₃	2009 ₄	2010 ₅	2011 ₆	2012 ₇	2013 ₈
Percentage of Online Shoppers	84.2	86.0	87.5	88.7	89.7	90.5

a. Align the input data to years after 2005.
   Plot the scatter plot for the data on the
   set of axes.

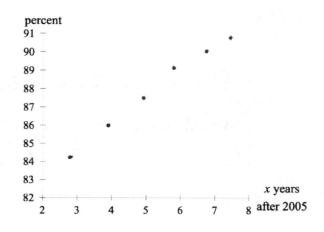

b. Describe the scatter plot by completing
   the following statements:

   The scatter-plot is (increasing)/decreasing.

   The scatter-plot has a single concavity;
   it is concave up/(down).

c. Complete the two models that might be used to fit the data.

quadratic: $Q(x) =$ _-0.125x² +2.626x +77.467_ gives the percent of Internet users who shop online, where x is the number of years after 2005, $3 \le x \le 8$.

logarithmic: $L(x) =$ ~~$(+0.62760e^{-0.23x})$~~ _____ gives the percent of Internet users who shop online, where x is the number of years after 2005, $3 \le x \le 8$.

$77.068 + 6.476 \ln x$

d. Both functions fit the data well. Which model should be used if the model is to be used for extrapolation past 2013? Explain.

logarithmic b/c we expect the # of online shoppers to continue to increase rather than ∆ direction and decrease (quadratic)

e. According to the model in part d) find the predicted percentage of online shoppers in 2014.

$Y_2(9) = 91.298\%$

> **Second differences** are found by taking the differences of the first differences. When the second differences are constant or fairly constant, a quadratic function should be considered when finding the best-fit function.

f. Complete the calculations in the tables below to find the **second differences** for the percent of U.S. Internet users who will shop online.

output data	84.2		86.0		87.5		88.7		89.7		90.5
first differences		1.8		1.5		1.2		1		0.8	
second differences			-0.3		-0.3		-0.2		-0.2		

Notice that the second differences are nearly constant. This is one reason we considered a quadratic function in part c.

Example 4: (CC5e p. 88)

The percentage of low birth-weight babies (babies born before 37 weeks of pregnancy and weighing less than 5.5 pounds), and the corresponding prenatal weight gain of the mother is given in the table.

Mother's Weight Gain (pounds)	18	23	28	33	38	43
Low Birth-weight Babies (percent)	48.2	42.5	38.6	36.5	35.4	35.7

a. Plot the scatter plot for the data.

b. Will the leading coefficient of a quadratic function for these data be positive or negative? Explain your answer.

positive

concave up

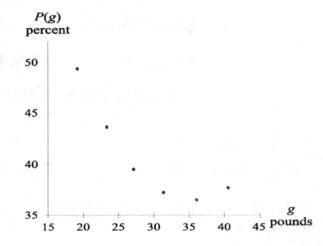

c. Find a quadratic model for the data.

$P(g) = 0.029g^2 - 2.286g + 79.685$ gives the % of low birth weight babies born to mothers whose prenatal weight gain was g pounds, $18 \leq g \leq 43$.

d. Find the percentage of low birth-weight babies born to mother's who gain 45 pounds in pregnancy.

36.4 %

Example 5: (CC5e pp. 91-92, Activities 7, 9, 11, 13)

What type(s) of function(s) might be appropriate to model the data represented by the scatter-plot: linear, exponential, logarithmic, or quadratic?

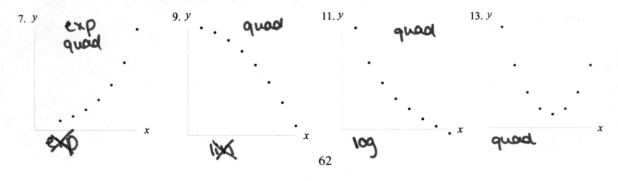

Section 1.10: Logistic Functions and Models

A quantity with exponential growth may have limiting factors that cause that quantity to level off. A **logistic function** either *increases* towards an upper limit or *declines* toward a lower limit as the input values increase.

A **logistic function** has an equation of the form $f(x) = \dfrac{L}{1 + Ae^{-Bx}}$, where A and B are nonzero constants and $L > 0$ is the **limiting value** of the function.

The graph of a logistic function has **two concavities**, with an inflection point. An inflection point is a point at which a function is increasing or decreasing the most or least rapidly on an interval around that inflection point.

The direction of a logistic function is determined by the sign of B:

- for $B < 0$, f is decreasing   • for $B > 0$, f is increasing

$-(eB)$

The graph of a logistic function of the form $f(x) = \dfrac{L}{1 + Ae^{-Bx}}$ is bounded by the horizontal axis and its limiting value. It has two horizontal asymptotes: $y = 0$ and $y = L$

- for $B < 0$, $\displaystyle\lim_{x \to -\infty} f(x) = L$ and $\displaystyle\lim_{x \to \infty} f(x) = 0$
- for $B > 0$, $\displaystyle\lim_{x \to -\infty} f(x) = 0$ and $\displaystyle\lim_{x \to \infty} f(x) = L$

Example 1:

a. Label each of the following graphs of $f(x) = \dfrac{L}{1 + Ae^{-Bx}}$ as either *increasing* or *decreasing*. Identify the *inflection point* by marking an "X" on the graph. Complete the limit statements that describe the end behavior.

b. Find the following for the function $f(x) = \dfrac{3.143}{1 + 2.251e^{0.466x}}$. Identify its graph below.

- $B = -0.466$ (Note that $B < 0$.)

- The equations of its two horizontal asymptotes are:

  $y = 0$, $y = 3.143$

c. Find the following for the function $f(x) = \dfrac{2.458}{1 + 3.331e^{-0.688x}}$. Identify its graph below.

- $B = 0.688$ (Note that $B > 0$.)

- The equations of its two horizontal asymptotes are:

  $y = 0$, $y = 2.458$

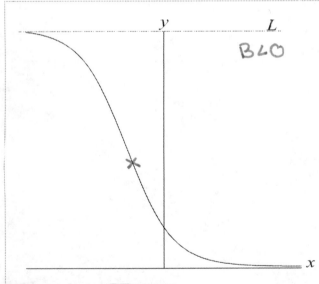

Increasing or ~~decreasing?~~

$\displaystyle \lim_{x \to -\infty} f(x) = \underline{L}$; $\displaystyle \lim_{x \to \infty} f(x) = \underline{0}$

$f(x) = \dfrac{3.143}{1 + 2.251e^{0.466x}}$

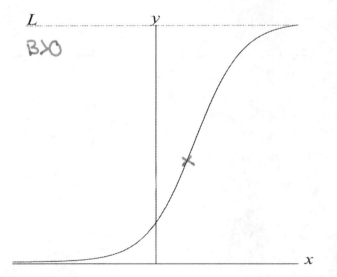

~~Increasing~~ or decreasing?

$\displaystyle \lim_{x \to -\infty} f(x) = \underline{0}$; $\displaystyle \lim_{x \to \infty} f(x) = \underline{L}$

$f(x) = \dfrac{2.458}{1 + 3.331e^{-0.688x}}$

Example 2: (CC5e p. 96)

The number of NBA players on the 2009-2010 roster who are taller than a given height are given in the table.

	0	2	4	6	8	10	12	14	16	18	20
Height, in inches	68	70	72	74	76	78	80	82	84	86	88
Number of NBA players	490	487	467	423	367	293	203	86	13	2	1

a. Align the data to the number of inches over 68. Verify the scatter-plot of the aligned data is shown to the right.

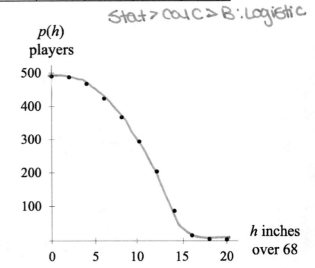

Stat > Calc > B: Logistic

b. Answer the following about the function p.

The function is *increasing* or (*decreasing*).

The function shows *zero, one,* or (*two*) concavities.

The function appears to be concave *up* or (*down*) near $h = 0$ and to be concave (*up*) or *down* near $h = 20$.

There appears to be an inflection point near $h = \underline{10}$.

c. Write a completely defined model for the (aligned) data.

$$p(h) = \frac{485.896}{1 + .007e^{.462h}}$$ gives the number of NBA players

on the 2009-2010 roster taller than ($h + 68$) inches

$0 \le h \le 20$.

Finding, storing, and viewing a logistic function:

- With the data in L1 and L2, **STAT** ▸ [CALC] ▼ to B [Logistic] **ENTER** returns Logistic on the Home Screen **VARS** ▸ [Y-VARS] **1** [Function] **1** [Y1] returns Y1 **ENTER**

    OR

    STAT ▸ [CALC] ▼ to B [Logistic] **ENTER** returns the Logistic Screen
    Xlist: **2ⁿᵈ 1** [L1]
    Ylist: **2ⁿᵈ 2** [L2]
    Store RegEQ: **VARS** ▸ [Y-VARS] **1** [Function] **1** [Y1]
    Move cursor to Calculate and hit **ENTER**

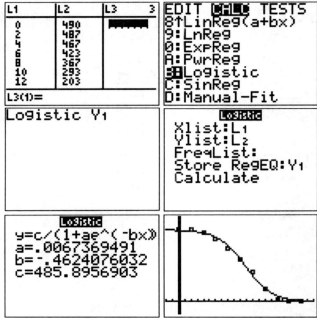

- Hit **ZOOM 9** [ZoomStat] to view the function and the scatter plot

d. Write the equations of the two horizontal asymptotes for the function.

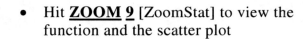

$$y = 0 \qquad y = 485.896$$

e. Describe the end behavior of the function model in part c).

$$\lim_{x \to -\infty} f(x) = \underline{485.896} \quad ; \quad \lim_{x \to \infty} f(x) = \underline{0}$$

f. As the heights of NBA players increase, the number of players taller than a particular height

   approaches ___0___.

g. Sketch the function model and the two horizontal asymptotes over the scatter plot given in part a.

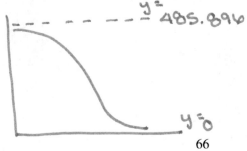

$$y = 485.896$$

$$y = 0$$

Example 3: (CC5e p. 97)

The total residential broadband (high-speed) access as a percentage of Internet access for specific years is shown in the table.

Year	2000	2001	2002	2003	2004	2005	2006	2007	2008	2009
	0	1	2	3	4	5	6	7	8	9
Broadband (percent)	10.6	19.3	29.1	41.7	54.1	64.7	78.5	87.8	92.7	95.8

a. What does the context suggest about the end behavior as the input values increase?

the percent of residential internet users w/ broadband should continue to ⊙rise

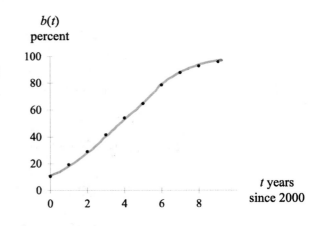

b. Align the input data to years after 2000. Find an appropriate model for the data.

$$b(t) = \frac{102.557}{1 + 7.464e^{-0.529t}}$$ gives the total residential broadband

access as a percent of Internet access for t years, $0 \le t \le 9$.

after 2000

c. State the equations of the two horizontal asymptotes.

$y = 0$ $y = 102.557$

d. In what year does the model predict that 99.9% of residences with Internet access will have broadband access?

$b(t) = 99.9$ $t = 10.663$ year 2011

e. In approximately what year is the percentage of residences with internet access who have broadband access increasing most rapidly?

$t = 45$ year 2005

Example 4: (CC5e pp. 94-95)

Suppose that a computer virus has attacked the computers of an international corporation. The worm is first detected on 100 computers. The corporation has 10,000 computers. As time passes, the number of infected computers can approach, but never exceed 10,000.

Hours	Infected Computers (thousand computers)
0	0.1
0.5	0.597
1	2.851
1.5	7.148
2	9.403
2.5	9.900

a. Does the scatter plot of the data indicate one or two concavities?

b. Write a completely defined logistic model for the data.

$$f(x) = \frac{10.000}{1+99.015e^{-3.676x}}$$ thousand computers gives at an international co. were infected by a computer virus x hours after virus detected, $0 \le x \le 2.5$.

c. Write the equations of the two horizontal asymptotes for the logistic function.

$$y=0 \quad y=10$$

d. According to the model, how many computers will be infected by the computer virus after 3 hours and 15 minutes?

$$f(3.25) = 9.994 \text{ thousand computers}$$

e. How long would it take for the computer virus to infect 5500 computers?

$$f(x) = 5500 \quad \underline{\underline{5.5}}$$

$$x = 1.315 \text{ hours}$$

1 hour
18.9 min

Section 1.11: Cubic Functions and Models

✗ complete previous semester exam for wed. 20 pts!

A **cubic** function has an equation of the form $f(x) = ax^3 + bx^2 + cx + d$, $a \neq 0$, b, c, and d are constants.

2 concavities

The graph of a cubic function $f(x) = ax^3 + bx^2 + cx + d$ has an **inflection point** because its graph shows a change in concavity. An inflection point is a point at which a function is increasing or decreasing the most or least rapidly on an interval around that inflection point.

The sign of a determines the behavior of a cubic function:

a<0 | C.D.
lim = -∞
x→∞
lim = ∞
x→-∞
C.U.

- For $a < 0$, f is concave up, followed by concave down, with end behavior
  $$\lim_{x \to -\infty} f(x) = \infty \text{ and } \lim_{x \to \infty} f(x) = -\infty$$

- For $a > 0$, f is concave down, followed by concave up, with end behavior
  $$\lim_{x \to -\infty} f(x) = -\infty \text{ and } \lim_{x \to \infty} f(x) = \infty$$

Some cubic functions appear to be strictly increasing or strictly decreasing. Other cubic functions change direction and have both increasing and decreasing intervals, showing both a relative maximum value and a relative minimum value.

Exam Wed. Sept. 14 5:30-7:00 Bracket 213

Formulas

$F(t) = P(1 + rt)$

$F(t) = Pe^{rt}$

$F(t) = P(1 + \frac{r}{n})^{nt}$

$APY = (e^r - 1) \cdot 100\%$

$APY = \left[(1 + \frac{r}{n})^n - 1\right] \cdot 100\%$

5 pts bonus on in class grade (quiz, etc.) for attending:

1. PAL session 8:00-9:30 ASC   or   2. CfC 9:00-12:00am M202, M203
   (Tuesday)   (Monday)

Example 1:

a. Label each of the following graphs of $f(x) = ax^3 + bx^2 + cx + d$ as either $a < 0$ or $a > 0$.

b. Identify the *inflection point* on each graph by marking an "X" on the graph. Note that the concavity changes at this point.

c. Complete the limit statements that describe the end behavior.

d. If a *relative maximum* and/or *relative minimum* occur, identify and label these points on the graph.

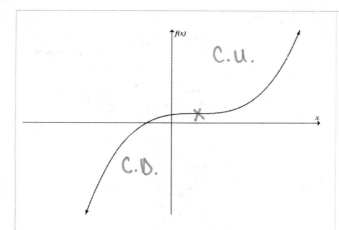

Is $a < 0$ or ⟨$a > 0$⟩?

$\lim_{x \to -\infty} f(x) = \underline{-\infty}$; $\lim_{x \to \infty} f(x) = \underline{\infty}$

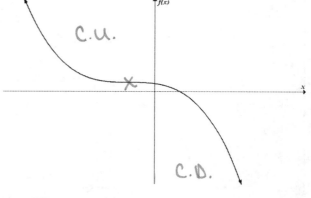

Is ⟨$a < 0$⟩ or $a > 0$?

$\lim_{x \to -\infty} f(x) = \underline{\infty}$; $\lim_{x \to \infty} f(x) = \underline{-\infty}$

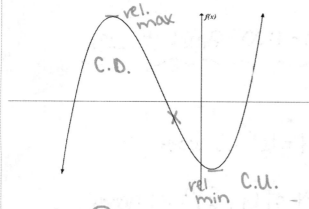

Is $a < 0$ or ⟨$a > 0$⟩?

$\lim_{x \to -\infty} f(x) = \underline{-\infty}$; $\lim_{x \to \infty} f(x) = \underline{\infty}$

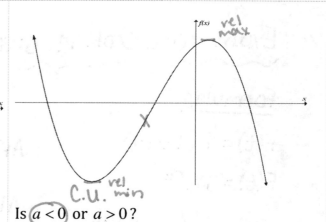

Is ⟨$a < 0$⟩ or $a > 0$?

$\lim_{x \to -\infty} f(x) = \underline{\infty}$; $\lim_{x \to \infty} f(x) = \underline{-\infty}$

Example 2: (CC5e p. 108, Activity 15)

The table shows the yearly monetary value of loss resulting from identity fraud between 2004 and 2008.

Year	Loss, in billion dollars
2004 ₀	60
2005 ₁	57
2006 ₂	51
2007 ₃	45
2008 ₄	48

a. Align the data to the number of years since 2004. Write a cubic model for the amount of loss due to identity fraud. stat> calc > 6:Cubic Reg

$f(x) = x^3 - 5.143x^2 + 1.571x + 59.914$ billion dollars gives the yearly monetary value of loss resulting from identity fraud x years since 2004, $0 \le x \le 4$.

Finding, storing, and viewing a cubic function:

- With the aligned data in L1 and L2, **STAT** ▸ [CALC] ▾ to 6 [CubicReg] **ENTER** returns CubicReg on the Home Screen. **VARS** ▸ [Y-VARS] **1** [Function] **1** [Y1] returns Y1 **ENTER**

OR

STAT ▸ [CALC] ▾ to 6 [CubicReg] **ENTER** returns the CubicReg Screen
Xlist: **2ⁿᵈ 1** [L1]
Ylist: **2ⁿᵈ 2** [L2]
Store RegEQ: **VARS** ▸ [Y-VARS] **1** [Function] **1** [Y1]
Move cursor to Calculate and hit **ENTER**

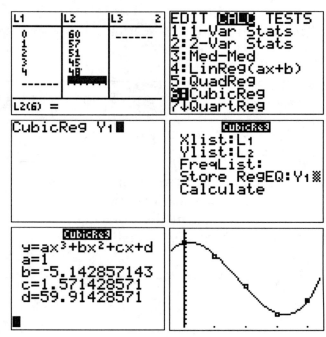

- Hit **ZOOM 9** [ZoomStat] to view the function and the scatter plot

b. Use the model to estimate the amount of loss in 2009. Comment on the usefulness of this estimate. y₁ (5)

$f(5) = 64.2$ billion dollars , we would expect it to increase due to the shape of the function

c. Does a model output value corresponding to an input of 2.5 make sense in context? Explain. halfway between 2006 to 2007

input values must be integers b/c output is yearly

d. Estimate the input and output values of the inflection point.

roughly 2006   (2, 51)

e. Interpret the inflection point value and location in a sentence.

Yearly loss from identity fraud was decreasing most rapidly approx. in 2006 when yearly loss was 51 billion.

Example 3: (CC5e p. 105)

The number of 20 to 24-year-olds who were employed full time during a given year is shown in the table below.

Year	2001	2002	2003	2004	2005	2006	2007
Employees, in thousands	9473	9233	9187	9226	9409	9580	9577

a. Align the data to the number of years since 2000 and view a scatter plot of the data. Why is a cubic model more appropriate for the data than a logistic model?

no evidence of 2 HA.

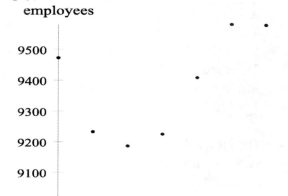

b. Write a completely defined cubic model for the data.

$p(t) = -12.917x^3 + 185.452x^2 - 729.345x + 10038.571$ thousand employees gives the # of 20-24 yr-olds who were employed full time t years since 2000, $1 \le t \le 7$.

c. What is the concern in using the model to extrapolate beyond 2007?

cubic model shows dec. in employment but there is no evidence to suggest that happens

d. Use the model in part b to estimate the employment of 20 to 24-year-olds in 2008.

$Y_1(8) = 9459.429$ *thousand full time employees*

e. According to the model, find the approximate time periods in which the number of 20 to 24-year-olds employees exceeded 9400 thousand.

3 possible answers

$P(t) = 9400$ $t = 1.224$

$t = 8.220$

$t = 4.914$

exceed 9400 from the end of 2000 to early 2002, and again from late 2008 to early 2009

late 2004 to 2005

Strategies for Choosing the Best-Fit Function to Model a Data Set

1. Look at the curvature of the scatter plot.

    • **No curvature** suggests a *linear* function.
    • **One concavity, with no inflection point**, suggests a *quadratic, exponential,* or *logarithmic* function.
    • **Two concavities, with an inflection point** suggests a *cubic* or *logistic* function.

2. Find the best fit among the functions (two functions, at most) with the same amount of concavity.

3. Consider the **end behavior** and the given **context** in choosing the best function to model the data, especially if two functions fit the data equally well.

4. *shapes of each function*

Example 4: (CC5e pp. 99, Activities 5, 7, 9)

a. For each of the following graphs, determine the amount of curvature displayed (no curvature, one concavity, two concavities).

b. For each of the following graphs, what type(s) of function(s) might be appropriate to model the data represented by each scatter-plot: linear, exponential, logarithmic, quadratic, logistic, or cubic?

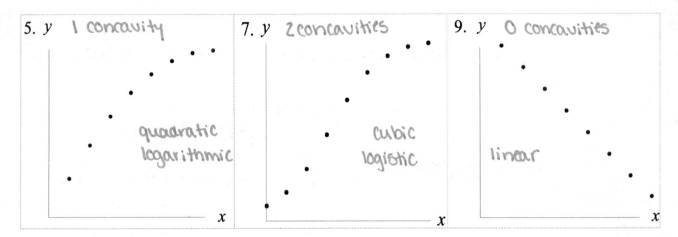

5. *y* I concavity

quadratic
logarithmic

x

7. *y* 2 concavities

cubic
logistic

x

9. *y* O concavities

linear

x

Example 5:

In 2008, a community began a local campaign to increase voter turnout in local elections. The percentages of all eligible voters voting in the yearly local elections are shown in the table below.

Year	2008	2009	2010	2011	2012	2013
Voter turnout, in percent	2.0	4.1	5.32	6.2	6.8	7.2

a. Examine the scatterplot of the data. What *two* functions would you consider for modeling this data?

b. If you were planning to use one of these models to estimate voter turnout in subsequent years, which of the two models do you think you would use and why?

c. Align the data to years after 2007. Write a completely defined model based on your answer to part b.

Example 6: (CC5e p. 99, based on Activity 16)

The age-specific likelihood for a woman to develop breast cancer in the next ten years is given in the table below.

Age	20	30	40	50	60	70
Likelihood of breast cancer, in percent	0.05	0.43	1.43	2.51	3.51	3.88

a. Examine the scatterplot of the data. What *two* functions would you consider for modeling this data?

logistic

cubic

b. If you were planning to use one of these models to predict the likelihood of breast cancer occurring in the next ten years for an 80-year old woman, which of the two functions do you think you would use to model the data and why?

logistic   we expect % of breast cancer to increase w/ age

c. Write a completely defined model using the function based on your answer to part b:

$$w(x) = \frac{4.039}{1 + 351.979e^{-0.129x}}$$ percent gives the likelihood that a woman who is x years of age will develop breast cancer within the next 10 years, $20 \leq x \leq 70$.

Example 7:

The table below is organized according to the amount of concavity displayed in a scatter plot. Use it to summarize the six functions studied in this chapter.

For each of the functions, sketch two possible graphs. Describe the end behavior using limit notation. List the special features (horizontal or vertical asymptote(s), maximum, minimum, inflection point, etc.) of each function. Write the equation(s) of any asymptotes.

SIX FUNCTION SUMMARY			
Function	**Graphs**	**End Behavior**	**Special Features**
No Curvature			
Linear $f(x) = ax + b$		When $a > 0$, $\lim\limits_{x \to \infty} f(x) = \infty$ $\lim\limits_{x \to -\infty} f(x) = -\infty$	$f(0) = b$ constant rate of change = slope
One Concavity (Up or Down)			
Exponential $f(x) = a(b^x)$		When $b > 1$, $\lim\limits_{x \to \infty} f(x) = \pm\infty$ $\lim\limits_{x \to -\infty} f(x) =$ $0 \leq b \leq 1 = 0$	concavity depends on sign of a $a > 0$ C.U. constant $a < 0$ C.D. percents HA = y=0 initial value a
Logarithmic $f(x) = a + b\ln x$	$b > 0$ C.U. $b < 0$ C.D.	When $b > 0$, $\lim\limits_{x \to 0^+} f(x) = \infty$ $\lim\limits_{x \to \infty} f(x) =$	V. A x=0 x>0 inverse of exp. func.
Quadratic $f(x) = ax^2 + bx + c$		When $a > 0$, $\lim\limits_{x \to \infty} f(x) = \infty$ $\lim\limits_{x \to -\infty} f(x) = \infty$	
Two Concavities			
Logistic $f(x) = \dfrac{L}{1 + ae^{-bx}}$	$b < 0$ dec. $b > 0$ inc.	When $b < 0$, $\lim\limits_{x \to \infty} f(x) = 0$ $\lim\limits_{x \to -\infty} f(x) = L$	2 HA y=0 y=L
Cubic $f(x) = ax^3 + bx^2 + cx + d$		When $a > 0$, $\lim\limits_{x \to \infty} f(x) = \infty$ $\lim\limits_{x \to -\infty} f(x) = -\infty$	

$a > 0$ C.D. → C.U.
$a < 0$ C.U. → C.D.

Section 2.1: Measures of Change over an Interval

The amount of **change,** the **percentage change,** or the **average rate of change** can be calculated between two points $(x_1, f(x_1))$ and $(x_2, f(x_2))$ by using the formulas in the table below.

Change finds the difference in two output values. Graphically, this is the amount of vertical change between the two points. $y_2 - y_1$

Percentage change expresses the amount of **change** as a percentage of the first output value.

Average rate of change divides the change by the length of the interval and expresses how quickly a quantity is changing on average over an interval. Graphically, this is the slope of the **secant line,** a line that connects the two points.

A sentence of **interpretation** for **change, percentage change, or average rate of change over an interval** uses ordinary conversational language to answer the questions:
- *When?* refers to the input interval.
- *What?* refers to the output description for the function.
- *Increased(es) or Decreased(es)?*
    For average rate of change, use the phrase "increased on average by" or "decreased on average by".
- *By how much?* refers to the change calculation, and includes its corresponding units.

	Formula (assume $x_1 < x_2$)	Units
Change	$f(x_2) - f(x_1)$	output units
Percentage change ✗ $\dfrac{new - old}{old} \cdot 100\%$	$\dfrac{f(x_2) - f(x_1)}{f(x_1)} \cdot 100\%$	percent
Average rate of change	$\dfrac{f(x_2) - f(x_1)}{x_2 - x_1}$	output units per input unit

Example 1: (CC5e p. 132)

The following graph shows the Social Security Advisory Board's estimates of the federal government's Social Security assets between 2002 and 2040 (in constant 2005 dollars).

a. Use the graph to estimate the output values for the points that correlate to 2012 and 2033. Write the two ordered pairs.

$$(12, 2.7) \quad (33, 2.2)$$

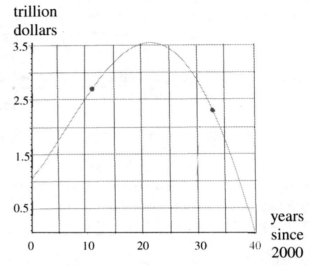

b. Calculate and interpret in a sentence the **change** in Social Security assets between 2012 and 2033.

$2.2 - 2.7 = -0.5$ trillion dollars; between 2012 and 2033 S.S. assets are expected to decrease by 0.5 trillion dollars

c. Calculate and interpret in a sentence the **percentage change** in Social Security assets between 2012 and 2033.

$\dfrac{2.2 - 2.7}{2.7} \cdot 100\% = -18.519\%$; Between 2012 and 2033 S.S. assets are expected to decrease by 18.519%.

d. Draw the **secant line** that cuts through the graph at input values 12 and 33. What is the slope of the secant line?

$\dfrac{2.2 - 2.7}{33 - 12} = -0.024$

e. Calculate and interpret in a sentence the **average rate of change** in Social Security assets between 2012 and 2033.

Between 2012 and 2033 S.S. assets are expected to decrease by an average of 0.024 trillion dollars per year.

Example 2: (CC5e p. 131)

The table shows temperatures on a typical day in May, in a certain Midwestern city.

Time, in hours after 7 am	0	1	2	3	4	5	6	7	8	9	10
Temperature, in degrees Fahrenheit $(°F)$	49	58	66	72	76	79	80	80	78	74	69

(8am is above the "1" column, 5pm is above the "10" column)

a. Find and interpret in a sentence the **change** in temperature between 8 A.M. and 5 P.M.

69-58 = 11°f ; Between 8am and 5pm on a typical day in may in a Midwest city increased by 11°f the temp.

b. Find and interpret in a sentence the **percentage change** in temperature between 8 A.M. and 5 P.M.

$$\frac{69-58}{58} \cdot 100 = 18.996\%$$

Between 8am and 5pm on a typical day in May in a Midwest city the temp. increased by 18.996%

c. Find and interpret in a sentence the **average rate of change** in temperature between 8 A.M. and 5 P.M.

$$\frac{69-58}{10-1} = 1.222°f$$

Between 8am and 5pm on a typical day in May in a Midwest city the temp. increased by an avg. of 1.222°f per hour.

d. How might the average rate of change in temperature between 8 A.M. and 5 P.M. be a misleading measure?

Doesn't account for an increase or decrease in temp.
Appear that temp. is constantly increasing each hour.

Example 3: (CC5e p. 133)

$f(t) = -0.8t^2 + 10t + 49$ degrees Fahrenheit gives the temperature of a certain Midwestern city on a day in May, t hours after 7 am.

a. Calculate the **change** in temperature between 11:00 am and 4:30 pm. Include units with your answer.

```
Plot1 Plot2 Plot3
\Y1◼-0.8X²+10X+4
9
\Y2=
\Y3=
\Y4=
\Y5=
\Y6=
```

```
Y₁(9.5)-Y₁(4)
```

$Y_1(9.5) - Y_1(4) = -4.4$

Between 11^{am} and 4:30 ^{pm} of a certain midwestern city on a day in May the temp. decreased by 4.4°F.

b. Calculate the **percentage change** between 11:00 am and 4:30 pm. Include units with your answer.

```
(Y₁(9.5)-Y₁(4))/
Y₁(4)◼
```

```
Ans*100
```

$Y_1(9.5) = 71.8$

$Y_2(4) = 76.2$

$$\frac{71.8 - 76.2}{76.2}$$

$$= -0.058 \cdot 100 \underset{=5.774}{}$$

Between 11^{am} and 4:30 ^{pm} of a certain Midwestern city on a day in May the temp. decreased by 5.774%.

c. Calculate the **average rate of change** between 11:00 am and 4:30 pm. Include units with your answer.

```
(Y₁(9.5)-Y₁(4))/
(9.5-4)
```

$Y_1^{(9.5)} = 71.8$

$Y_1(4) = 76.2$

$$\frac{71.8 - 76.2}{9.5 - 4} = -0.8$$

Between 11^{am} and 4:30 ^{pm} of a certain Midwestern city on a day in May the temp. decreased by an avg. of 0.8°f per hour.

Example 4: (CC5e p. 135, similar to Activity 11)

Kelly Services, Inc., a leading global provider of staffing services, had a revenue of 4850 million dollars in 2004 and a revenue of 5700 million dollars in 2007.

a. Write a sentence of interpretation for the amount of change in Kelly Services' revenue between 2004 and 2007.

$$5700 - 4850 = 850$$

Between 2004 and 2007 ∨ the revenue of Kelly Services, Inc. increased by 850 million dollars.

b. Write a sentence of interpretation for the percentage change in Kelly Services' revenue between 2004 and 2007.

$$\frac{5700 - 4850}{4850} \cdot 100 = 17.526$$

Between 2004 and 2007 the revenue of Kelly Services increased by 17.526%.

c. Write a sentence of interpretation for the average rate of change in Kelly Services' revenue between 2004 and 2007.

$$\frac{5700 - 4850}{2007 - 2004} = 283.333$$

Between 2004 and 2007 the revenue of Kelly Services increased by an avg. of 283.333 million dollars per year.

Example 5:

$W(x) = 1.608(1.271^x)$ thousand megawatts gives the cumulative capacity for wind power worldwide over the past x years since 1990, $0 \le x \le 17$.

a. Since W is an exponential function, it has constant percentage change. Find the constant percentage change and use it to complete the following sentence:

$(b-1) \cdot 100\%$
$(1.271-1) \cdot 100$

Between 1990 and 2007, the cumulative capacity for wind power worldwide increased by ___27.1___ % each year.

b. Calculate the percentage change in the cumulative capacity between 1990 and 2007 and complete the following sentence:

Between 1990 and 2007, the cumulative capacity for wind power worldwide increased by ___548.13___ %. or $\frac{f(17) - 1.608}{17 - 0} \cdot 100 = 548.127$

c. Explain the difference in the answers in part a and part b.

a) % change from 1 year to next

b) % change over 17 years

Section 2.2: Measures of Change at a Point – Graphical

The **(instantaneous) rate of change** of a continuous function f at a point x is given by the **slope** of the **tangent line** to the graph at that point (unless the tangent line is vertical at x or there is a sharp corner at x). It is denoted by $f'(x)$ and read as "f *prime of x*". The unit of measure for rate of change is **output units per input unit**.

The **slope of a graph** at a point refers to the slope of the tangent line to the graph at that point.

The **percentage rate of change** at a point expresses the rate of change as a percent. If the rate of change $f'(a)$ exists for input a and $f(a) \neq 0$, then

$$\textbf{percentage rate of change } = \frac{\textit{rate of change at a po} \text{int}}{\textit{value of the function at that po}\text{int}} \cdot 100 = \frac{f'(a)}{f(a)} \cdot 100\, \%$$

The unit of measure for percentage rate of change is **% per input unit**.

A sentence of **interpretation** for **rate of change** or **percentage rate of change** at a point uses ordinary conversational language to answer the questions:
- *When?* refers to the single point.
- *What?* refers to the output description for the function.
- *Increas**ing** or Decreas**ing**?*
- *By how much?* refers to the rate of change or percentage rate of change calculation, and includes its corresponding units.

Example 1:

Examples of graphs with a tangent line are shown below. Describe the concavity of the graph at the point of tangency and state whether the tangent line lies above the graph, below the graph, cuts through the graph, or coincides with the graph.

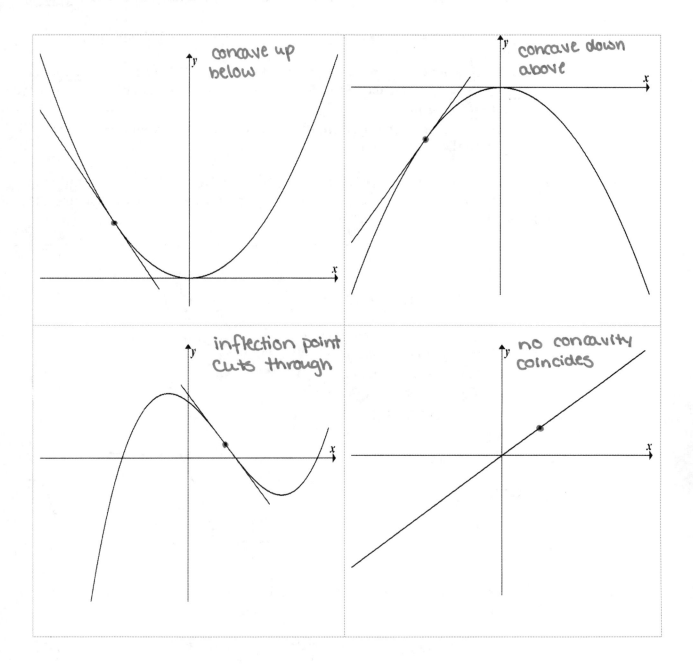

To draw a **tangent line** to a graph at a point, draw a line that goes through that point (called the **point of tangency**) and follows the slope of the graph.

- If the graph is **concave up** at the point of tangency, the tangent line lies below the graph.
- If the graph is **concave down** at the point of tangency, the tangent line lies above the graph.
- If there is an **inflection point** at the point of tangency, the tangent line cuts through the graph. It lies above the concave down portion and below the concave up portion of the graph.
- If the graph is of a **linear function**, the tangent line at the point of tangency will coincide with the graph of the line.

Use the idea of **local linearity** to help draw a tangent line. Notice that over a small input interval, the curve appears to be linear. Extend this apparent straight line while using the above information to draw a tangent line.

Example 2: (CC5e p. 147, Activity 1)

a. Draw a tangent line at each labeled point on the graph. State whether the graph is concave up, concave down, or has an inflection point at each labeled point.

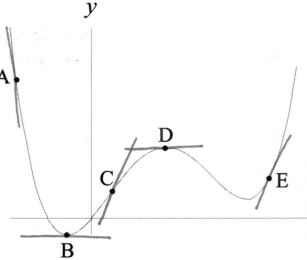

A: up

B: up

C: inflection

D: down

E: up

b. State whether the instantaneous rate of change is positive, negative or zero at each of the labeled points.

A: neg   B: zero   C: pos   D: zero   E: pos

c. Is the graph steeper at point *A* or at point *C*? A

d. Is the slope greater at point *A* or at point *C*? C

Example 3: (CC5e p. 143)

The graph shows the mean plasma concentration of acetaminophen in adults, in micrograms per milliliter ($\mu g / mL$), t hours after being dosed with two 500 mg caplets of Tylenol.

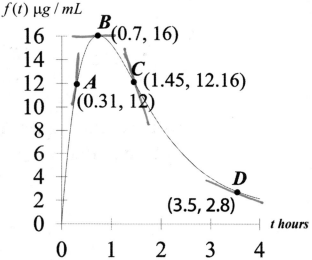

$f(t)$ $\mu g / mL$

B (0.7, 16)

C (1.45, 12.16)

A (0.31, 12)

D (3.5, 2.8)

t hours

- The slope of the line tangent to the graph at point A is approximately <u>22.4</u> $\mu g / mL$ per hour. The input at point A is 0.31 hours.

- The slope of the graph is zero at point <u>B</u>.

- Mean plasma concentration is decreasing most rapidly at point <u>C</u>, where the rate is <u>-7.61</u> $\mu g / mL$ per hour.

- The instantaneous rate of change of mean plasma concentration at point D is approximately <u>-1.67</u> $\mu g / mL$ per hour.

a. Draw tangent lines to the curve at each of the points A, B, C, and D.

b. List points A, B, C, and D in order from **least to greatest slope**.

<u>least</u>   C   D   B   A   <u>greatest</u>

c. List points A, B, C, and D in order from **least to greatest steepness**.

<u>least</u>   B   D   C   A   <u>greatest</u>

d. Write a sentence of interpretation for the **rate of change** in mean plasma concentration at each of the points A and C.

A: .31 hours (18.6 min) after being dosed with 2 500mg Tylenol tablets, the mean plasma concentration in adults is increasing by 22.4 $\mu g/mL$ per hour

C: 1.45 hours (1 hour 22min) after being dosed with 2 500mg Tylenol tablets, the mean plasma concentration in adults is decreasing by ~~2.67~~ 7.61 $\mu g/mL$ per hour.

e. Find the **percentage rate of change** in mean plasma concentration of acetaminophen 18.6 minutes (0.31hours) after being dosed with two 500 mg caplets of Tylenol. Write a sentence of interpretation.

$$\frac{f'(a)}{f(a)} \cdot 100 \qquad \frac{22.4}{12} \cdot 100 = 186.667\%$$

0.31 hours after being dosed w/ 2 500mg caplets of Tylenol the mean plasma concentration of ace. is inc. by 186.667% per hour

The **tangent line at point** T can be defined as follows:
Given a point T and close points P_n on the graph of a smooth continuous function, the **tangent line at point** T is the limiting position of the secant lines through point T and increasingly close points P_n.

Example 4:

P. 140
Figure 2.11
2.12

Draw secant lines through P_1 and T, P_2 and T, etc. on the left side of T. Repeat on the right side of T by drawing secant lines through P_5 and T, P_6 and T, etc. on the right side of T. Finally, draw the tangent line at T, noting how it is the limiting position of the secant lines.

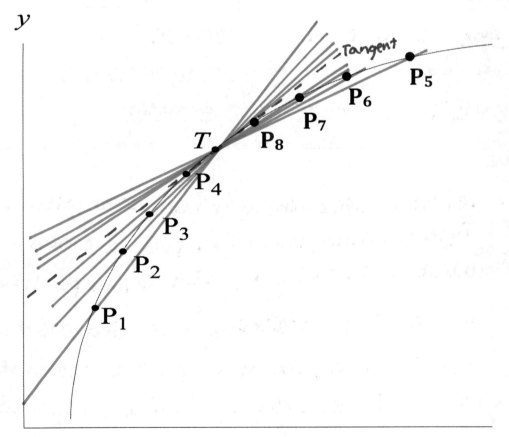

Section 2.3: Rates of Change – Notation and Interpretation

= slope of tangent line at x

The **(instantaneous) rate of change** of a function f at a point x is also referred to as the **derivative of f at x.** It is denoted by $f'(x)$, read as "f prime of x", or

$\dfrac{df}{dx}$, read as " d-f d-x ".   *$f'(x)$ = derivative of f at x*

The rate of change, or derivative, at a specific input a can be denoted as $f'(a)$, read as "f prime evaluated at a", or $\left. \dfrac{df}{dx} \right|_{x=a}$, read as "d-f d-x evaluated at a ".

The unit of measure for a rate of change or a derivative f' is **output units of f per input unit of f** .

Recall:
A sentence of **interpretation** for a **derivative** or **percentage rate of change** at a point uses ordinary conversational language to answer the questions:
- *When?* refers to the single point.
- *What?* refers to the output description for the function.
- *Increas**ing** or Decreas**ing**?*
- *By how much?* refers to the rate of change or percentage rate of change calculation, and includes its corresponding units.

function name → $\dfrac{df}{dx}$ *derivative of f*
                        derivative of x
              ↑
           variable

$f'(5)$ = derivative of f at $x=5$

$\left. \dfrac{df}{dx} \right|_{x=5}$

$s(t)$ → *$s'(t)$* $\dfrac{ds}{dt}$

Example 1: (CC5e p. 157, Activity 3)

The function f gives the weekly profit, in thousand dollars, that an airline makes on its flights from Boston to Washington D.C. when the ticket price is p dollars.

Given: $f(65) = 15$, $f'(65) = 1.5$, and $f'(90) = -2$.
    point   increasing   decreasing

a. On the basis of the given information, sketch a graph of f on the axes provided.

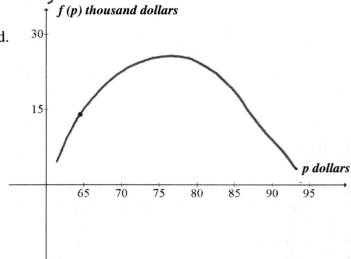

b. Write a sentence of interpretation for each of the following:

- $f(65) = 15$ When the ticket price is $65, the weekly profit to the airline on flights from Boston to washington D.C. is $15 thousand dollars.

- $f'(65) = 1.5$ When the ticket price is $65, the weekly profit to the airline … is increasing by 1.5 thousand dollars per dollar of tickets price.

c. Find the percentage rate of change for the function at $p = 65$. Include units with the answer.

$$\frac{f'(65)}{f(65)} \cdot 100 = \frac{1.5}{15} \cdot 100 = 10\% \text{ per dollar of ticket price}$$

Average Rate of Change	*instantaneous* Rate of Change/Derivative
Measures how rapidly a quantity *changes* on average between two points.	Measures how rapidly a quantity *is changing* at a single point.
Graphically finds the slope of the secant line between two points.	Graphically finds the slope of the tangent line at a single point on a continuous and smooth graph.
Requires two points	Requires a continuous function at a point that is not a sharp corner and does not have a vertical tangent.

Example 2: (CC5e, p. 153)

The figure to the right shows Apple Corporation's annual net sales, in trillion dollars, over an eight year period.

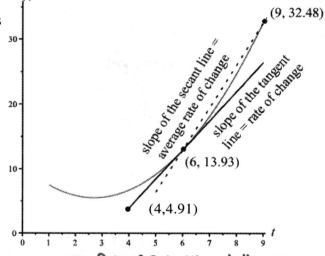

a. Find and interpret the average rate of change between year 6 and year 9.

$$\frac{32.48-13.93}{9-6} = 6.183 \text{ trillion dollars per year}$$

Between year 6 and 9, Apple Co's annual net sales increased by an average of 6.183 trillion dollars per year.

b. Find the slope of the graph at $(6, 13.93)$. Write the answer using both notations for the derivative.

$$\frac{13.93-4.91}{6-4} = 4.51$$

1. $s'(6) = 4.51$

2. $\left.\frac{ds}{dt}\right|_{t=6} = 4.51$

c. Write a sentence of interpretation for the derivative found in part b.

At year 6 (end of) Apple's annual net sales were increasing by 4.51 trillion dollars per year.

d. Write a sentence of interpretation for the percentage rate of change at $(6, 13.93)$.

$$\frac{4.51}{13.93} \cdot 100 = 32.376\% \text{ per year}$$

At year 6 (end of) Apple's annual net sales were increasing by 32.376% per year.

89

Example 3: (CC5e p. 156)

$C(h)$ is the average concentration, in ng/mL, of a drug in the bloodstream h hours after the administration of a dose of 360 mg. On the basis of the following information sketch a graph of C:

- $C(0) = 124$ ng/mL point

- $C(4) = 252$ ng/mL and point
  $C'(4) = 48$ ng/mL per hour
  increasing

- The concentration after 24 hours is 35.9 ng/mL higher than it was when the dose was administered. 159.9

- The concentration of the drug is increasing most rapidly after 4 hours.
  inflection point

- The maximum concentration of 380 ng/mL occurs after 8 hours.
  max. point

- Between $h = 8$ and $h = 24$, the concentration declines at a constant rate of 14 g/mL.
  negative slope

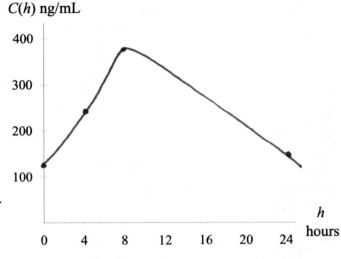

Example 4: (CC5e p. 155)

The graph shows the temperature T, in $^\circ$C, of the polar night region as a function of k, the number of kilometers above sea level.

a. Sketch a tangent line and estimate its slope at 45 km. Include units with the answer.

$(45, -30)$ $(35, -50)$ $\dfrac{-50 + 30}{35 - 45}$

$= 2\,^\circ\text{C per km}$

b. Use derivative notation to express the slope of the graph of T when $k = 45$.

$T'(45) = 2$ $\dfrac{dT}{dk}\Big|_{k=45} = 2$

c. Write a sentence interpreting the rate of change of T at 45 km.

At 45 km above sea level, the temp. of the polar night region is increasing by 2°C per km.

Summary of Measures of Change		
	Formula (assume $x_1 < x_2$)	**Units**
Change	$f(x_2) - f(x_1)$	<u>output</u> units of f
Percentage change	$\dfrac{f(x_2) - f(x_1)}{f(x_1)} \cdot 100\%$	<u>percent</u>
Average rate of change	$\dfrac{f(x_2) - f(x_1)}{x_2 - x_1}$	<u>output</u> units of f per <u>input</u> unit of f
Instantaneous rate of change *or* **rate of change** *or* **derivative at** $x = a$	$f'(a)$	<u>output</u> units of f per <u>input</u> unit of f
Percentage rate of change at $x = a$	$\dfrac{f'(a)}{f(a)} \cdot 100\%$	<u>%</u> per <u>input</u> unit of f

Handwritten annotations:
2.1

increased/
increases

2points
↑
↓
1point

slope of secant

slope of tangent

increasing

2.2

Section 2.4: Rates of Change – Numerical Limits and Nonexistence

The rate of change, or derivative, of a function $f(x)$, at input a, is the limit of secant

slopes: $f'(a) = \lim\limits_{x \to a} \dfrac{f(x) - f(a)}{x - a}$, provided the limit exists. $\lim\limits_{x \to a^-} x = \lim\limits_{x \to a^+} x$

Graphically, $f'(a)$ is the slope of the line tangent to the graph of $f(x)$ at input a.

$f'(a)$ can be estimated **numerically** by calculating slopes of secant lines between $(a, f(a))$ and nearby points $(x, f(x))$ and then finding the limit of the secant slopes as nearby points get closer to the point of tangency. Points on both sides of a must be used in order to verify that the limit exists at a.

Example 1: (CC5e p.160)

Estimate $f'(4)$ for the function $f(x) = 2\sqrt{x}$, both graphically and numerically.

a. Graphically estimate $f'(4)$ by finding the slope of the tangent line to $f(x)$ at $x =$ ___4___ .

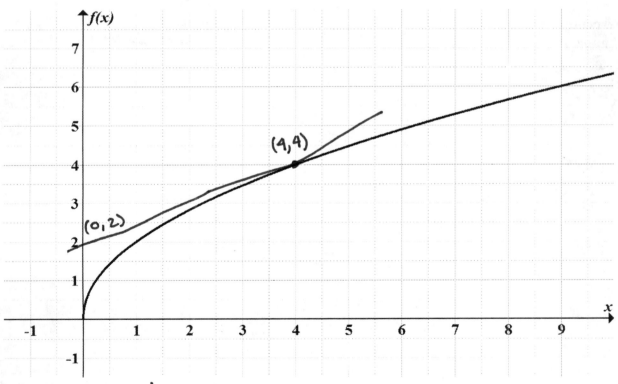

(4,4)

(0,2)

Graphically, $f'(4) \approx$ __$\frac{1}{2}$__ .

$$\frac{4-2}{4-0} = \frac{1}{2}$$

b. Numerically estimate $f'(4)$ by finding the limit of the secant slopes.

➤ Let $(x, f(x))$ be a point very close to the point $(4, f(4))$.
Write the slope formula for the secant line connecting these two points.

$$\frac{f(x) - f(a)}{x - 4}$$

➤ If a nearby point has input $x = 3.9$, what is the slope of the secant line between the points $(3.9, f(3.9))$ and $(4, f(4))$? Enter the answer in the table below, rounding to four decimal places. Repeat for other input values as points get closer and closer to $x = 4$, from both the left and the right.

$x \to 4^-$	$\dfrac{f(x) - f(4)}{x - 4}$	$x \to 4^+$	$\dfrac{f(x) - f(4)}{x - 4}$
3.9	.5032	4.1	.4969
3.99	.5003	4.01	.4997
3.999	.50003	4.001	.49996
3.9999	.500003	4.0001	.49999

$$y_1 = 2\sqrt{x} \qquad y_2 = \frac{(y_1(x) - y_1(4))}{(x - 4)}$$

Numerically estimating a rate of change:

- Enter *f(x)* into Y1.

- Enter the formula for the slope of the secant line into Y2:
  (**Y1 (X) - Y1 (4)) / (X - 4)**

- **2ND WINDOW** [TBLSET] returns the table setup.

- **2ND GRAPH** [TABLE] returns the table.

- Use **DEL** to clear any values in the X column.

- In the X column, type **3.9 ENTER 3.99 ENTER 3.999 ENTER 3.9999 ENTER**. The function values are in the Y1 column and the slope of the secant lines between each entered *x* value and *x* = 4 are in the Y2 column.

- Move the cursor over the values in Y2 to see the unrounded slopes.

- Repeat for *x* values to the right of 4.

> The **limit** of the slopes of the secant lines from the left, $\lim\limits_{x \to 4^-} \dfrac{f(x) - f(4)}{x - 4}$ = ___.5___

The **limit** of the slopes of the secant lines from the right, $\lim\limits_{x \to 4^+} \dfrac{f(x) - f(4)}{x - 4}$ = ___.5___

Since the left-hand and right-hand limits are equal, the limit of the slopes of the secant lines *exists* and $\lim\limits_{x \to 4} \dfrac{f(x) - f(4)}{x - 4}$ = ___.5___ .

Numerically, $f'(4) \approx$ ___.5___

Example 2: (CC5e p.161)

A multinational corporation invests 432 billion of its assets in the global market, resulting in an investment with a future value of $F(t) = 32(1.12^t)$ billion dollars after t years. The graph of $F(t)$ is shown to the right.

exponential growth
concave up $b > 1$

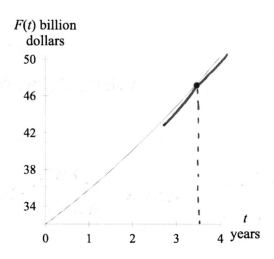

$F(t)$ billion dollars

a. Draw the line on the graph of $F(t)$ whose slope represents the rate of change of the future value of the investment at $t = 3.5$, in the middle of the fourth year.

tangent

b. Find the secant slopes between $(t, F(t))$ and $(3.5, F(3.5))$ and enter them in the table. Round answers to three decimal places.

$t \to 3.5^-$	$\dfrac{F(t) - F(3.5)}{t - 3.5}$	$t \to 3.5^+$	$\dfrac{F(t) - F(3.5)}{t - 3.5}$
3.49	5.389	3.51	5.395
3.499	5.3917	3.501	5.3923
3.4999	5.3920	3.5001	5.3921
3.49999	5.3920	3.50001	5.3920
3.499999	~~5.3920~~	3.500001	6.3920

5.3920

c. Find the left-hand and right-hand limits of the secant slopes.

$$\lim_{t \to 3.5^-} \frac{F(t) - F(3.5)}{t - 3.5} = \underline{5.392} \qquad \text{and} \qquad \lim_{t \to 3.5^+} \frac{F(t) - F(3.5)}{t - 3.5} = \underline{5.392}$$

d. $F'(3.5) = \lim_{t \to 3.5} \dfrac{F(t) - F(3.5)}{t - 3.5} = \underline{5.392} \quad = \dfrac{dF}{dt}\bigg|_{t=3.5}$

e. Complete the following sentence of interpretation for the answer to part d.

In the middle of the fourth year, the value of the multinational corporation's investment is

_increasing by 5.392 billion dollars per year._____ .

f. Find and interpret the percentage rate of change when $t = 3.5$.

$$\frac{f'(3.5)}{f(3.5)} \cdot 100 = \frac{5.392}{47.579} \cdot 100 = 11.333\% \text{ per year}$$

In the middle of the 4th year, the value of the multinational corporation's investment is increasing by 11.333% per year.

If the derivative of a function exists at a point, the function is said to be **differentiable** at that point. If the derivative of a function exists for every point whose input is in an open interval, the function is **differentiable over that open interval.**

The **derivative does not exist**:

- at a point P where the function is **not continuous.**
  At such a point, a tangent line cannot be drawn. The derivative does not exist because the limit of the secant slopes does not exist.

- at a point P where the function **has a sharp point** (the function is not smooth).
  At such a point, a tangent line cannot be drawn. The derivative does not exist because the limit of the secant slopes does not exist.

- at a point P where the function is continuous but **the tangent line is vertical.**
  At such a point, the derivative does not exist because the slope of the vertical line is undefined.

Example 3: (CC5e p. 165-166, Activities 15 and 17)

Identify input values (other than endpoints) at which the function is **not differentiable**.
State the reason(s) the function is not differentiable at each input value identified.

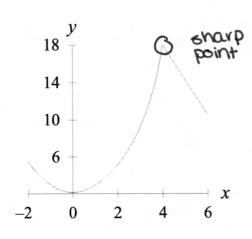

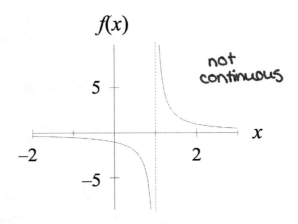

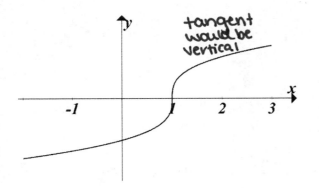

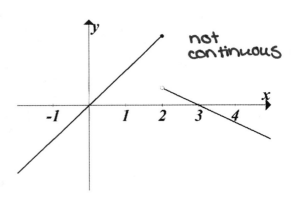

Section 2.5: Rates of Change Defined over Intervals

The rate of change, or derivative, of a function $f(x)$, at any input x on an interval, is the limit of secant slopes between $(x, f(x))$ and nearby point $(x+h, f(x+h))$:

$f'(x) = \lim\limits_{h \to 0} \dfrac{f(x+h) - f(x)}{h}$, provided the limit exists.

This is called the **limit definition of the derivative.**

Example 1:

$f(x+h)$ is found in the numerator of the limit definition for $f'(x)$. Find and simplify $f(x+h)$ for each of the functions below.

$f(x) = 3x - 4$	$f(x+h) =$
$f(x) = x^2 + 1$	$f(x+h) =$
$f(x) = 3x^2 - 2x + 1$	$f(x+h) =$
$f(x) = \dfrac{1}{x}$	$f(x+h) =$
$f(x) = \sqrt{x}$	$f(x+h) =$
$f(x) = x^3$	$f(x+h) =$

Example 2: Use the limit definition to find the derivative $f'(x)$ for $f(x) = 2x^2 - 1$.

a. Let $(x+h, f(x+h))$ be a point very close to the point of tangency $(x, f(x))$.
The formula for the slope of a secant line connecting these two points is given.

Simplify: $\dfrac{f(x+h) - f(x)}{(x+h) - x} =$

b. $f'(x)$ is the limit of the secant slopes, as $h \to 0$, i.e. $f'(x) = \lim\limits_{h \to 0} \dfrac{f(x+h) - f(x)}{h}$.

Follow each of the steps below to find $f'(x)$ for $f(x) = 2x^2 - 1$, using the limit definition.

1. Write the general limit definition of the derivative	$f'(x) = \lim\limits_{h \to 0} \dfrac{f(x+h) - f(x)}{h}$
2. Rewrite the limit definition using the given function. This step will require finding $f(x+h)$.	$= \lim\limits_{h \to 0} \dfrac{[\qquad\qquad\qquad] - [\qquad\qquad\qquad]}{h}$
3. Simplify the algebraic expression, showing one step at a time: *3a) Expand $(x+h)^2$*	$= \lim\limits_{h \to 0}$
3b) Distribute	$= \lim\limits_{h \to 0}$
3c) Combine like terms	$= \lim\limits_{h \to 0}$
3d) Factor out and cancel a common factor of h	$= \lim\limits_{h \to 0}$
4. Show the limit of a completely simplified algebraic expression.	$= \lim\limits_{h \to 0}(4x + 2h)$
5. Evaluate the limit as $h \to 0$.	$=$
6. Conclusion. State the derivative formula.	Thus, $f'(x) = 4x$

c.   Use the derivative formula $f'(x) = 4x$ to find the following.

$f'(-2) =$ $\qquad\qquad\qquad$ $f'(-1) =$ $\qquad\qquad\qquad$ $f'(0) =$

$f'(1) =$ $\qquad\qquad\qquad$ $f'(2) =$ $\qquad\qquad\qquad$ $f'(3) =$

Example 3: (CC5e pp. 169-70)

a.   Use the limit definition to find the derivative $f'(x)$ for $f(x) = -1.6x^2 + 15.6x - 6.4$.
     Clearly show all steps, as illustrated in the previous example, including equal signs and limit
     notation.

b.   The amount of coal used quarterly for synthetic-fuel plants in the United States between 2001
     and 2004 can be modeled as $f(x) = -1.6x^2 + 15.6x - 6.4$ million short tons, where x is the
     number of years since the beginning of 2000.

     Find $f'(3.5)$ and write a sentence of interpretation.

c. Find the percentage rate of change in the amount of coal used quarterly in synthetic-fuel plants when $x = 3.5$. Include units with the answer.

Example 4: In finding the derivative of $f(x) = 2x^2 - x + 3$ below, there is a missing parentheses in step 2, there are four incorrect terms due to distribution errors in step 3b, two limit notations missing, and one crucial missing step.

Write-in the missing parentheses, correct the four terms, write in the limits, and fill in the missing step.

$$f'(x) = \lim_{h \to 0} \frac{f(x+h) - f(x)}{h}$$

$$= \lim_{h \to 0} \frac{[2(x+h)^2 - (x+h) + 3] - 2x^2 - x + 3}{h}$$

$$= \lim_{h \to 0} \frac{[2(x^2 + 2xh + h^2) - (x+h) + 3] - [2x^2 - x + 3]}{h}$$

$$= \lim_{h \to 0} \frac{2x^2 + 2xh + 2h^2 - x + h + 3 - 2x^2 - x + 3}{h}$$

$$= \frac{4xh + 2h^2 - h}{h}$$

$$= \frac{h(4x + 2h - 1)}{h}$$

$$=$$

$$= 4x - 1$$

Thus, $f'(x) = 4x - 1$

Example 5: (CC5e pp. 168-9)

The pressure on a scuba diver underwater is $f(x) = \dfrac{1}{33}x + 1$ atm at x feet below the surface of the water.

a. Use the limit definition to find the equation for the rate-of-change of f.

b. Find $f(100)$, $f'(100)$, and the percentage rate of change in the pressure on a scuba diver that is 100 feet below the water. Include units with all answers.

Example 6: (CC5e pp. 170-71)

Compare three methods for finding the derivative for the function $f(x) = x^2$ at $x = 1$.

a. The figure shows a graph of the function $f(x) = x^2$. Use a tangent line to **graphically** *estimate*

$$\left.\frac{df}{dx}\right|_{x=1} = f'(1) \approx \underline{\hspace{2cm}}.$$

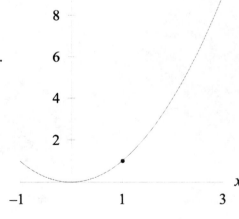

b. Use the limit of the slopes of secant lines to **numerically** *estimate*. Round entries in the table to three decimal places.

$x \to 1^-$	$\dfrac{f(x)-f(1)}{x-1}$	$x \to 1^+$	$\dfrac{f(x)-f(1)}{x-1}$
0.9		1.1	

$$\lim_{x \to 1^-} \frac{f(x)-f(1)}{x-1} = \qquad\qquad \lim_{x \to 1^+} \frac{f(x)-f(1)}{x-1} =$$

Conclusion: $f'(1) = \lim\limits_{x \to 1} \dfrac{f(x)-f(1)}{x-1} =$

c. Find a formula for $f'(x)$ using the **limit definition** of the derivative, clearly showing all steps. Then use the formula to evaluate $f'(1)$.

Section 2.6: Rate-of-Change Graphs

A **slope graph** of a function (or **rate-of-change graph** or **derivative graph**) is the graph that results from plotting the slopes of the function.

If the function graph is continuous, with no sharp corners or points that would have vertical tangent lines, then the **slope graph** of the function will be continuous.

If the function graph is continuous, but has a point with a vertical tangent, the slope graph will have a vertical asymptote at that point. If the function graph is continuous, but has a sharp corner, the **slope graph** will not be continuous at that point.

If the function graph is not continuous at a point, the **slope graph** will not be continuous at that point.

Example 1:

The quadratic function $f(x) = 2x^2 - 1$, has derivative $f'(x) = 4x$. This can be verified using the limit definition of the derivative. Therefore, the graph of $f'(x) = 4x$ is the slope graph of $f(x) = 2x^2 - 1$.

It is possible to sketch the slope graph without knowing the derivative formula.

a. The tangent lines at $x = -2$, $x = -1$, $x = 0$, $x = 1$, and $x = 2$ are drawn on the graph of the quadratic. Write the slopes of each of these tangent lines directly on the graph of the quadratic.

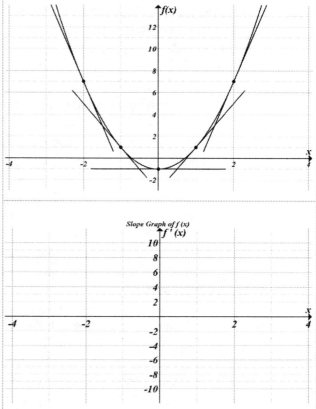

b. Plot the **slopes** of the tangent lines at $x = -2$, $x = -1$, $x = 0$, $x = 1$, and $x = 2$ on the **slope graph**. Since the slope of the tangent line at $x = -2$ is -8, plot the point $(-2, -8)$. Repeat for the slopes at $x = -1$, $x = 0$, $x = 1$, and $x = 2$.

c. Draw a line through the points to sketch a slope graph for $f(x) = 2x^2 - 1$.

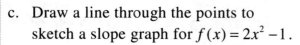

d. Find the equation of the line drawn in part c.

To sketch a slope graph from a graph of a function, it is not necessary to calculate exact slopes of tangent lines. Follow the steps below to sketch a slope graph.

Step 1: Find points on the graph of $f(x)$ with a slope of *zero*. Since relative maxima or relative minima have horizontal tangents, the function has a slope of zero at these points. These are *x-intercepts* on the **slope graph**.

Identify any points on the graph of $f(x)$ in which the slope *does not exist*. The slope does not exist at input values that have a sharp point, a discontinuity, or a vertical tangent. The **slope graph** has *breaks* (either open circles or a vertical asymptote) at such points.

Step 2: Examine each interval between the *x*-intercepts or breaks.

If the function is *increasing*, with *positive* slopes, the **slope graph** lies *above* the *x*-axis on that interval.

If the function is *decreasing*, with *negative* slopes, the **slope graph** lies *below* the *x*-axis on that interval.

Step 3: If the graph of the function is *concave up*, slopes are increasing and the **slope graph** is *increasing*. If the function is *concave down*, slopes are decreasing and the **slope graph** is *decreasing*.

Note that the steeper the tangent lines are, the further away the **slope graph** will be from the *x*-axis at those input values.

Since an inflection point on the graph of $f(x)$ is a point at which the function is increasing or decreasing the most or least rapidly, that is the point at which the **slope graph** has a *relative maximum* or *relative minimum* (except in the case of a vertical tangent).

Example 2:

Draw the slope graph for the following quadratic function by following the above three steps.

- What input value has a slope of zero? _____ Graph (1,0) on the slope graph.

- For $x < 1$, slopes are positive. The slope graph is _____ *(above/below)* the x-axis on this interval. Since the graph of the parabola is concave down, and the slopes are becoming less steep (from left to right), the slope graph is _____ *(increasing/decreasing)* on this interval.

- For $x > 1$, slopes are negative. The slope graph is _____ *(above/below)* the x-axis on this interval. Since the graph of the parabola is concave down, and the slopes are becoming steeper (from left to right), the slope graph is _____ *(increasing/decreasing)* on this interval.

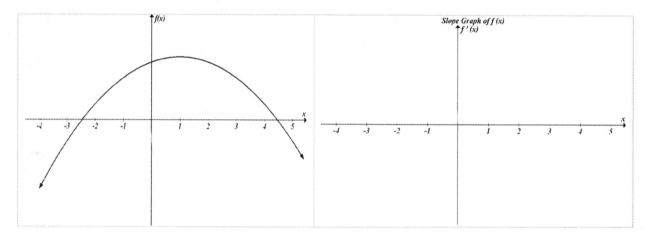

Example 3:

The graph of a cubic function $f(x)$ is shown below on the interval $0 < x < 6.5$.

a. The slope is zero when $x =$ _____ and $x =$ _____.

b. For $0 < x < a$, the graph of f is increasing, so the slopes are _____ *(positive/negative)*.

For $0 < x < a$, the graph is _____ *(concave up/concave down)*. The tangent lines become less steep as x approaches a from the left, so the slopes are _____ *(increasing/decreasing)*.

c. For $a < x < c$, the graph of f is decreasing, so the slopes are _____ *(positive/negative)*.

On the interval $a < x < c$, the graph of f has an inflection point at $x =$ _____. This is the point where f is decreasing _____ (*most rapidly/least rapidly*).
$f'(b)$ is a _____(*relative maximum/relative minimum*) on $0 < x < 6.5$.

d. For $c < x < 6.5$, the graph of f is _____(*increasing/decreasing*), so the slopes are _____ (*positive/negative*).

    For $c < x < 6.5$, the graph is _____(*concave up/concave down*). The tangent lines become steeper for $x > c$, so the slopes are _____ (*increasing/decreasing*).

e. Sketch a graph on f' on the axes provided.

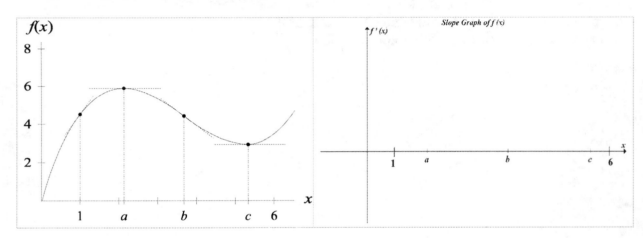

Example 4:

Draw the slope graph for the following cubic function.

$f(x)$ is increasing_____ (*most rapidly/least rapidly*) at approximately $x = 1.5$, where $f'(x)$ has a _____ (*relative maximum/relative minimum*)..

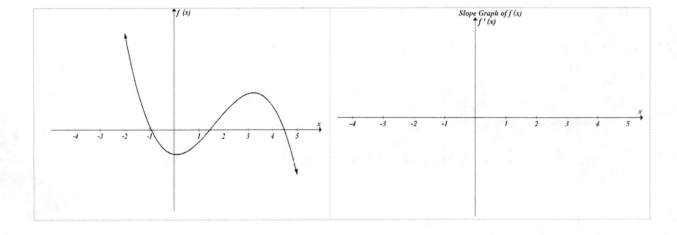

Example 5:

Draw the slope graph for the following cubic function.

$f(x)$ is decreasing_____ (*most rapidly/least rapidly*) at approximately $x =$ ___ , where
$f'(x)$ has a _____ (*relative maximum/relative minimum*).

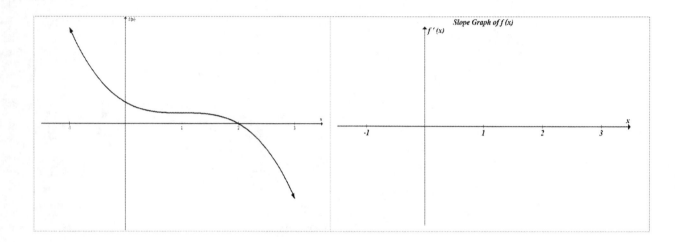

Example 6:

Draw the slope graph for the following linear function. Note that the slope is constant.

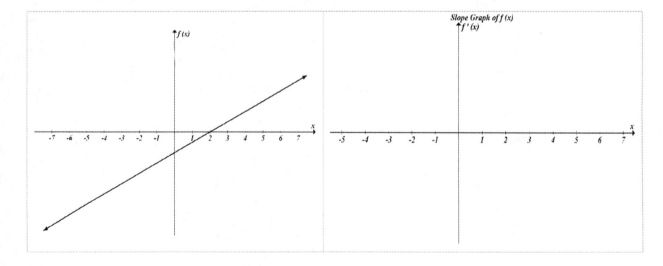

Example 7:

Draw the slope graph for the following function. This function is not smooth, since it *has a sharp point at* $x = 3$. The derivative does not exist at x=3 because a tangent line cannot be drawn at a sharp point. The slope graph has _____ at $x = 3$.

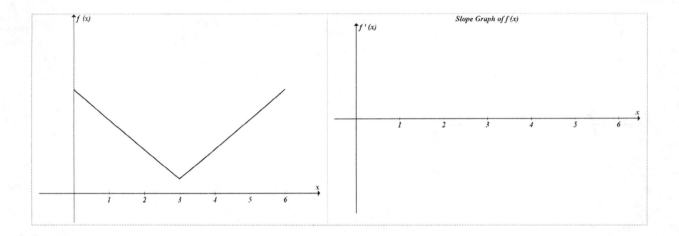

Example 8:

Draw the slope graph for the following function. This function *is not continuous at* $x = 2$.
The derivative does not exist at $x = 2$ because a tangent line cannot be drawn at a *discontinuity*.

The slope graph has _____ at $x = 2$.

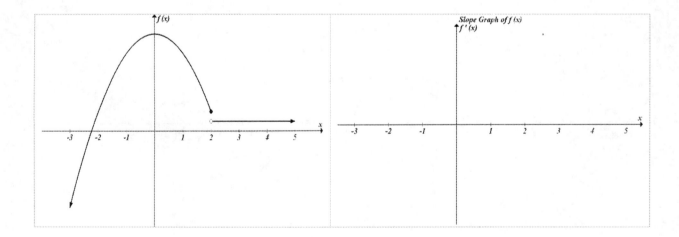

Example 9:

Draw the slope graph for the following function. This function *has a vertical tangent at* $x = 1$.
The derivative does not exist at $x = 1$ because the slope of a vertical tangent line is undefined.
The slope graph has _____ at $x = 1$.

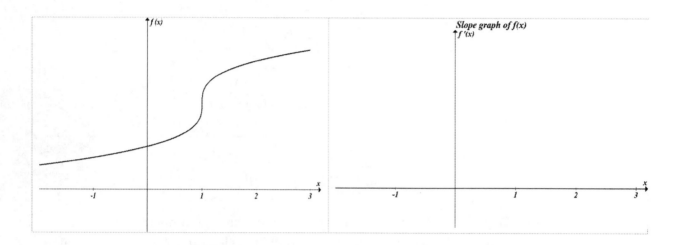

Example 10:

Draw the slope graph for the following logistic function.
$f'(x)$ has a _____ (*relative maximum/relative minimum*) at approximately $x =$ ___ .

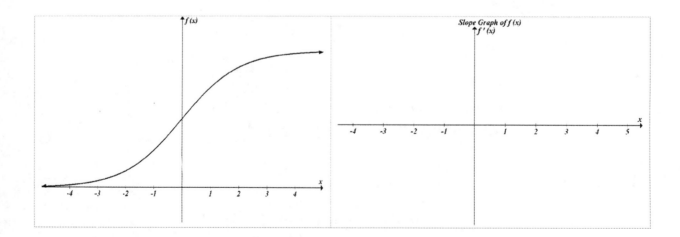

Example 11:

Draw the slope graph for the following exponential function.

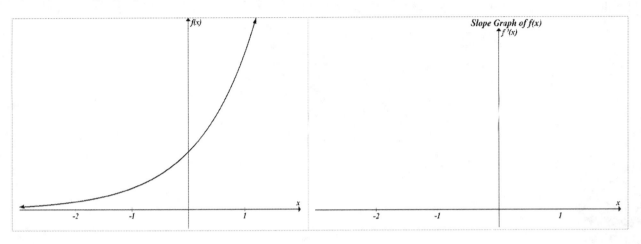

Example 12:

Answer the questions using the graph of $y = f(x)$ shown below and the points labeled points A, B, C, D and E. For parts a - e, list all x-values that apply. Sketch the slope graph on the axes below.

a. $f'(x) > 0$ at $x = $ _____

b. $f'(x) < 0$ at $x = $ _____

c. $f'(x)$ does not exist at $x = $ _____

d. $f'(x) = 0$ at $x = $ _____

e. A horizontal tangent line would be drawn at $x = $ _____.

f. The average rate of change between point A and B is the same as the instantaneous rate-of-change at $x = $ _____.

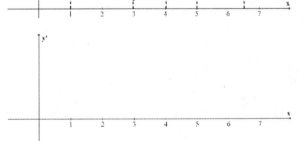

g. The tangent line at $x = $ _____ lies above the graph of $y = f(x)$.

h. The tangent line at $x = $ _____ lies below the graph of $y = f(x)$.

i. The tangent line at $x = $ _____ cuts through the graph of $y = f(x)$.

j. A tangent line cannot be drawn at $x = $ _____.

Example 13: (CC5e pp. 178-79)

A scatter plot of the population data for Cleveland from 1810 through 1990 is shown below.

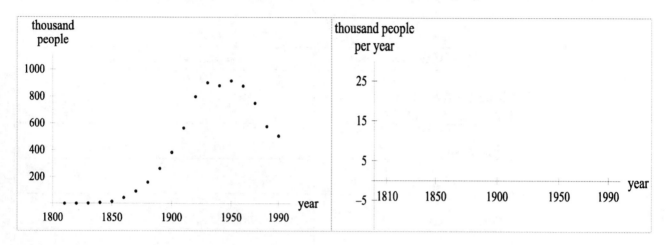

a. Sketch a smooth curve over the scatter plot. The curve should have one relative maximum and two inflection points.

b. What are the approximate input values at the inflection points?

c. Draw tangent lines and estimate the slope at the inflection points.

d. Sketch the slope graph on the axes shown to the right.

e. Identify the input units and output units on the slope graph.

Example 14: Suppose that $f(x)$ is a continuous and differentiable function.

a. For each characteristic of the graph of $f(x)$ in the table below, describe the corresponding feature on the graph of $f'(x)$.

Graph of $f(x)$ is/has	Graph of $f'(x)$ is/has...
Relative Maximum/Minimum (not at a sharp point)	
Increasing	
Decreasing	
Concave up	
Concave down	
Inflection point (without a vertical tangent)	

b. If a function is continuous, but is not differentiable at a point because it has a sharp point, its slope graph will have _____ at that point.

c. If a function is continuous, but is not differentiable at a point because it has a vertical tangent, its slope graph will have _____ at that point.

d. If a function is not continuous at a point, then its slope graph will have

_____ at that point.

Section 3.1: Simple Rate-of-Change Formulas

Constant Rule for Derivatives:
- If $f(x) = b$, where b is a constant, then $f'(x) = 0$.

Simple Power Rule for Derivatives:
- If $f(x) = x^n$, then $f'(x) = nx^{n-1}$, where x is any non-zero real number and n is a constant.

Constant Multiplier Rule for Derivatives:
- If $f(x) = c \cdot g(x)$ where c is a constant, then $f'(x) = c \cdot g'(x)$

Sum and Difference Rules for Derivatives:
- If $h(x) = (f + g)(x) = f(x) + g(x)$ then $h'(x) = f'(x) + g'(x)$
- If $h(x) = (f - g)(x) = f(x) - g(x)$ then $h'(x) = f'(x) - g'(x)$

Example 1:

Find the derivative of each of the following functions using the Constant Rule.

$y = 5$	$\dfrac{dy}{dx} =$
$f(x) = \pi$	$f'(x) =$
The speed of a car with its cruise control set is $s(t) = 65$ mph where t is time in minutes.	$s'(t) = $ _____ mph per minute

Rules of Exponents
For integer constants $m > 0$, $n > 0$, and $x \neq 0$,

$$x^{\frac{1}{n}} = \sqrt[n]{x} \qquad\qquad x^{\frac{m}{n}} = \sqrt[n]{x^m} \qquad\qquad x^{-n} = \frac{1}{x^n}$$

Example 2:

Find the derivative of each of the following functions using the Power Rule. If necessary, first use the Rules of Exponents to rewrite the function in the form $f(x) = x^n$.

$y = x^2$	$\dfrac{dy}{dx} =$
$f(x) = x^5$	$f'(x) =$
$g(x) = \sqrt{x} = \underline{\qquad}$	$g'(x) =$
$p(t) = \sqrt[3]{t} = \underline{\qquad}$	$p'(t) =$
$s(t) = \dfrac{1}{t^2} = \underline{\qquad}$	
$s(r) = \dfrac{1}{r} = \underline{\qquad}$	
$f(x) = x$	
$t(x) = \dfrac{1}{\sqrt{x}} = \underline{\qquad}$	
$g(x) = \dfrac{1}{\sqrt[3]{x^2}} = \underline{\qquad}$	

Example 3:

Identify "c" and "$g(x)$" for each of the following functions and find the derivative of each using the Constant Multiplier Rule.

$f(x) = 5x^3$ $c = \underline{\hspace{1cm}}$; $g(x) = \underline{\hspace{2cm}}$	$f'(x) =$
$j(x) = \dfrac{1}{2x^5} = \underline{\hspace{2cm}}$ $c = \underline{\hspace{1cm}}$; $g(x) = \underline{\hspace{2cm}}$	

Example 4:

Find the derivative of each of the following functions using the Sum and Difference Rules.

$p(x) = 5x^3 - 3.5x^2 + 9x - 6\pi^2$	
$f(x) = \dfrac{3x^2 - 4x + 8}{2x} = \underline{\hspace{3cm}}$ (*Hint*: Rewrite as 3 terms)	

Example 5: (CC5e p. 199, Activity 31)

$n(x) = -0.00082x^3 + 0.059x^2 + 0.183x + 34.42$ million people gives the number of Americans age 65 or older, x years after 2000, with projections through 2050.

a. What is the projected number of Americans 65 years of age and older in 2030? Include units with the answer.

b. How quickly is the projected number of Americans age 65 or older changing in 2030? Include units with the answer.

Evaluating the derivative function at a point:

- Enter $n(x)$ in Y1
- **2nd QUIT** returns to the Home Screen
- **MATH** ▼ to 8 [nDeriv(] **ENTER** returns nDeriv(on the Home Screen
- Complete the nDeriv statement with **Y1 , X , 30**). **ENTER** returns the value of the derivative at $x = 30$.

OR

- **MATH** ▼ to 8 [nDeriv(] **ENTER** returns the first screen on the Home Screen.
- Fill in the blanks as shown in the second screen. **ENTER** returns the value of the derivative at $x = 30$.

c. Calculate the percentage rate of change of $n(x)$ in 2030. Include units in the answer.

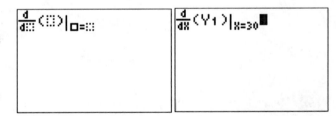

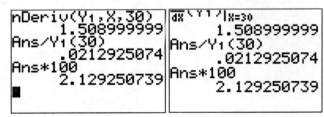

A **rate-of-change model** is a statement that describes the relationship between an output variable and an input variable of a derivative equation in context. It includes the following:

- a derivative equation
- an output description, with (derivative) units
- an input description, with units
- an input data range

d. Find the derivative of $n(x) = -0.00082x^3 + 0.059x^2 + 0.183x + 34.42$ and write a rate-of - change model.

$n'(x) =$ _____ million people per _____

gives the **rate of change** in the number of Americans 65 years of age and older, x years after 2000, with projections through 2050.

Example 6:

The number of student tickets sold for a home basketball game at State University is represented by $S(w)$ tickets when w is the winning percentage of the team.

The number of nonstudent tickets sold for the same game is represented by $N(w)$ hundred tickets when the winning percentage of the team is w.

a. $T(w) =$_____ tickets gives the total number of tickets sold for a home basketball game at State University, when w is the winning percentage of the team.

b. Use simple rate-of-change formulas to express the derivative of $T(w)$ and write a rate-of-change model for the total number of tickets sold.

$T'(w) =$ _____ tickets per _____
gives the _____ in the total number of tickets sold for a home basketball game at State University, when w is the winning percentage of the team.

Example 7: (CC5e p. 197)

The data in the table give the maintenance costs for vehicles driven for 15,000 miles in the U.S. from 1993 through 2000. The maintenance costs given are yearly averages.

Year	1993	1994	1995	1996	1997	1998	1999	2000
Maintenance costs, in dollars	360	375	390	420	420	465	540	585

a. Write a quadratic model, where t is the number of years since 1993, for the maintenance cost for a vehicle driven 15,000 miles.

b. Write a rate-of-change model for the maintenance cost model.

c. How rapidly were maintenance costs changing in 1998? Write a sentence of interpretation.

Example 8: (CC5e p. 198, Activities 1, 5, 9, 13, 17, 21, and 25)

For each function given in the first column, write the derivative formula in the second column.

$y = 17.5$	
$f(x) = x^5$	
$x(t) = t^{2\pi}$	
$f(x) = -0.5x^2$	
$f(x) = 5x^3 + 3x^2 - 2x - 5$	
$g(x) = \dfrac{-9}{x^2}$	
$f(x) = \dfrac{3x^2 + 1}{x}$	

Section 3.2: Exponential, Logarithmic, and Cyclic Rate-of-Change Formulas

---

e^x **Derivative Rule:**

- If $f(x) = e^x$, then $f'(x) = e^x$

Exponential Derivative Rule:

- If $f(x) = b^x$, then $f'(x) = (\ln b)b^x$

Natural Logarithm Rule for Derivatives:

- If $f(x) = \ln x$, $x > 0$, then $f'(x) = \dfrac{1}{x}$

(Optional)
Sine Rule for Derivatives:

- If $f(x) = \sin x$, then $f'(x) = \cos x$

Cosine Rule for Derivatives:

- If $f(x) = \cos x$, then $f'(x) = -\sin x$

Note: The e^x Derivative Rule is a special case of the Exponential Derivative Rule since $f(x) = e^x$ has derivative $f'(x) = (\ln e)e^x = e^x$ because $\ln e = 1$.

Example 1:

Find the derivative of each of the following functions using the Exponential Rules.

$y = 2^x + x^2$	$\dfrac{dy}{dx} =$
$f(x) = 2(1.5^x) - 3x$	$f'(x) =$
$g(t) = 4e^t - 3e^2$	

Example 2:

Find the derivative of each of the following functions using the Logarithmic Rule.

$y = 3\ln x$	
$f(x) = 2\ln x + 2^x - 3\ln(2)$	
$g(t) = 5 - 8\ln t$	
$j(x) = 3.2\left(0.7^x\right) + 1.5 - \pi^2$	

Example 3: (CC5e pp. 205-206)

Optimal weekly weight loss can be modeled as a function of the dieter's starting weight. The data in the table shows the optimum weekly weight loss for dieters originally weighing between 140 and 220 pounds.

	140	150	180	220
Body weight in pounds	140	150	180	220
Body weight – 130 pounds	10			
Optimal weight loss, in pounds	1.1	2	3	4

a. Fill in the table by subtracting 130 pounds from each input value to align the input to the amount of weight over 130 pounds.

b. Examine the scatterplot and find a completely defined logarithmic model for the optimum weight loss.

$p(w) =$

c. Write a completely defined rate-of-change model for the optimal weight loss model.

$$p'(w) =$$

d. What is the optimum weekly weight loss for a person with a body weight of 200 pounds? Include units with the answer.

e. How quickly is the optimum weekly weight loss for a person with a body weight of 200 pounds changing? Include units with the answer.

f. Find the percentage rate of change in optimum weekly weight loss for a person with a body weight of 200 pounds. Include units with the answer.

Example 4 (Optional): (CC5e pp. 209-210, Activities 3, 9, 13)

Find the derivative of the following function using the Sine and Cosine Rules.

$n(x) = 14\sin x$	
$n(x) = 6\ln x - 13\sin x$	
$f(t) = 0.07\cos t - 4.7\sin t$	
$g(t) = 13\sin t + 5\cos t$	

Section 3.3: Rates of Change for Functions That Can Be Composed

Given two functions $f(t)$ and $t(x)$, the derivative of the composition $f(t(x))$ is given by the First Form of the Chain Rule: $\dfrac{df}{dx} = \dfrac{df}{dt} \cdot \dfrac{dt}{dx}$

Note that $f(t(x))$ can be written in typical function notation as $f(x)$. It follows that the derivative of the composition can be denoted as $\dfrac{df}{dx}$.

To use the First Form of the Chain Rule:
i. Find the derivative of each of the two given functions.
ii. Multiply the two derivatives together.
iii. Rewrite in terms of a single input variable.

Example 1: (CC5e p.213)

Given $f(t) = 3t^2$ and $t(x) = 4 + 7\ln x$, find the derivative of the composition $f(t(x))$.

a. Find: $\dfrac{df}{dt} =$ and $\dfrac{dt}{dx} =$

b. Multiply: $\dfrac{df}{dx} = \dfrac{df}{dt} \cdot \dfrac{dt}{dx} =$

c. What is the input variable for the composition function $f(x)$? _____

  Rewrite $\dfrac{df}{dx}$ in terms of x: $\dfrac{df}{dx} =$

Example 2:

Given $f(t) = 1000e^t$ and $t(x) = 0.025x^2 + 1$, find the derivative of the composition $f(t(x))$.

a. Find: $\dfrac{df}{dt} =$ and $\dfrac{dt}{dx} =$

b. Multiply: $\dfrac{df}{dx} = \dfrac{df}{dt} \cdot \dfrac{dt}{dx} =$

c. What is the input variable for the composition function $f(x)$? _____

  Rewrite $\dfrac{df}{dx}$ in terms of x: $\dfrac{df}{dx} =$

Example 3: (CC5e pp. 211-212)

$t(h)$ degrees Fahrenheit gives the temperature h hours after sunset, $0 \le h \le 12$.

$f(t)$ gives the number of cricket chirps in one minute when the temperature is t degrees Fahrenheit, $50 \le t \le 75$.

a. Use the input/output diagram to identify units for the composition $f(t(h))$.

    input units: _____

    output units: _____

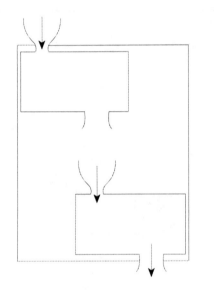

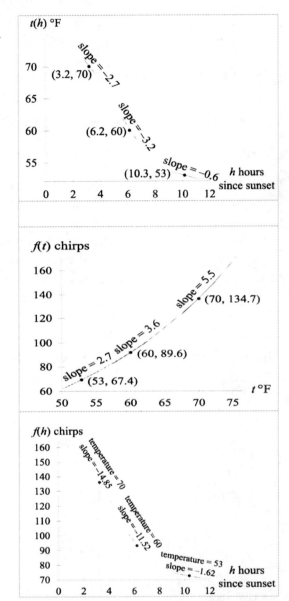

$f(h) =$_____ **gives the number of cricket chirps in one minute, h hours after sunset, $0 \le h \le 12$.**

b. Use the graphs to find the number of cricket chirps in one minute 3.2 hours after sunset. Include units with the answer.

c. Use the graphs and the First Form of the Chain Rule to determine how quickly the number of cricket chirps in one minute is changing with respect to time, 3.2 hours after sunset. Include units with each derivative.

Example 4: (CC5e p.213)

$A(v)$ dollars represents the average cost to produce a student violin when v violins are produced.

$v(t)$ represents the number of student violins produced in year t.

In 2011, 10,000 violins are produced and production is increasing by 100 violins per year.

When 10,000 violins are produced, the average cost to produce a student violin is \$142.10, and the average cost is decreasing by \$0.15 per violin.

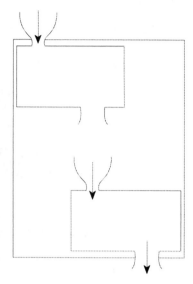

a. Use the input/output diagram to identify units for the composition $A(v(t))$, or $A(t)$.

   input units: _____   output units: _____

b. Use the given information to find the average cost to produce a student violin in 2011. Include units with your answer.

   Since $v(2011) =$ _____ _____ and $A(10,000) =$ _____ _____,

   the average cost to produce a student violin in 2011 was _____ _____.

c. Use the given information and the First Form of the Chain Rule to determine how quickly the average cost to produce a student violin is changing with respect to time, in 2011. Include units with each derivative.

   $$\left.\frac{dA}{dt}\right|_{t=2011} = \left.\frac{dA}{dv}\right|_{\substack{v=10,000 \\ (t=2011)}} \cdot \left.\frac{dv}{dt}\right|_{t=2011} = \underline{\hspace{4cm}} \cdot \underline{\hspace{4cm}}$$

   $$= \underline{\hspace{8cm}}$$

d. Write a sentence of interpretation for your answer to part c.

Example 5: (CC5e p.217, Activity 21)

$f(t) = 0.123t^3 - 3.3t^2 + 22.2t + 55.72$ percent gives the occupancy rate for the month at a motel where $t = 1$ is the end of January, etc.

$r(f) = -0.0006f^3 + 0.18f^2$ thousand dollars gives the monthly revenue where $f\,\%$ is the occupancy rate at the motel.

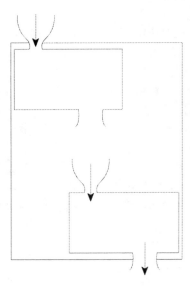

a. Use the input/output diagram to identify units for the composition function $r(f(t))$, or $r(t)$.

input units: _____

output units: _____

b. Find the monthly revenue at the end of July ($t = 7$). Include units with the answer.

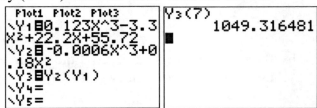

c. Find the rate of change in monthly revenue at the end of July ($t = 7$). Include units with the answer.

```
nDeriv(Y3,X,7)
      -105.7918473
```

$$\frac{d}{dx}(Y_3)\big|_{x=7}$$
```
      -105.7918473
```

Example 6:

Functions $g(h)$ and $h(x)$ can be composed as $g(h(x))$.

Given $h(-1) = 5$, $g(5) = 0.2$, $\dfrac{dh}{dx}\bigg|_{x=-1} = 3$, and $\dfrac{dg}{dh}\bigg|_{h=5} = -1.5$, find the following:

a. $g(h(-1)) =$

b. $\dfrac{dg}{dx}\bigg|_{x=-1} =$

Section 3.4: Rates of Change of Composite Functions

A composite function $f(x) = g(h(x))$ has an *outside function g* and an *inside function h* .

Its derivative is given by the Second Form of the Chain Rule: $f'(x) = g'(h(x)) \cdot h'(x)$

The Second Form of the Chain Rule says that the derivative of a composition function is found

by multiplying: $\begin{pmatrix} \text{the } \textit{derivative of the outside} \\ \text{function evaluated at the} \\ \text{inside function} \end{pmatrix} \bullet \begin{pmatrix} \text{the } \textit{derivative of} \\ \textit{the inside function} \end{pmatrix}$

Example 1:

$f(x) = (x^3 - 5x^2)^{2/3}$ is a composite function $f(x) = g(h(x))$.

a.   Note that $f(x)$ takes the form $f(x) = (\textit{inside function})^{2/3}$. The outside function is

   $g(h) = h^{2/3}$. Circle the "inside function" in $f(x) = (x^3 - 5x^2)^{2/3}$.

Outside function: $g(h) = h^{2/3}$	Inside function: $h(x) = x^3 - 5x^2$

b.   Write the derivative of the outside function and the inside function in the table below.
     Note that the derivative of the outside function uses the Power Rule.

Derivative of outside function: $g'(h) = \frac{2}{3} h^{-1/3}$	Derivative of inside function: $h'(x) = 3x^2 - 10x$

c.   Use the Second Form of the Chain Rule to find the derivative of the composition:

$$f'(x) = g'(h(x)) \cdot h'(x) = \frac{2}{3} (\textit{inside function})^{-1/3} \cdot (\textit{derivative of the inside function})$$

$$= \frac{2}{3} (x^3 - 5x^2)^{-1/3} \cdot (3x^2 - 10x)$$

129

Example 2:

$f(x) = \ln(x^3 - 5x^2)$ is a composite function $f(x) = g(h(x))$.

a. Note that $f(x)$ takes the form $f(x) = \ln(\textit{inside function})$. The outside function is
$g(h) = \ln(h)$. Circle the "inside function" in $f(x) = \ln(x^3 - 5x^2)$.

Outside function:	Inside function:

b. Write the derivative of the outside function and the inside function in the table below.
Note that the derivative of the outside function uses the Natural Logarithm Rule.

Derivative of outside function:	Derivative of inside function:

c. Use the Second Form of the Chain Rule to find the derivative of the composition:

$$f'(x) = g'(h(x)) \cdot h'(x) = \frac{1}{\textit{inside function}} \cdot (\textit{derivative of the inside function})$$

$$= \frac{1}{x^3 - 5x^2} \cdot (3x^2 - 10x)$$

Example 3:

$f(x) = e^{(x^3 - 5x^2)}$ is a composite function $f(x) = g(h(x))$.

a. Note that $f(x)$ takes the form $f(x) = e^{(\textit{inside function})}$. The outside function is $g(h) = e^h$.
Circle the "inside function" in $f(x) = e^{(x^3 - 5x^2)}$.

Outside function:	Inside function:

b. Write the derivative of the outside function and the inside function in the table below.
Note that the derivative of the outside function uses the e^x Rule.

Derivative of outside function:	Derivative of inside function:

c. Use the Second Form of the Chain Rule to find the derivative of the composition:
$$f'(x) = g'(h(x)) \cdot h'(x) = e^{(\textit{inside function})} \cdot (\textit{derivative of the inside function})$$

$$= e^{(x^3 - 5x^2)} \cdot (3x^2 - 10x)$$

Example 4:

$f(x) = 2^{(x^3 - 5x^2)}$ is a composite function $f(x) = g(h(x))$.

a. Note that $f(x)$ takes the form $f(x) = 2^{(inside\ function)}$. The outside function is $g(h) = 2^h$.
    Circle the "inside function" in $f(x) = 2^{(x^3 - 5x^2)}$.

Outside function:	Inside function:

b. Write the derivative of the outside function and the inside function in the table below.
    Note that the derivative of the outside function uses the Exponential Rule.

Derivative of outside function:	Derivative of inside function:

c. Use the Second Form of the Chain Rule to find the derivative of the composition:

$$f'(x) = g'(h(x)) \cdot h'(x) = (\ln 2) \cdot 2^{(inside\ function)} \cdot (derivative\ of\ the\ inside\ function)$$
$$= (\ln 2) \cdot 2^{(x^3 - 5x^2)} \cdot (3x^2 - 10x)$$

Example 5:

Use the Second Form of the Chain Rule to find the derivative of each function. Verify that each function is a composite function by identifying the outside function g and the inside function h. Identify the Rate-of-Change Rule used in finding the derivative of the outside function. Use proper notation.

a. $f(x) = (-3x^2 + 2x - 5)^{-2}$

$f'(x) =$

b. $f(x) = \sqrt{-3x^2 + 2x - 5}$

$f'(x) =$

c. $f(x) = (\ln x)^{-2}$

d. $f(x) = 3\sqrt{\ln x}$

e. $f(x) = \ln(-3x^2 + 2x - 5)$

f. $f(x) = 2\ln(\sqrt{x})$

g. $f(x) = 0.5e^{(-3x^2 + 2x - 5)}$

h. $f(x) = 2^{(-3x^2 + 2x - 5)}$

Example 6:

Use Addition and Subtraction Rules to find the derivative of the function. Apply the Chain Rule for terms that require it.

$$f(x) = e^{2x^3} + 2\ln x - 5\sqrt{x} - \pi^2$$

$$f'(x) =$$

The Chain Rule can be used multiple times for a function of the form $f(x) = g(h(k(x)))$.

The derivative is: $f'(x) = g'\big(h(k(x))\big) \cdot h'(k(x)) \cdot k'(x)$.

Example 7:

Find the derivative of $f(x) = e^{\left(\sqrt{-3x^2 + 2x - 5}\right)}$.

Example 8:

Find the derivative of each function. Use proper notation.

a. $f(x) = 5 - 3\ln\left(x^2 + 1\right)$

b. $s(t) = 2e^{3t^2}$

c. $f(x) = 12e^{0.5x} - \pi x + e^2$

d. $f(x) = 6\sqrt[3]{x^2 + 5x}$

e. $f(x) = \dfrac{5}{7(x^3 - x)^2}$ Hint: Before taking the derivative, rewrite the function using a negative

exponent for the denominator: $f(x) = \dfrac{5}{7}(x^3 - x)^{-2}$

f. $f(x) = \dfrac{15.2}{1 + 2.4e^{0.3x}}$ Hint: Before taking the derivative, rewrite the function using a negative

exponent for the denominator: $f(x) = 15.2(1 + 2.4e^{0.3x})^{-1}$

g. $f(x) = 2^{\ln x}$

h. $f(x) = 3\sqrt{x^2 + 1}$

Example 9:

Write a completely defined rate of change model for each of the models given below.

a. A model for the average number of chirps each minute by a cricket is $f(t) = 7.8e^{0.0407t}$ chirps when the temperature is t degrees Fahrenheit.

b. The temperature on an average late-summer evening in south-central Michigan can be modeled as $t(h) = \dfrac{24}{1 + 0.04\,e^{(0.6h + 0.02)}} + 52$ degrees Fahrenheit, h hours after sunset.

Section 3.5: Rates of Change for Functions That Can Be Multiplied

If two functions $g(x)$ and $h(x)$ are multiplied together, the derivative of their product $f(x) = (g \cdot h)(x) = g(x) \cdot h(x)$ is given by the Product Rule: $f'(x) = g'(x) \cdot h(x) + g(x) \cdot h'(x)$

The Product Rule says that the derivative of a product function is found by:

$$\left(\begin{array}{c} \text{derivative of} \\ \text{the first function} \end{array} \right) \bullet \left(\begin{array}{c} \text{second} \\ \text{function} \end{array} \right) + \left(\begin{array}{c} \text{first} \\ \text{function} \end{array} \right) \bullet \left(\begin{array}{c} \text{derivative of} \\ \text{the second function} \end{array} \right)$$

Example 1:

Given $g(x) = 5x^6$ and $h(x) = \ln x$, find the derivative of their product.

a. The product function is $(g \cdot h)(x) = g(x) \cdot h(x) =$

b. The derivative of the product function is

$(g \cdot h)'(x) = g'(x) \cdot h(x) + g(x) \cdot h'(x)$

$= (\underline{\hspace{2cm}}) \cdot (\underline{\hspace{2cm}}) + (\underline{\hspace{2cm}}) \cdot (\underline{\hspace{2cm}})$

$= \underline{\hspace{8cm}}$

Note: The functions and their derivatives can be organized in a table.

First function: $g(x) = 5x^6$	Second function: $h(x) = \ln x$
Derivative of first function: $g'(x) = 30x^5$	Derivative of second function: $h'(x) = \dfrac{1}{x}$

Example 2:

Given $g(x) = 2(3^x)$ and $h(x) = 3x^2 - 2x + 1$, find the derivative of their product.

a. The product function is $(g \cdot h)(x) = g(x) \cdot h(x) =$

b. The derivative of the product function is

$(g \cdot h)'(x) = g'(x) \cdot h(x) + g(x) \cdot h'(x)$

$= (\underline{\hspace{2cm}}) \cdot (\underline{\hspace{2cm}}) + (\underline{\hspace{2cm}}) \cdot (\underline{\hspace{2cm}})$

$= \underline{\hspace{8cm}}$

Note: The functions and their derivatives can be organized in a table.

First function:	Second function:
Derivative of first function:	Derivative of second function:

Example 3: (CC5e pp. 226-227)

$s(x)$ million students gives the number of full time students enrolled in American public colleges and universities, where x is the number of years since the fall semester, 1999.

$t(x)$ thousand dollars per student gives the average tuition paid by a full-time student in an American public colleges and universities, where x is the number of years since the fall semester, 1999.

a. Identify the input and output units for the product

$$E(x) = s(x) \cdot t(x).$$

input units:

output units:

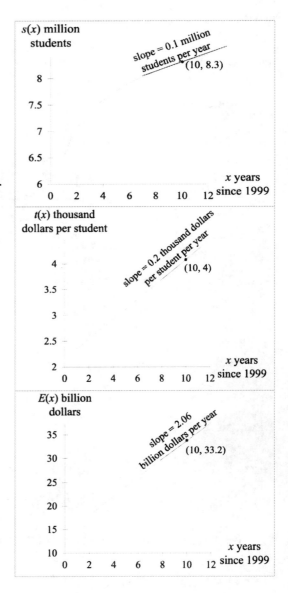

b. Use the graphs to find the total amount spent on tuition by students enrolled full time in American public colleges and universities in the fall semester of 2009. Include units with the answer.

c. Use the graphs and the Product Rule to determine how quickly the amount spent on tuition by students enrolled full time in American public colleges and universities was changing in the fall semester of 2009. Include units with each factor and in the answer.

Example 4: (CC5e p.228)

$f(m)$ layers gives the number of laying hens in month m, where $m = 1$ is January, etc.

$g(m)$ eggs per layer gives the laying capacity for one laying hen in month m, where $m = 1$ is January, etc.

In March 2010, a poultry farmer had 30,000 laying hens and he was increasing his flock by 500 laying hens per month.

In March 2010, the monthly laying capacity was 21 eggs per hen and the laying capacity was increasing by 0.2 eggs per hen per month.

a. Identify units for the product $(f \cdot g)(m)$.

   input units: output units:

b. Use the given information to find the egg production in March 2010.
    Include units in each blank.

   Since $f(3) =$ _____ and $g(3) =$ _____ ,

   egg production in March 2010 was _____ .

c. Use the given information and the Product Rule to determine how quickly egg production was changing in March 2010. Include units with each factor and in the answer.

   $$\left. \frac{d(f \cdot g)}{dm} \right|_{m=3} = f'(3) \cdot g(3) + f(3) \cdot g'(3) =$$

d. Write a sentence of interpretation for your answer to part c.

Example 5: (CC5e p.230-231)

$f(x) = 3.09x + 54.18$ gives the percent of post-secondary students with some form of financial aid where $x = 1$ represents fall 2000, $x = 2$ represents fall 2001, etc.

$s(x) = 0.76\ln x + 6.5$ million students gives the full-time enrollment in American public colleges and universities where $x = 1$ represents fall 2000, $x = 2$ represents fall 2001, etc.

a. Write a model for the number of full-time students with some form of financial aid.
   (*Convert the units for function $f(x)$ to a decimal.*)

b. How many students had financial aid in fall 2010? Include units with the answer.

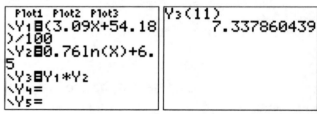

c. How quickly was the number of students with financial aid changing in fall 2010? Include units with the answer.

Example 6: (CC5e p.232, Activity 5)

$s(x) = 15 + \dfrac{2.6}{x+1}$ dollars gives the value of one share of a company's stock where x is the number of weeks after the stock is first offered.

An investor buys some of the stock each week and owns $n(x) = 100 + 0.25x^2$ shares after x weeks.

The value of the investor's stock is $v(x) = s(x) \cdot n(x)$ dollars x weeks after the stock is first offered.

a. What is the value of the investor's stock 10 weeks after the stock was first offered?

b. How quickly is the value of the investor's stock changing 10 weeks after the stock was first offered?

Example 7:

Use the table below to find the derivative of $f(x) = g(x) \cdot h(x)$ when $x = -1$. Include work.

	$g(x)$	$g'(x)$	$h(x)$	$h'(x)$
$x = -1$	5	0.02	-8	-0.025

a. $f'(x) =$

b. $f'(-1) =$

Section 3.6: Rates of Change of Product Functions

The derivative of a product $f(x) = g(x) \cdot h(x)$ is given by the Product Rule:

$$f'(x) = g'(x) \cdot h(x) + g(x) \cdot h'(x)$$

The Product Rule says that the derivative of a product function is found by:

$$\left(\begin{array}{c} \text{derivative of} \\ \text{the first function} \end{array} \right) \bullet \left(\begin{array}{c} \text{second} \\ \text{function} \end{array} \right) + \left(\begin{array}{c} \text{first} \\ \text{function} \end{array} \right) \bullet \left(\begin{array}{c} \text{derivative of} \\ \text{the second function} \end{array} \right)$$

Example 1:

$f(x) = x^{2/3}(x^3 - 5x^2)$ is a product $f(x) = g(x) \cdot h(x)$.

a. Identify the first and second functions.

First function: $g(x) =$ Second function: $h(x) =$

b. Find the derivatives:

$g'(x) =$ $h'(x) =$

First function: $g(x) = x^{2/3}$	Second function: $h(x) = x^3 - 5x^2$
Derivative of first function: $g'(x) = \frac{2}{3}x^{-1/3}$	Derivative of second function: $h'(x) = 3x^2 - 10x$

c. Use the Product Rule to find the derivative of $f(x) = x^{2/3}(x^3 - 5x^2)$.

$$f'(x) = g'(x) \cdot h(x) + g(x) \cdot h'(x) =$$

Example 2:

$f(x) = e^{2x}\sqrt{x^3 - 5x^2}$ is a product $f(x) = g(x) \cdot h(x)$.

a.   Identify the first and second functions.

First function: $g(x) =$ Second function: $h(x) =$

b.   Find the derivatives. Note that the first and second functions are compositions and finding their derivatives will require the Chain Rule.

$g'(x) =$ $h'(x) =$

First function:	Second function:
Derivative of first function:	Derivative of second function:

c.   Use the Product Rule to find the derivative of $f(x) = e^{2x}\sqrt{x^3 - 5x^2}$.

$f'(x) = g'(x) \cdot h(x) + g(x) \cdot h'(x) =$

Example 3:

Use the Product Rule to find the derivative of each function. Verify that each function is a product by identifying the two functions that are being multiplied (call the first function g and the second function h). Use proper notation.

a. $f(x) = \left(4x^2 - x + 1.5\right)\left[2\left(5^x\right)\right]$

$f'(x) =$

b. $f(x) = \dfrac{-2\left(3^x\right)}{\sqrt{x}} = $ _____

$f'(x) =$

c. $f(x) = 2.5x\,\sqrt{x^3 - x} = $ _____

d. $f(x) = (6x-4)^5(2x+1)$

e. $f(x) = \dfrac{2x^3 + 7x}{3x - 5} = $ _____

f. $f(x) = 2(5^x)(\ln x)$

Example 4: (CC5e pp. 234-235, 235-336)

Write a rate of change model for each of the following models.

a. $f(t) = 110te^{-0.7t}$ ng/mL gives the concentration levels of the active ingredient in Ambien in the bloodstream t hours after a single 5 mg dose is taken orally.

b. The production level at a plant manufacturing radios can be modeled as

   $f(x) = 10.54x^{0.5}(2 - 0.13x)^{0.3}$ thousand radios where x thousand dollars has been spent on modernizing plant technology.

Example 5: (CC5e pp. 236-237)

Kish Industries develops and produces deck laminates for naval vessels.
$C(q) = 500 + 190\ln q$ thousand dollars gives the production costs to develop and produce q thousand gallons of deck laminate.

a. Write an equation for the average cost to produce a gallon of deck laminate when q thousand gallons of deck laminate are produced.

b. Rewrite the average cost function in part a) as a product (instead of a quotient).

c. Find the derivative of the average cost function. Include the output units.

Section 4.1: Linearization and Estimates

For a point $(c, f(c))$ and a nearby point $(c+h, f(c+h))$ on a differentiable function f, the rate of change $f'(c)$ can be used to **approximate the amount of change** between the two points. $f'(c)$ can also be used to **approximate the value** of $f(c+h)$.

Recall from section 2.1 that **change** between $(c, f(c))$ and a nearby point $(c+h, f(c+h))$ is defined as the difference between output values: $f(c+h) - f(c)$, for $h > 0$.

An **estimate of change** between $(c, f(c))$ and a nearby point $(c+h, f(c+h))$ is given by: $f'(c) \cdot h$. Graphically, $f'(c) \cdot h$ is the vertical distance between points at $x = c$ and $x = c + h$ on the tangent line to f at $x = c$.

$f(c+h) \approx f(c) + f'(c) \cdot h$ gives an **estimate of the output value** $f(c+h)$ by finding the output value for $x = c + h$ on the tangent line to f at $x = c$. It is found by adding the estimated amount of change to $f(c)$.

The **linearization of a function f at a point c** is the equation of the line tangent to the function at point c. This equation can be found using the point-slope formula of a line, with a point on the tangent line $(c, f(c))$ and its slope $f'(c)$.

The linearization of f at point c is given by the formula $f_L(x) = f(c) + f'(c) \cdot (x - c)$.

Example 1: (CC5e p. 252)

As shown in the graph to the right, $g(10) = 5$ and $g'(10) = 2$.

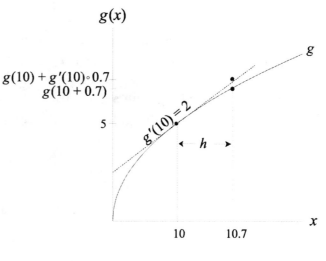

a. Approximate the amount of **change** between $g(10)$ and $g(10.7)$.

$g(10) + g'(10) \circ 0.7$
$g(10 + 0.7)$

The amount of change, $g(10.7) - g(10)$, can be estimated by $g'(10) \cdot 0.7 =$

b. Approximate the output value of $g(10.7)$.

$g(10.7) \approx [g(10) + \text{estimated change}] =$

c. The estimate in part b is an *underestimate/overestimate* because the function is *concave up/concave down* and the tangent line lies *below/above* the graph.

d. Write a linearization for $g(x)$ at $c = 10$.

$g_L(x) =$

e. Use the linearization in part d to approximate $g(10.7)$. Verify that the answer is the same as found in part b.

Example 2: (CC5e p. 255, Activity 5)

a. If $f(3) = 17$ *and* $f'(3) = 4.6$, write a linearization for f at input $c = 3$.

b. Use the linearization to estimate $f(3.5)$.

Example 3: (CC5e pp. 250-251)

$p(t)$ cents is the average retail price of a pound of salted, grade A butter, t years since 1990.

Use the graph of p along with a tangent line at $t = 8$ to complete the following statements.

a. $p(8) =$ _____ and $\dfrac{dp}{dt}\Big|_{t=8} =$ _____

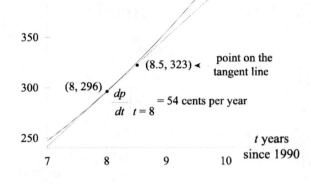

b. Estimate the **change** in the price of butter from the end of December, 1998 until the end of June, 1999.

$p'(8) \cdot 0.5 =$

c. Estimate the price of butter at the end of June, 1999.

$p(8.5) \approx p(8) + p'(8) \cdot 0.5 =$

d. Is the estimated price of butter found in part c an *underestimate or overestimate*?

e. Write a **linearization** for the function p at $c = 8$.

Example 4: (CC5e pp. 253-254)

$f(t) = -12.92t^3 + 185.45t^2 - 729.35t + 10038.57$ thousand employees gives the number of 20-24 year old full-time employees over a six-year period, $1 \le t \le 7$. Assume that the six-year period represents the *previous* six years, so that $t = 7$ represents **current** full-time employment.

The graph to the right shows $f(t)$ on the interval $1 \le t \le 7$.

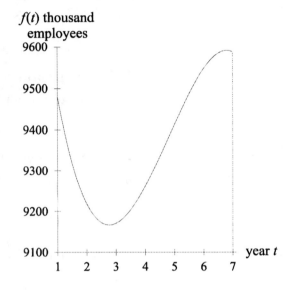

f(t) thousand employees

a. Find $f(2)$ and $f'(2)$. Include units.

b. Find the linearization $f_L(t)$ at $c = 2$.

$$f_L(t) = f(c) + f'(c) \cdot (t - c) =$$

c. Estimate $f(3)$ using the linearization found in part b. Is this an underestimate or an overestimate of the model's prediction of the number of 20-24 year old full-time employees when $t = 3$?

d. Find $f(3)$ using the given function $f(x)$. Compare your answer to your answer to part c.

Section 4.2: Relative Extreme Points

A **relative extreme point** $(c, f(c))$ is a point on a function f at which a relative maximum or a relative minimum occurs.

A function has a **relative maximum** at input c if the output $f(c)$ is *greater than or equal to* any other output in some open interval around c. $f(c)$ is referred to as a relative maximum value.

A function has a **relative minimum** at input c if the output $f(c)$ is *less than or equal to* any other output in some open interval around c. $f(c)$ is referred to as a relative minimum value.

If a function $f(x)$ is defined on a closed interval $a \le x \le b$, then a relative extreme point does **not** occur at endpoints $x = a$ or $x = b$.

Example 1: (similar to CC5e p. 267)

a. Identify each of the points at inputs *a, b, c, d, e* and *g* in the graph of $f(x)$ shown to the right as a *relative maximum, a relative minimum, or neither.*
For each relative extreme point, find the slope of the function at that point.

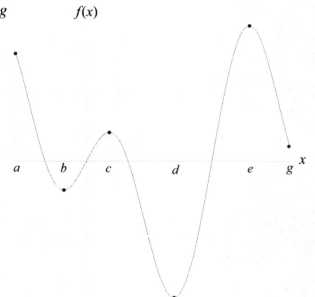

f(x)

a: _____; _____

b: _____; _____

c: _____; _____

d: _____; _____

e: _____; _____

g: _____; _____

b. What is the slope of the function at each of the relative extreme points?

A **critical point** of a function f is a number c in the domain of f at which $f'(c) = 0$ or $f'(c)$ does not exist.

A critical point identifies the location of all **possible** relative extreme points. If f has a relative maximum or minimum value at c and $f'(c)$ exists, then $f'(c) = 0$. However, if $f'(c) = 0$, there is not necessarily an extreme point at $x = c$.

The First Derivative Test (to determine whether a relative extreme point occurs at a critical point):

For a critical point c of a function f that is continuous on some open interval around c :

- If f' changes from positive to negative as x increases through c, then f has a relative maximum at c.

- If f' changes from negative to positive as x increases through c, then f has a relative minimum at c.

- If f' does not change sign as x increases through c (from positive to negative or vice versa), then f does not have a relative extreme point at c.

Graphically, the first derivative test says that for a function that is continuous on an open interval around c with $f'(c) = 0$, if the slope graph **crosses** (not just touches) the input axis at $x = c$, there is a relative extreme point at the critical point $x = c$. For a function that is continuous on an open interval around c with $f'(c)$ not existing, if the slope graph **is on opposite sides** of the input axis at $x = c$, there is a relative extreme point at $x = c$.

If a function f is not continuous at a point c, then $f'(c)$ does not exist. Examine the graph of f to determine whether a relative extreme point exists at the critical point $x = c$.

Example 2: (CC5e p. 258)

Given: $f(x) = 0.4x^2 - 2x + 10$

a. Identify the critical point on the graph of $f(x)$ by marking an "X" on the point at which $f'(c) = 0$.

b. Write the equation whose solution identifies the critical point(s).

c. Solve the equation to identify the critical point.

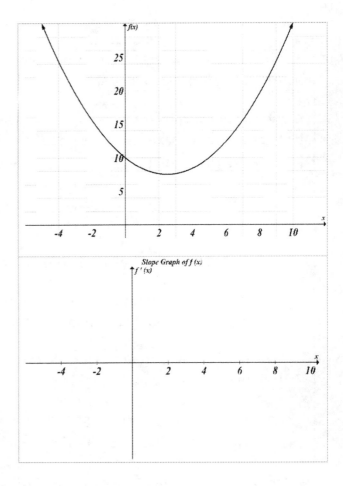

d. Draw the slope graph of $f(x) = 0.4x^2 - 2x + 10$ and verify that the slope graph **crosses** the x-axis at the critical point $x = c$.

e. Circle the terms that correctly complete the statement.

f' is *positive/negative* for $x < c$ and *positive/negative* for $x > c$.

f. Does the function have a *relative maximum, a relative minimum, or neither* at the critical point in part c)?

Example 3:

a. Identify the critical point on the graph of $f(x)$ by marking an "X" on the point at which $f'(c) = 0$.

b. Draw the slope graph of $f(x)$.

c. Does the slope graph **cross** the x-axis at the critical point $x = c$?

d. Circle the terms that correctly complete the statement.

f' is *positive/negative* for $x < c$ and *positive/negative* for $x > c$.

e. Does the function have a *relative maximum, a relative minimum, or neither* at the critical point?

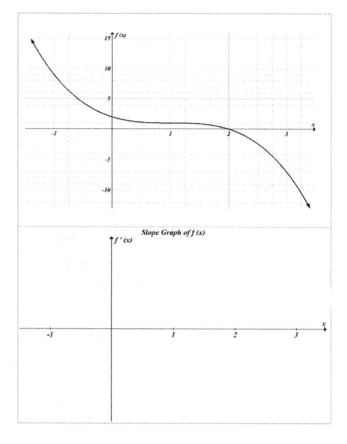

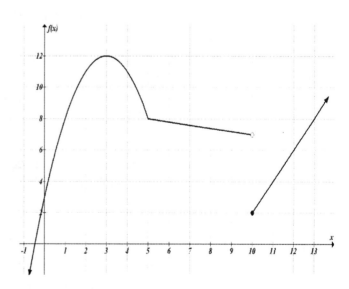

Example 4:

Consider the three critical points on the graph of the function *f:*

a. A critical point of $f(x)$ occurs at $x =$ ___ . If the function is continuous at this point, discuss what happens to the slope graph near this critical point. If the function has a *relative maximum or a relative minimum* at this critical point, mark it on the graph.

b. A second critical point of $f(x)$ occurs at $x =$ _____ . If the function is continuous at this point, discuss what happens to the slope graph near this critical point. If the function has a *relative maximum or a relative minimum* at this critical point, mark it on the graph.

c.   A third critical point of $f(x)$ occurs at $x =$ ____ . If the function is continuous at this point, discuss what happens to the slope graph near this critical point. If the function has a *relative maximum or a relative minimum* at this critical point, mark it on the graph.

Example 5: (CC5e pp. 257-259)

The population of Kentucky can be modeled as $p(x) = 0.395x^3 - 6.67x^2 + 30.3x + 3661$ thousand people where x is the number of years since 1980, $0 \le x \le 10$.

a.   Use your calculator to verify that the graph to the right is the graph of $p(x)$ on the interval $0 \le x \le 10$.

b.   Label and mark an "X" on the graph of $p(x)$ for the relative maximum and the relative minimum. Does the graph of $p'(x)$ confirm your findings? Explain.

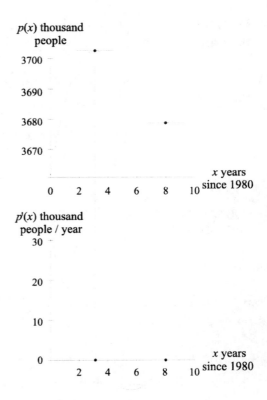

c.   Use your calculator to find the following, correct to three decimal places, on the given interval. (See calculator directions on the next page.)

Relative minimum: $x =$ _____ ; $p($ $) =$ _____

Relative maximum: $x =$ _____ ; $p($ $) =$ _____

d.   What was the population of Kentucky at the relative maximum?

What was the population of Kentucky at the relative minimum?

Finding relative maximum and relative minimum points:

- Enter $p(x)$ into Y1

- Set the window using **WINDOW** Xmin = **0** and Xmax = **10**

- **ZOOM 0** [ZOOMFIT] returns the graph of p.

- **2ND TRACE** [CALC] **4** [maximum] returns the second screen.

- Use ◄ as many times as necessary to position the cursor to the *left* of the relative maximum of p
- **ENTER** marks the left bound

- Use ► as many times as necessary to position the cursor to the *right* of that relative maximum
- **ENTER** marks the right bound

- Use ◄ as many times as necessary to position the cursor at the approximate relative maximum. **ENTER** returns the x and y coordinates of the relative maximum.

- Repeat the process to find the relative minimum using **2ND TRACE** [CALC] **3** [minimum].

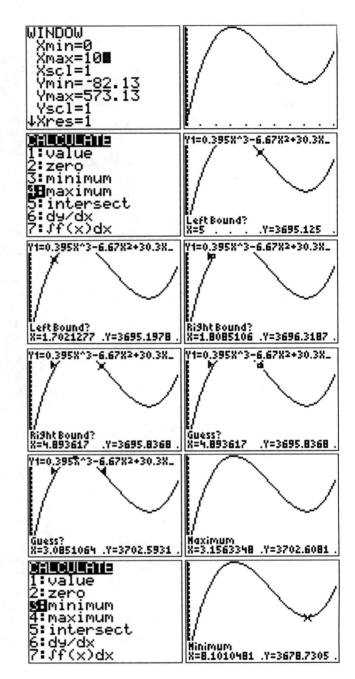

Using critical points as an alternate method for finding relative maximum and relative minimum points:

- Enter $p(x)$ into Y1 and $p'(x)$ into Y2 using nDeriv(Y1, X, X). Recall: *nDeriv* is found using MATH 8.
- Move the cursor to Y1 and press ENTER to un-highlight it

- Set the window using **WINDOW** Xmin = **0** and Xmax = **10**
- **ZOOM 0** [ZOOMFIT] returns the graph of p'. There are two places where p' crosses the horizontal axis.

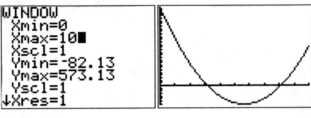

- **2ND TRACE** [CALC] **2** [zero] returns the second screen.

- Use ◄ as many times as necessary to position the cursor to the *left* of the first *x*-intercept (zero) of p'
- **ENTER** marks the left bound

- Use ► as many times as necessary to position the cursor to the *right* of that *x*-intercept of p'
- **ENTER** marks the right bound

- Use ◄ as many times as necessary to position the cursor at the approximate zero. **ENTER** returns a solution to $p'(x) = 0$

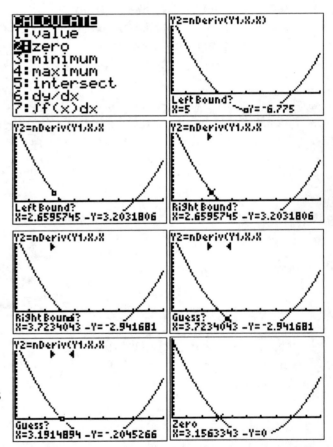

- Return to the Home Screen and **Y1 ENTER** returns the output value of the stored *x-value*. Since the last *x*-value was the location of the relative maximum, *x*= 3.1563, the value returned is the output value (with no intermediate rounding of the input value).

Y1	
	3702.608113

- Repeat the process to find the second critical point and the corresponding minimum.

Example 6: (CC5e p. 262)

TW Cable Company actively promoted sales in a town that previously had no cable service. Once TW saturated the marker, it introduced a new 50-channel system, raised rates, and began a new sales campaign. As the company began to offer its expanded system, a different company, CC Network, began offering satellite service with more channels than TW and at a lower price. TW Cable's revenue for 26 weeks after it began its sales campaign is given by $R(x) = -3x^4 + 160x^3 - 3000x^2 + 24,000x$ dollars, where x is the number of weeks since TW Cable Company began its new sales campaign.

a. Use your calculator to verify that the graph to the right is the graph of $R(x)$ on the interval $0 \le x \le 26$.

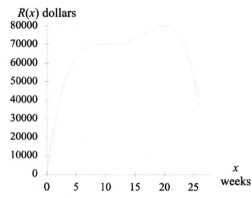

b. One critical point occurs at approximately $x = 10$. Explain how the derivative graph shows there is not a relative extreme at this critical point.

c. A relative maximum does occur at a second critical point. Mark the relative maximum with an "X" on the graph of $R(x)$. Also mark the graph of $R'(x)$ by circling the point on $R'(x)$ at which the relative maximum occurs on $R(x)$.

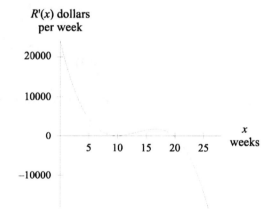

d. Use your calculator to find the second critical point.

When did TW Cable Company's revenue peak during the period shown in the graph?

What was its revenue at that time?

Section 4.3: Absolute Extreme Points

A function *f* has an **absolute maximum** at input *c* if the output $f(c)$ is greater than (or equal to) every other output value on the domain of the function.

A function *f* has an **absolute minimum** at input *c* if the output $f(c)$ is less than (or equal to) every other output value on the domain of the function.

The output $f(c)$ is referred to as the *maximum* (value) or the *minimum* (value) of *f*.

If a function *f* is defined on a closed interval $a \le x \le b$, the absolute maximum or absolute minimum may occur at either endpoint $x = a$ or $x = b$ <u>or</u> an absolute extreme value may occur where a relative extreme value occurs.

To find an absolute extreme on a closed interval $a \le x \le b$, compare the relative extreme values in the interval with the output values at the endpoints $f(a)$ and $f(b)$.
The largest of these values is the absolute maximum and the smallest of these values is the absolute minimum.

Example 1: (CC5e p. 269)

Identify absolute extreme points for the following functions on the domain of all real numbers.

a.

f(x)

$f(x) = e^x$
Absolute maximum? (*yes/no*);
If yes, where? _____

Absolute minimum? (*yes/no*);
If yes, where? _____

b.

g(x)

$g(x) = x^2$
Absolute maximum? (*yes/no*);
If yes, where? _____

Absolute minimum? (*yes/no*);
If yes, where? _____

Example 2: (CC5e p. 271, Activities 3, 4)

Identify absolute extreme points for the following functions on the given domain

For each extreme point, indicate whether the derivative at that point is zero or does not exist.

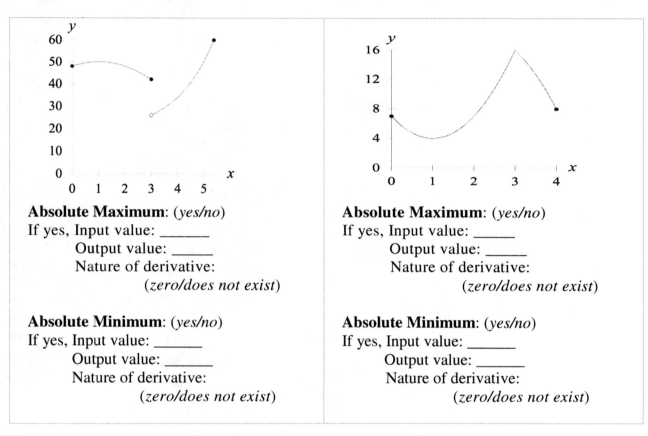

Absolute Maximum: (*yes/no*)
If yes, Input value: _____
       Output value: _____
       Nature of derivative:
           (*zero/does not exist*)

Absolute Minimum: (*yes/no*)
If yes, Input value: _____
       Output value: _____
       Nature of derivative:
           (*zero/does not exist*)

Absolute Maximum: (*yes/no*)
If yes, Input value: _____
       Output value: _____
       Nature of derivative:
           (*zero/does not exist*)

Absolute Minimum: (*yes/no*)
If yes, Input value: _____
       Output value: _____
       Nature of derivative:
           (*zero/does not exist*)

Example 3: (similar to CC5e p. 267)

The function *f*, defined on a closed interval, is shown to the right.

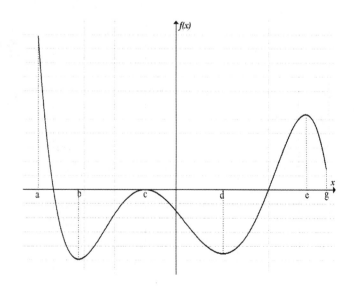

a. Label each of the points at inputs *a, b, c, d, e,* and *g* with all that apply: *relative maximum, relative minimum, absolute maximum, absolute minimum.*

b. Can an *absolute extreme* value occur at an endpoint of a closed interval?

c. Can a *relative extreme* value occur at an endpoint of a closed interval?

Example 4:

The population of Kentucky can be modeled as

$p(x) = 0.395x^3 - 6.67x^2 + 30.3x + 3661$

thousand people where x is the number of years since 1980, $0 \le x \le 10$.

$p(x)$ thousand people

3700

3690

3680

3670

0   2   4   6   8   10 x years since 1980

a. Label and mark an "X" on the graph of $p(x)$ for the absolute maximum and the absolute minimum.

b. In section 4.2, we found the following:

$p'(x)$ thousand people / year

30

20

10

0

2   4   6   8   10 x years since 1980

Relative minimum:

$x =$ _____; $p(_____) =$ _____

Relative maximum:

$x =$ _____; $p(_____) =$ _____

c. Find $p(0) =$ _____ and $p(10) =$ _____ .

d. Comparing the relative extreme points and the endpoints, determine the absolute extreme points:

Absolute minimum: $x =$ _____; $p(_____) =$ _____

Absolute maximum: $x =$ _____; $p(_____) =$ _____

e. Between the years 1980 and 1990, Kentucky's population was *lowest* in _____, at which time the population was _____.

Between the years 1980 and 1990, Kentucky's population was *highest* _____ years after 1980, at which time the population was _____.

Example 5: (CC5e pp. 268-269)

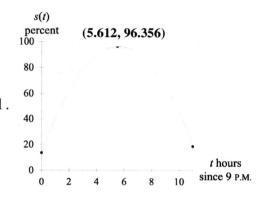

$s(t) = -2.63t^2 + 29.52t + 13.52$ percent gives the percentage of people aged 15 and older in the United States who are sleeping t hours after 9:00 pm, $0 \le t \le 11$.

a.   Write a sentence of interpretation for the ordered pair $(5.612, 96.356)$.

b.   Identify the absolute maximum on the closed interval $0 \le t \le 11$. Interpret the answer.

Absolute maximum: $t =$ _____; $s($_____$) =$ _____

The highest percentage of people, 15 years and older in the U.S., who are sleeping occurs

_____ hours after 9 pm, at which time _____ percent of people 15 years and older

are sleeping.

c.   Find the absolute minimum on the closed interval $0 \le t \le 11$. Interpret the answer.

Absolute minimum: $t =$ _____; $s($_____$) =$ _____

The lowest percentage of people, 15 years and older in the U.S., who are sleeping occurs

_____ hours after 9 pm, at which time _____ percent of people 15 years and older

are sleeping.

Example 6: (CC5e pp. 271-272, Activity 15)

$f(h) = -0.865h^3 + 12.05h^2 - 8.95h + 123.02$ cubic feet per second (cfs) gives the flow rate of a river in the first 11 hours after the beginning of a severe thunderstorm, h hours after the storm began.

a. What are the flow rates for $h = 0$ and $h = 11$?

b. Identify the absolute maximum on the closed interval $0 \leq h \leq 11$.

Absolute maximum: $h = $ _____; $f($_____$) = $ _____

In the first eleven hours after a severe thunderstorm, the flow rate for a river was *highest*

_____ hours after the storm began. At that time, the flow rate was _____ cfs.

c. Find the absolute minimum on the closed interval $0 \leq t \leq 11$. Hint: Compare the relative minimum to $f(0)$. Interpret the answer.

Absolute minimum: $h = $ _____; $f($_____$) = $ _____

In the first eleven hours after a severe thunderstorm, the flow rate for a river was *lowest*

_____ hours after the storm began. At that time, the flow rate was _____ cfs.

Example 7:

A clothing manufacturer determines that the cost of producing x jackets is $C(x) = 2500 + 0.25x^2$ dollars, and sets the sales price of $p(x) = 150 - 0.5x$ dollars per jacket, $0 \leq x \leq 200$.

a. Find the total revenue from the sale of x jackets.

b. Find the total profit from the sale of x jackets.

c. How many jackets must the manufacturer produce and sell in order to maximize profit?

d. What is the maximum profit?

Section 4.4: Inflection Points and Second Derivatives

The **second derivative** of a function $f(x)$ is the derivative of the derivative function $f'(x)$. It is denoted by $f''(x)$ and read as "*f double prime of x*". The unit of measure for the second derivative is *output units of f' per input unit of f'*, or (*output units of f per input unit of f*) *per input unit of f.*

An **inflection point** is a point at which a continuous function f changes concavity. On a graph of a differentiable function f, it is either the point of greatest slope (*most rapid change*) or the point of least slope (*least rapid change*) and it corresponds to a relative extreme point of $f'(x)$.

If there is an **inflection point** at $x = c$, then $f''(c) = 0$ or $f''(c)$ does not exist. Solutions to the equation $f''(c) = 0$ or points at which $f''(c)$ does not exist are the *possible* location of inflection points of the function $f(x)$.

Second Derivatives and Concavity:
- On an interval on which $f''(x) > 0$, a function f is concave up.
- On an interval on which $f''(x) < 0$, a function f is concave down.

For a continuous function f, if f'' changes from positive to negative as x increases through c, or from negative to positive as x increases through c, then f has an inflection point at c. Graphically, if the second derivative graph crosses the x-axis or lies on opposite sides of the x-axis at c, f has an inflection point at c.

Example 1: (CC5e p. 273)

The population of Kentucky can be modeled as
$p(x) = 0.395x^3 - 6.67x^2 + 30.3x + 3661$ thousand people
where x is the number of years since 1980, $0 \le x \le 13$.

a. Find the equation and write the output units for $p'(x)$.

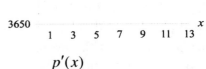

b. Find the equation and write the output units for $p''(x)$.

c. Place an "X" on the graph of $p(x)$ that indicates the inflection point, the point at which the population of Kentucky is *decreasing most rapidly* on the given interval.

d. The graph of $p'(x)$ has a *relative maximum /relative minimum* at the inflection point on $p(x)$.

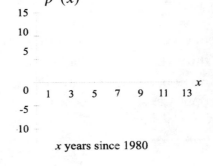

e. Use the calculator to find the point at which the population of Kentucky is *decreasing most rapidly* on the given interval.

Between 1980 and 1993, Kentucky's population was decreasing most rapidly _____ years after 1980.

Finding both coordinates of an inflection point:

- Enter $p(x)$ in Y1

- Enter **nDeriv (Y1, X, X)** or
  $\frac{d}{dx}(Y_1)\Big|_{X=X}$ in Y2 using **MATH 8**

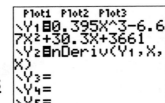

- In **WINDOW**, set Xmin = **0** and Xmax = **13**
- **ZOOM 0** [ZoomFit] returns the graphs of p and p' which are difficult to see in this example. If both functions are visible, refer to example 7 at the end of this section for an alternate method.

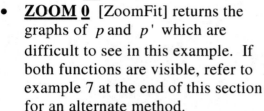
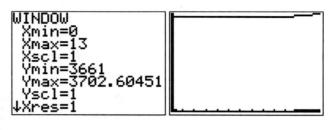

- Turn Y1 off and ZoomFit again to view the graph of p' by itself.

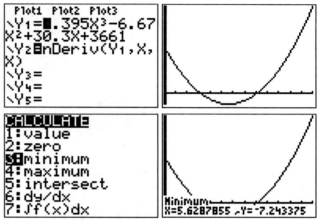

- Find the relative minimum of $p'(x)$ using the process outlined in the previous section. The x-coordinate of the relative minimum of p' is the same as the x-coordinate of the inflection point of p.

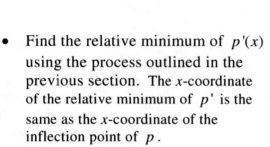

f. How quickly is the population changing at that time?

g. What is Kentucky's population at that time?

- Return to the Home Screen and evaluate **Y1 ENTER** which finds the y-coordinate of the inflection point (with no intermediate rounding of the input value).

h. The graph of $p''(x) = $ _____ at the inflection point on $p(x)$.

Solve the equation $p''(x) = 0$. Is the solution the same as the solution in part e?

i. The change in concavity at the inflection point is indicated by a change in sign on the second derivative graph from *positive to negative / negative to positive*.

On the interval to the left of the inflection point, the graph of $p(x)$ is *concave up/concave down* and the graph of $p''(x)$ lies *above the x-axis/below the x-axis.*

On the interval to the right of the inflection point, the graph of $p(x)$ is *concave up/concave down* and the graph of $p''(x)$ lies *above the x-axis/below the x-axis.*

Example 2: (CC5e p. 279)

The three graphs, g, g', and g'', are shown below.

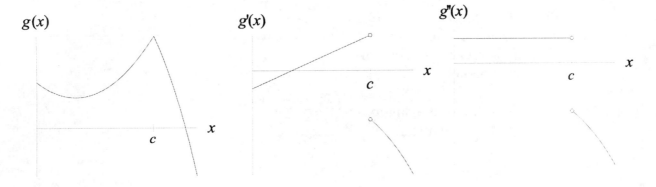

$g(x)$ $g'(x)$ $g''(x)$

a. At an input value of $x = c$, is there a change in concavity in $g(x)$?

    Does the function $g(x)$ have an inflection point at $x = c$?

b. Which is correct: $g''(c) = 0$ or $g''(c)$ does not exist?

c. For input values $x < c$, $g''(x) > 0 / g''(x) < 0$ and $g(x)$ is concave *up/down.*

    For input values $x > c$, $g''(x) > 0 / g''(x) < 0$ and $g(x)$ is concave *up/down.*

Second Derivative Test for Relative Extrema (to determine whether a critical point is a relative extreme point):

Suppose a function f is continuous over an interval containing c,
- If $f'(c) = 0$ and $f''(c) > 0$, then f has a relative minimum at c.
- If $f'(c) = 0$ and $f''(c) < 0$, then f has a relative maximum at c.

Example 3:

In section 4.2, $p(x) = 0.395x^3 - 6.67x^2 + 30.3x + 3661$ was found to have a critical point at $x = 3.156$. The *first derivative test* confirmed that there is in fact a relative maximum at this point (see graphs in Example 1 above). The *second derivative test* also confirms this: $p''(3.156) > 0 / p''(3.156) < 0$, which means that $p(x)$ is concave *up/down* at $x = 3.156$, and thus a relative maximum occurs at $x = 3.156$.

Example 4: (CC5e p. 277)

The figure to the right shows graphs of a function f, its first derivative f', and its second derivative f'', on the interval $0 \le x \le 5$.

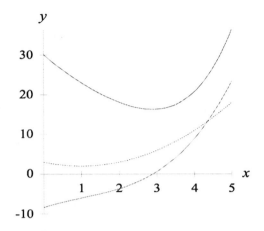

a. Identify and label the graphs of $f(x)$, $f'(x)$, and $f''(x)$.

Complete the following statements:

b. The graph of the function f is concave _up/down_ on the given interval and has a relative

maximum/minimum near $x = 3$.

c. The graph of the first derivative f' lies _above/below_ the x-axis for $x < 3$, lies _above/below_

the x-axis for $x > 3$, and is _increasing/decreasing_ on the interval $0 \le x \le 5$.

f' has a _____ near $x = 3$.

d. The graph of the second derivative f'' lies _above/below_ the x-axis and is _positive/negative_

on the interval $0 \le x \le 5$.

Example 5: (part a, CC5e p. 274)

Use relative extreme points, inflection points, direction, and concavity to determine which of the three graphs shown is the graph of $f(x)$, $f'(x)$, or $f''(x)$.

a.

167

b.

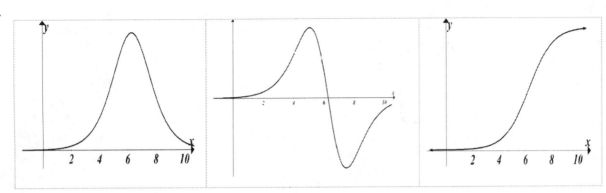

c.

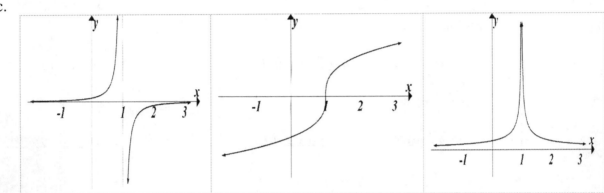

Example 6:

The derivative graph to the right shows the rate of change in last year's production level of jet skis at a manufacturing company. 1= end of January, etc.

Complete the following statements by naming the appropriate months.

a. Last year, the production of jet skis was increasing from the end of _____through the end of _____ and again from the end of _____through the end of _____.

b. Last year, the production of jet skis was decreasing most rapidly at the end of _____.

c. Last year the production of jet skis reached a relative maximum at the end of _____.

d. Last year the production of jet skis reached a relative minimum at the end of _____.

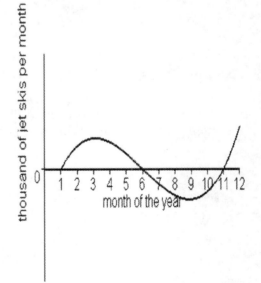

Rate of Change in Production

Example 7:

Suppose that $f(x)$ is a continuous and differentiable function.

a. Using the graph of $f'(x)$ shown to the left below, complete the following statements.

At $x \approx -1.3$, $f(x)$ has a(n) *relative maximum/ relative minimum/inflection point.*

At $x \approx 5.3$, $f(x)$ has a(n) *relative maximum/ relative minimum/inflection point.*

b. Using the graph of $f''(x)$ shown to the right below, complete the following statements.

At $x = 2$, $f(x)$ has a(n) *relative maximum/ relative minimum/inflection point.*

On the interval $x < 2$, $f(x)$ is *concave up/concave down.*

On the interval $x > 2$, $f(x)$ is *concave up/concave down.*

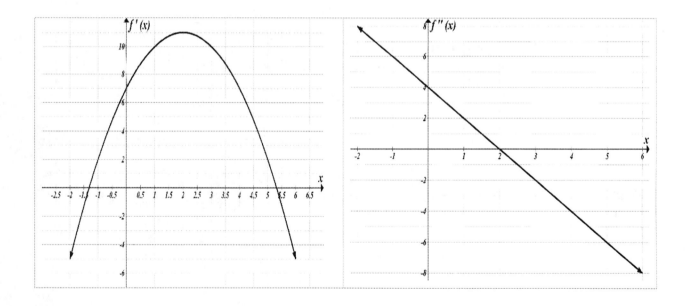

> If an inflection point appears on an *increasing* function that is *concave down to the right* of the inflection point, that point is regarded as the **point of diminishing returns** since each additional unit of input results in a smaller gain in output.

Example 8: (CC5e p. 276)

$p(t) = \dfrac{83}{1 + 5.94e^{-0.969t}}$ percent gives the percentage of new material that an average college student retains after studying for t hours without a break, $0 \le x \le 8$.

The graphs of p, p', and p'' are shown to the right.

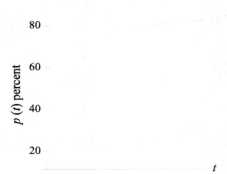

a. How much of the material is retained by a student who has not started studying $(t = 0)$?

b. What is the point of diminishing returns? After how many hours of study is a student's retention rate increasing most rapidly?

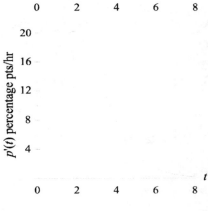

c. At the point of diminishing returns, how quickly is the retention rate changing and what is the retention rate? Include units with your answers.

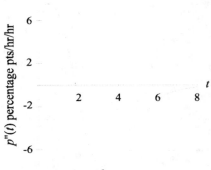

d. Why is the second derivative graph below the x-axis to the right of the point of diminishing returns?

Another example of finding both coordinates of an inflection point:

- Enter $p(t)$ in Y1 and $p'(t)$ in Y2

- Set the WINDOW and ZOOMFIT to get the graph of Y1 and at Y2.

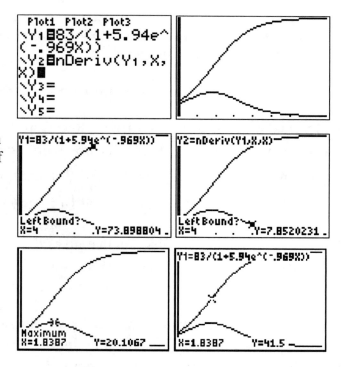

- Use the process described earlier in this section to find the maximum of $p'(t)$. *Initially the header indicates Y1 is selected. Use ▾ to select the derivative function Y2.*

- The first screen shows the maximum of $p'(t)$.
- Use ▴ to move the cursor to the function and obtain the output value at the inflection point.

Example 9:

Suppose that $f(x)$ is a continuous and differentiable function. For each characteristic of the graph of $f(x)$ in the table below, describe the corresponding feature on the graph of $f'(x)$. Then, in the last three rows, also describe the corresponding feature on the graph of $f''(x)$.

Graph of $f(x)$ is/has	Graph of $f'(x)$ is/has...	Graph of $f''(x)$ is/has...
Relative Maximum/Minimum (not at a sharp point)		
Increasing		
Decreasing		
Concave up		
Concave down		
Inflection point (without a vertical tangent)		

Section 4.5: Marginal Analysis

In **marginal analysis,** a decision to increase production is analyzed by weighing potential benefits against potential costs.

In marginal analysis the decision is based on **a unit change in input.**

Marginal analysis uses **derivatives**. Recall from section 4.1 that an **estimate of change** between $(q, f(q))$ and a nearby point $(q+h, f(q+h))$ on a function $f(x)$ is given by $f'(q) \cdot h$. Using $h = 1$ in this formula finds an estimate in the amount of change between $(q, f(q))$ and a point $(q+1, f(q+1))$ and is given by $f'(q) \cdot 1 = f'(q)$.

If $C(q)$ is a continuous function that gives the cost of producing q units, then an estimate of the cost of producing **one** additional unit is given by $C'(q)$ and is called the **Marginal Cost of producing the q+1st unit.**

If $R(q)$ is a continuous function that gives the revenue from selling q units, then an estimate of the revenue generated by selling **one** additional unit is given by $R'(q)$ and is called the **Marginal Revenue from selling the q+1st unit.**

A sentence of **interpretation** for **marginal cost or marginal revenue** does not use the word "marginal" and may be written in the same manner as a sentence of interpretation for a derivative. Or, more commonly in economics, it may take the following form:

> *The additional cost of producing the **q+1st** unit is $C'(q)$ dollars (or the output units of C).*

or

> *The additional revenue from selling the **q+1st** unit is $R'(q)$ dollars (or the output units of C).*

Marginal cost or marginal revenue is measured in cost or revenue units per **single** production unit.

Example 1: (CC5e pp. 285)

$C(x)$ hundred dollars gives the cost of producing x thousand microwave ovens. When 2.4 thousand microwave ovens are produced, the total cost of production is 96 hundred dollars and costs are increasing by 13 hundred dollars per thousand microwave ovens.

a. Write the following sentence using derivative notation.
    When 2.4 thousand microwave ovens are produced, the total cost of production is increasing by 13 hundred dollars per thousand microwave ovens.

b. Marginal cost is measured in cost units per **single** production unit.

    Convert the derivative to the new units:

    $C'(2.4) = $ _____ dollars per microwave oven

c. What is the marginal cost for the 2401st microwave oven?

d. Write a sentence of interpretation for marginal cost, using the form commonly used in economics.

    The _____ cost of producing the _____ *st* microwave

    oven is _____ dollars.

Example 2: (CC5e pp. 289, based on Activity 15)

$C(x) = 0.16x^3 - 8.7x^2 + 172x + 69.4$ dollars gives the hourly production costs where x television sets are produced each hour, $5 \le x \le 35$.

a. What are the hourly production costs when five television sets are produced each hour? Include units with the answer.

b. How quickly are production costs changing when five television sets are produced each hour? Include units with the answer.

c. Find the linearization for $C(x)$ with respect to $x=5$.

$C_L(x) =$

d. Write a sentence of interpretation for the marginal cost at a production level of five television sets, using the form commonly used in economics.

The _____ cost of producing the _____ *th* television

set each hour is _____ dollars.

e. Complete the following statements using marginal analysis.

The *additional* cost of producing the *21st* television set each hour is _____ *dollars*.

When 30 television sets are produced each hour, the hourly cost of production is increasing

by _____ dollars per additional television set.

Example 3: (CC5e p. 284)

$C(q)$ million dollars gives the cost of producing q million barrels of crude oil at a certain oil field, $0 < q < 17$.

$R(q)$ million dollars gives the revenue from the sale of q million barrels of crude oil at a certain oil field, $0 < q < 17$.

The graphs of C and R are shown to the right.

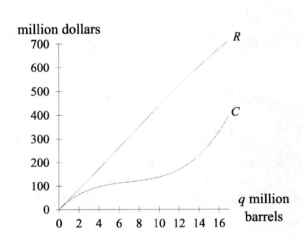

a. $C'(10) = 10.720$. Convert the units before filling in the blanks in the following sentences of interpretation for marginal cost.

When _____ million barrels of crude oil are produced, the cost of production is increasing by _____**dollars per barrel.**

Or, using the form commonly used in economics,

The _____ cost to produce the _____*st* barrel of crude oil is _____ **dollars.**

b. $R'(10) = 43.090$. Convert the units before filling in the blanks in the following sentences of interpretation for marginal revenue.

When _____ million barrels of crude oil are sold, revenue is increasing by _____**dollars per barrel.**

Or, using the form commonly used in economics,

The _____ revenue from the sale of the _____*st* barrel of crude oil is _____ **dollars.**

c. If the revenue from the sale of 10 million barrels of crude oil is 438.9 million dollars, estimate the revenue from the sale of 10,000,001 barrels of oil. Include units with your answer.

Profit Maximization Rule (optional):

For a cost function $C(q)$ and a revenue function $R(q)$, a profit function is given by $P(q) = R(q) - C(q)$, when producing and selling q units.

Profit is maximized when $P'(q) = R'(q) - C'(q) = 0$ or $R'(q) = C'(q)$.
Profit is maximized when **marginal revenue equals marginal cost.**

Since a solution to this equation may produce a minimum profit, check the graph of the profit function to verify that profit is maximized.

---

d. (Optional) The graph showing both marginal revenue and marginal cost is shown to the left below and the graph of the profit function, $P(q) = R(q) - C(q)$ is shown to the right below.

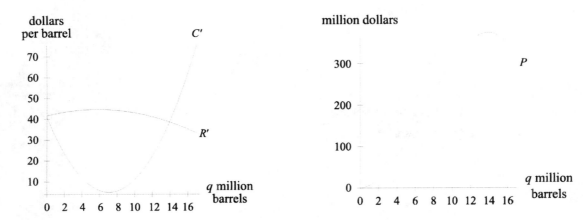

Estimate the input value where the profit is maximized by finding the input value at the intersection of the marginal cost and the marginal revenue. Include units with the answer.

Use the graph of $P(q)$ to verify that the input value occurs where the profit is maximized.

Example 4: (CC5e pp. 285-286)

Each council of Girl Scouts has costs associated with their annual cookie sales. The council sets the price for cookies sold in their region.

During a recent campaign, one council set the sales price at $4.00 per box.

$C(q) = 0.23q^3 - 0.98q^2 + 2.7q + 0.2$ million dollars gives the Girl Scout council's total cost associated with this campaign when q million boxes are sold, $0 < q < 4$.

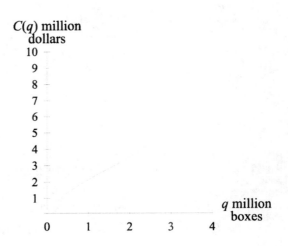

a. Complete the derivative model:

$C'(q) =$ _____ dollars per box gives the rate of change in the costs associated with Girl Scout cookie sales in one council's region when q million boxes are sold, $0 < q < 4$.

b. Complete the model for revenue:

$R(q) =$ _____ million dollars gives the revenue from the sale of Girl Scout cookie sales in one council's region when q million boxes are sold, $0 < q < 4$.

c. Complete the derivative model:

$R'(q) =$ _____ dollars per box gives the rate of change in the revenue from the sale of Girl Scout cookies in one council's region when q million boxes are sold, $0 < q < 4$.

d. Complete the model for profit:

$P(q) =$ _____ million dollars gives the profit from the sale of Girl Scout cookie sales in one council's region when q million boxes are sold, $0 < q < 4$.

e. What is the marginal cost when 2 million box of Girl Scout cookies are produced (the marginal cost for 2,000,001st box)?

f. (Optional) Profit is maximized at _____ million dollars when _____ boxes are sold.

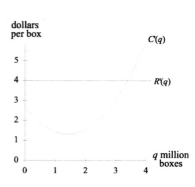

(Optional)
A **Production function** $Q(k)$ gives the quantity of output that can be produced by a given amount of input k, called a **production factor**, when all other production factors are held constant. Production factors may be labor costs, capital expenditures, natural resources, etc.

Marginal Product refers to the change in production level resulting from **one** additional unit of the variable production factor k.

Example 5 (optional): (CC5e pp. 287)

$Q(k)$ automobiles represents the output for a Honda automobile plant in Dongfeng, China when its production factor of capital investment is k million U.S. dollars.

Current production is $Q(200) = 119,200$ and $Q'(200) = 600$.

a. When _____ million U.S. dollars are invested, the Honda automobile plant in

   Dongfeng produces _____ automobiles and its output is increasing by

   _____ automobiles per million U.S. dollars in capital investment.

b. By increasing investment by one million U.S. dollars, production will increase to

   _____ automobiles at the Dongfeng plant.

c. The **marginal product** with respect to capital is _____ automobiles per U.S. dollar

   in capital investment.

Section 5.1: An Introduction to Results of Change

Previously the change in $F(x)$ from $x = a$ to $x = b$ was found as $F(b) - F(a)$. How can the change in $F(x)$ from $x = a$ to $x = b$ be found when only $F'(x)$ is given? Change can be measured as it accumulates over an interval. The results of change can be found using the area between a function and the input axis.

A simple example:

A barrel contains five gallons of water.

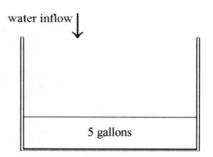

Between 4:00 pm and 6:00 pm water flows into the tank at the rate of 3 gallons per hour. Graph the rate function.

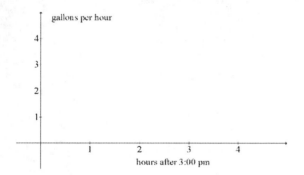

How much water flowed into the barrel over the two hour period?

Graph the amount of water in the barrel as a function of time.

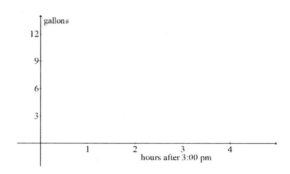

What is the slope of this graph?

At 6 pm, how much water is in the barrel? _____ gallons.

Example 1: Area as Accumulated Change

An example of *accumulated change* is distance as an accumulation of velocity over time. Suppose a train leaves a station and begins a journey. The graph shows the train's progress over 2 hours:

- The train leaves the station and steadily increases its speed from 0 to 60 mph.
- Once the train attains the speed of 60 mph, it maintains that speed for the next 50 minutes.
- After one hour of travel, the train steadily decreases its speed to 20 mph.
- The train maintains this speed until it has travelled a total of 2 hours.

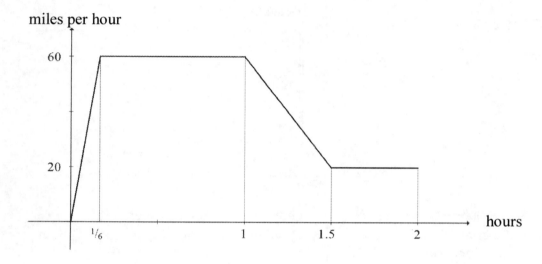

Compute the distance travelled in each leg of the journey:

The distance travelled over the length of the journey is _____

Example 2: Signed Area and Negative Accumulation

A grain silo is opened by a mechanized door which takes 6 seconds to fully open. During the first 6 seconds of activation, grain is dispensed at a rate of $g(t) = -50t$ cubic feet per second, t seconds after activation.

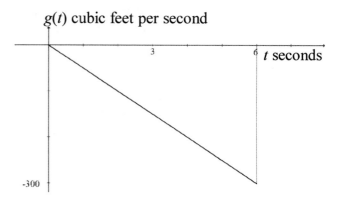

a. How quickly is the grain dispensing 3 seconds after the silo is opened?

b. Write a sentence interpreting $g(3)$.

> A **sentence of interpretation** for a **rate of change** uses ordinary conversational language to answer the questions *when?*, *what?*, *increasing or decreasing?* and *by how much?*
> 　　*When?* refers to the single input and does not necessarily involve time.
> 　　*What?* refers to the output description for the function.
> 　　*Increasing or Decreasing?* conveys if the rate was positive or negative.
> 　　*By how much?* refers to the rate of change, and includes its corresponding units.

c. Shade the region trapped between $g(t)$ and the t axis between $t = 0$ and $t = 6$.

d. The units on the height and width of the area of the region between the time axis and the rate graph **must** make sense when multiplied.

Units for height (vertical)		Units for width (horizontal)		Units for the Area
	×		=	

e. The **area** of the region shaded in part c is _____.

f. Write a sentence interpreting the **signed area** of the region shaded in part c.

> A **sentence of interpretation** for **change** uses ordinary conversational language to answer the questions *when?*, *what?*, *increased or decreased?* and *by how much?*
> 　　*When?* refers to the input interval and does not necessarily involve time.
> 　　*What?* refers to the output description for the function.
> 　　*Increased or Decreased?* conveys if the change was positive or negative.
> 　　*By how much?* refers to the change calculator and includes its corresponding units.

If the rate-of-change function, f, of a quantity function, F, is continuous over the interval $a < x < b$, the **accumulated** change in the quantity F between input values of a and b is equal to the area (or *signed* area) of the region between the graph of the rate-of-change function f and the horizontal axis, provided the graph of f **does not cross** the horizontal axis between a and b.

Area is always positive, but accumulated change can be either positive or negative, depending on the context of the problem. If the trapped area is *above* the horizontal axis, the accumulated change is *positive*; if the trapped area is *below* the horizontal axis, the accumulated change is *negative*.

Example 3: More Accumulated Change

The convention for data is that it is considered to be collected at the end of any time period (e.g., on December 31st of any year.

The graph of the rate of change in the population of a city from the end of 1900 to the end of 1975 is shown in the figure.

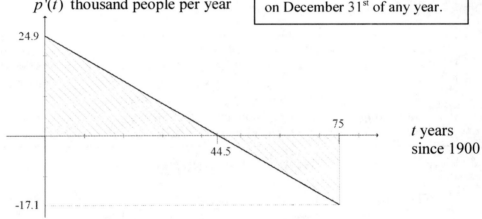

a. Calculate the signed area of each region.

b. The population _____ by _____ thousand people

between the end of 1900 and mid-1945.

c. The population _____ by _____ thousand people

between the mid-1945 and the end of 1975.

d. Between the end of 1900 and the end of 1975 the population _____ by

_____ thousand people.

Example 4: Some Connections between $f(x)$ and $f'(x)$

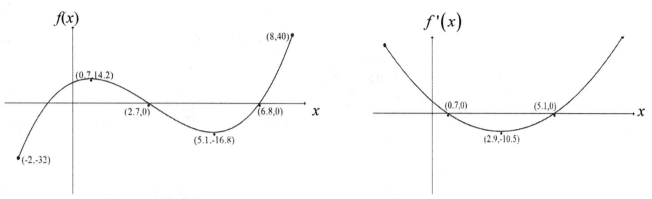

The accumulation function $f(x)$ has a relative maximum at $x = 0.7$ and a relative minimum at $x = 5.1$. $f'(x) = 0$ and crosses the x-axis at both of these x values. Complete the following using this word bank: *above/below, positive/negative, increasing/decreasing, rapidly/slowly, maximum/minimum/inflection point.*

a. On the interval $-2 < x < 0.7$, f' is _____ the x-axis; the rate of

    change is_____ , so the accumulation function f is _____ .

b. When $x = 0.7$, the rate of change is zero, the accumulation function is neither increasing

    nor decreasing.   This point is a *relative* _____ of $f(x)$.

c. On the interval $0.7 < x < 5.1$, f' is _____ the x-axis; the rate of

    change is_____ , so the accumulation function f is _____ .

d. When $x = 5.1$, the rate of change is zero, the accumulation function is neither increasing

    nor decreasing.   This point is a *relative* _____ of $f(x)$.

e. On the interval $5.1 < x < 8$, f' is _____ the x-axis; the rate of

    change is_____ , so the accumulation function f is _____ .

f. Finally, f' appears to have a relative minimum at about $x = 2.9$. this is where the

    accumulation function is _____ most _____ ,

    indicating an _____ .

Example 5: Interpreting a Rate of Change Function

The figure shows the rate of change of cost, in dollars per case, for an orchard in Florida at various production levels during grapefruit season, where n is the number of cases produced.

Use the graph of $c'(n)$ to complete the statements about $c(n)$. Write NA if the statement cannot be completed using the information provided.

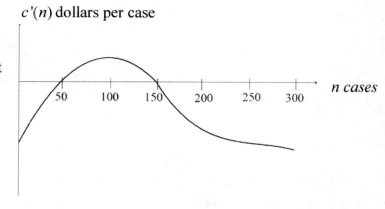

a. Cost is increasing when grapefruit production is between _____ and _____ cases.

b. The cost to produce 100 cases is _____ dollars.

c. The cost is lower than at nearby costs at a production level of _____ cases of grapefruit.

d. The cost is higher than at nearby costs at a production level of _____ cases.

e. The cost is increasing most rapidly when _____ cases of grapefruit are produced.

f. The unit of measure for the area between $c'(n)$ and the n-axis and between production levels of 50 and 100 cases is _____.

g. What does the area mentioned in part f represent?

Example 6: Answering Quantity Questions from a Rate of Change Graph

$C(u)$ dollars gives the cost to produce one thousand units at various production levels, where u equals the number of thousand units produced.

$c(u) = C'(u) =$ the rate of change of the cost in dollars per thousand units where u thousand units are produced. Use the graph of $c(u)$ to complete the statements.

Write NA if the statement cannot be completed using the information provided.

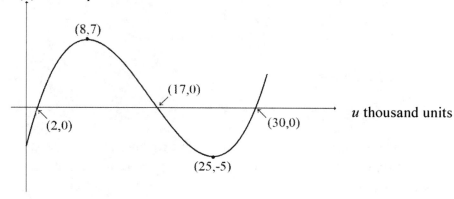

a. Cost is increasing when production is between _____ and _____ thousand units.

b. The cost when 25,000 units are produced is _____.

c. Cost is higher than nearby costs at a production level of _____ thousand units.

d. The cost is increasing most rapidly when _____ thousand units are produced.

e. Costs are lower than nearby costs when _____ or _____ thousand units are produced.

f. The cost is decreasing most rapidly when _____ thousand units are produced.

g. The units of measure for the area of the region between $c(u)$ and the u-axis are _____ .

Section 5.2: Limit of Sums and the Definite Integral

The examples in Section 5.1 were chosen so that geometric formulas for the area of a triangle, a rectangle, or a combination of rectangles and triangles could be used to calculate the areas of regions between the rate-of-change graph and the horizontal axis. Most situations are not that simple and a series of rectangles is used to approximate the area under a curve.

Example 1: Area of a Circle

Consider a circle centered at the origin with radius $r = 2$.
The equation of the circle is $x^2 + y^2 = 4$.
The formula for the area of a circle is $A = \pi r^2$

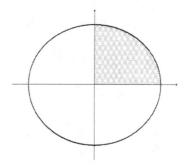

- The area of this circle = _____

- The area of the shaded region = _____

The equation for the top semicircle is $f(x) = \sqrt{4 - x^2}$.

The area of the shaded region can be *approximated* by using left rectangles, right rectangles or midpoint rectangles. The *height* of each rectangle is determined by the function at the left, right or midpoint of each sub-interval.

Use four rectangles of each type to approximate the shaded area.

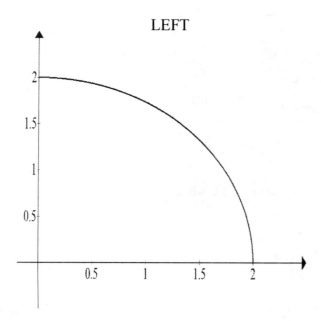

LEFT

$n = 4$ is the number of rectangles to be used.

$$\Delta x = \frac{b - a}{n} = \frac{2 - 0}{4} = 0.5$$
This is the base (width) of each rectangle.

$f(0), f(0.5), f(1)$, and $f(1.5)$ are the heights of the four <u>left</u> rectangles.

The sum of the areas of the four rectangles is:

$0.5 \cdot f(0) + 0.5 \cdot f(0.5) + 0.5 \cdot f(1) + 0.5 \cdot f(1.5)$
or $0.5[f(0) + f(0.5) + f(1) + f(1.5)] = 3.496$

This approximation is an _____
of the exact area.

The sum $0.5 \cdot f(0) + 0.5 \cdot f(0.5) + 0.5 \cdot f(1) + 0.5 \cdot f(1.5)$ can be notated using summation notation:

$$\sum_{i=1}^{4} f(x_i)\Delta x = \sum_{i=1}^{4} (\text{height of } i^{th} \text{ rectangle})(\text{width of } i^{th} \text{ rectangle}).$$

$$\sum_{i=1}^{4} f(x_i)\Delta x = f(x_1)\Delta x + f(x_2)\Delta x + f(x_3)\Delta x + f(x_4)\Delta x = f(0)\cdot(0.5) + f(0.5)\cdot(0.5) + f(1)\cdot(0.5) + f(1.5)\cdot(0.5)$$

Note: Summation notation is discussed here as it is used in the definition of the definite integral. Being able to read and understand summation notation is a required skill. Being able to write summation notation is not.

RIGHT

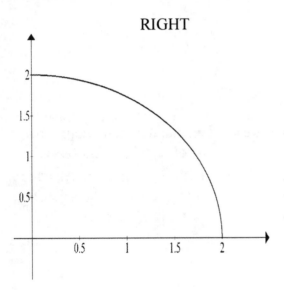

MIDPOINT

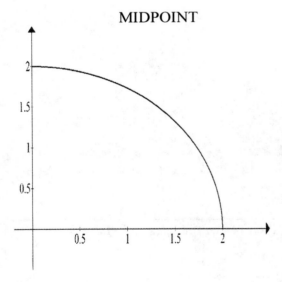

In general, should left, right or midpoint rectangles be used to find the best approximation?

How could the estimate be improved?

As n, the number of rectangles increases, the estimate of the area under the curve improves.

In general, as the number of rectangles increases without bound ($n \to \infty$), the sum of the areas of the rectangles approaches the exact area of the shaded region (π in this example).

In mathematical terms, the area of the region between the graph of f and the x-axis from a to b is given by a **limit of sums** as n increases without bound.

$n \to \infty$	$\sum\limits_{i=1}^{n} \sqrt{4-(x_i)^2}\,\Delta x$
16	3.146952
50	3.142566
100	3.141937
500	3.141623
1000	3.141604
2000	3.141597

$$\lim_{n \to \infty}\left[\sum_{i=1}^{n} f(x_i)\Delta x\right] \approx 3.1416 \approx \pi$$

Better Estimates of Areas

Suppose n rectangles of equal width are used to approximate the area of a region R between a graph of a function f and the input axis from a to b. As the number of rectangles **increases without** bound ($n \to \infty$), the **region** *covered* by the rectangles more closely approximates region R, and the **sum of the areas** of the rectangles approaches the *area* of region R. The area of the region between the graph of f and the x-axis from a to b is given by a **limit of sums** as n increases without bound.

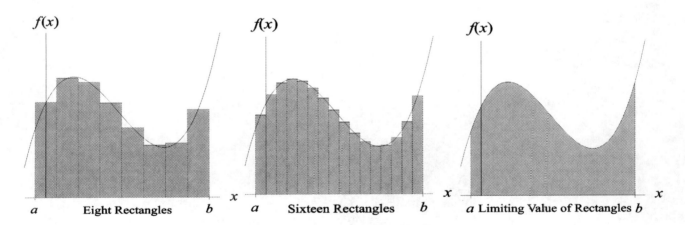

| $f(x)$ | $f(x)$ | $f(x)$ |

a Eight Rectangles b a Sixteen Rectangles b a Limiting Value of Rectangles b

---

For a continuous, nonnegative function f from a to b, the **area** of the region R between the graph of f and the x – axis from a to b is given by:

$$\left.\begin{array}{c}\text{Area of the}\\\text{region } R\end{array}\right\} = \lim_{n \to \infty}\left[\sum_{i=1}^{n} f(x_i)\Delta x\right]$$

where x_i is the midpoint of the ith subinterval of length $\Delta x = \dfrac{b-a}{n}$ between a and b.

Example 2: Estimating the Area Under a Curve in Context

A professor assigns online homework. From previous experience, the professor expects that the rate of change in the number of students logging on to the homework website on a particular evening can be modeled as

$s(x) = 1.5x^3 - 20x^2 + 35x + 250$ students per hour, x hours after 3:00 pm.

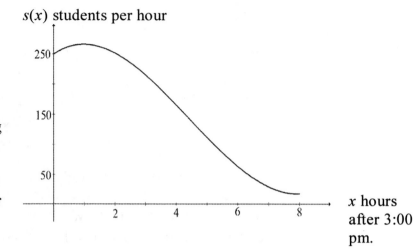

$s(x)$ students per hour

x hours after 3:00 pm.

Estimate the change in the number of students logging on to the website between 3:00 pm and 9:00 pm using three midpoint rectangles.

a. Identify the following:

$n =$ _____ $a =$ _____ $b =$ _____ $\Delta x =$ _____

b. Draw three midpoint rectangles on the graph above.

c. Complete the table by finding the height and the area of each rectangle.

Rectangle Index	Midpoint x_i	Height $s(x_i)$	Width/Base Δx	Area $s(x_i) \cdot \Delta x$
1				
2				
3				

d. Find the sum of the three areas found in part c.

e. Interpret the answer found in part d.

The Definite Integral

Let f be a continuous function defined on an interval from a to b. The *accumulated change* (or **definite integral**) of f from a to b is $\int_a^b f(x)\,dx = \lim_{n\to\infty} \sum_{i=1}^{n} f(x_i)\Delta x$ where x_i is the midpoint of *i*th subinterval of length $\Delta x = \dfrac{b-a}{n}$ in the interval from a to b.

- The sign $\int$ is called an **integral sign**.
- The values a and b identify the input interval.
- f is the function.
- dx is the symbol that reminds us of the width Δx of each subinterval.
- dx also indicates that the function will be integrated with respect to x.

  Notations for different functions: $\int_a^b g(p)\,dp$, $\int_a^b R(t)\,dt$, $\int_a^b P'(z)\,dz$.

- When a and b are specific numbers, $\int_a^b f(x)\,dx$ is known as a **definite integral.**

	Summation	Integral
symbol	$\sum_{i=1}^{n} f(x_i)\Delta x$	$\int_a^b f(x)\,dx$
height	$f(x_i)$	$f(x)$
width	Δx	dx
The notation at top and bottom of the symbol indicates	the number of rectangles to be used in the estimate	the upper and lower bounds of the interval

Note: The definite integral can be more generally defined without specifying midpoint rectangles:

If f is a function defined for $a \le x \le b$ and the interval $[a,b]$ is divided into n subintervals of equal width $\Delta x = \dfrac{b-a}{n}$ and x_i^* is any sample point in the ith subinterval, the definite integral of f from a to b is $\int_a^b f(x)\,dx = \lim_{n\to\infty} \sum_{i=1}^{n} f\left(x_i^*\right)\Delta x$.

Example 3: Using Technology to Evaluate a Definite Integral

In Example 1, the area under $f(x) = \sqrt{4 - x^2}$ (the area between the curve and the x-axis) in the interval $0 \le x \le 2$ was estimated using 4 left rectangles, 4 right rectangles and 4 midpoint rectangles. If one were to sum the areas of an *infinite* number of rectangles, the area under the curve would equal $\pi \approx 3.142$.

Using geometry, it is clear that the area of a circle with radius 2 is 4π, therefore the area of one quadrant of the circle is π.

Using technology, this area is found using the **function integration** facility, *fnInt*.

$$\int_0^2 f(x)dx = \underline{\hspace{2cm}}$$

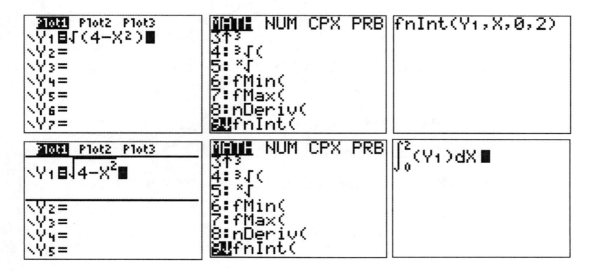

Note: Unless otherwise instructed to do so, the *fnInt* command may be used to evaluate any definite integral.

Example 4: Relating Signed Areas and Accumulation

The rate of change of the per capita consumption of wine in the United States from the end of 1970 through the end of 2008 can be modeled as

$w(x) = -0.0004768x^3 + 0.03408x^2 - 0.704x + 3.816$ pints per year where x is the number of years since (the end of) 1970.   Check: $w(2) = 2.5405056$

a. Estimate the change in the per capita consumption of wine between 1970 and 2008 using two right rectangles. Draw the rectangles on the graph.

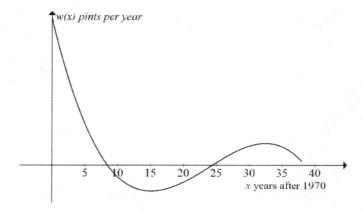

b. Find the input values where w crosses the horizontal axis. Round values to three decimal places.

c. Find the interval(s) when wine consumption was increasing.

d. Find the interval(s) when wine consumption was decreasing.

e. Find the *signed* areas of R_1, R_2, and R_3. Show the notation that lead to your answers.

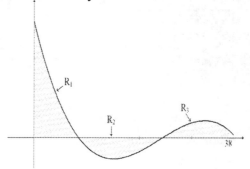

f. Using a single integral, calculate the change in per capita wine consumption over the 38-year period.

g. Show how the change in per capita wine consumption over the 38-year period can be found using the signed areas that were found in part e.

Section 5.3: Accumulation Functions

Given a **rate-of-change function** for a certain quantity, the **accumulation of change** in that quantity can be calculated using the signed areas of the regions between the rate-of-change curve and the horizontal axis.

The **accumulation function** of a function f, denoted by $A(x) = \int_a^x f(t)\,dt$, gives the accumulation of the signed area between the horizontal axis and the graph of f from a to x.

The constant a is the input value at which the accumulation is *zero*; the constant a is called the initial input value.

Example 1: Accumulation over Time (Revisiting Example 1 from Section 5.1)

Suppose a train leaves a station and begins a journey. The graph shows the train's progress over 2 hours:

- The train leaves the station and steadily increases its speed from 0 to 60 mph.
- Once the train attains the speed of 60 mph, it maintains that speed for the next 50 minutes.
- After one hour of travel, the train steadily decreases its speed to 20 mph.
- The train maintains this speed until it has travelled a total of 2 hours.

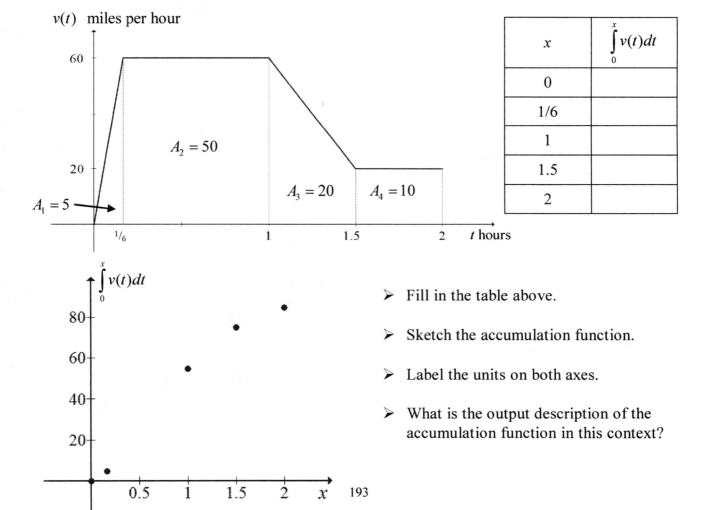

x	$\int_0^x v(t)\,dt$
0	
1/6	
1	
1.5	
2	

$A_2 = 50$

$A_3 = 20$ $A_4 = 10$

$A_1 = 5$

➢ Fill in the table above.

➢ Sketch the accumulation function.

➢ Label the units on both axes.

➢ What is the output description of the accumulation function in this context?

193

Example 2: Sketching Accumulation Functions

The rate of change function $f(t)$ has intervals where the function is negative as well as intervals where the function is positive.

Shade the area between the graph and the t-axis in the interval $[-3.14, 3.14]$.

There are four regions shown in the interval $[-3.14, 3.14]$. The area between the curve and the t-axis for each of these regions is equal to 1.

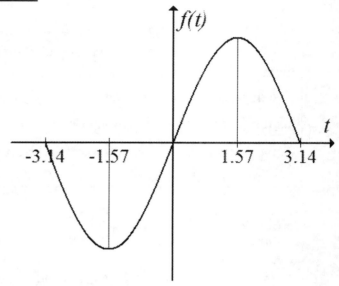

$F(x) = \int_{-3.14}^{x} f(t)dt$ is an accumulation function.

Complete the table of accumulation function values

interval	-3.14 to -1.57	-1.57 to 0	0 to 1.57	1.57 to 3.14
Signed area				

x	-3.14	-1.57	0	1.57	3.14
$F(x) = \int_{-3.14}^{x} f(t)dt$					

interval	-3.14 to -1.57	-1.57 to 0	0 to 1.57	1.57 to 3.14
$F(x)$ is increasing or decreasing ($f(t)$ is above or below the t-axis)				
Slower or faster				
Concavity of $F(x)$				

Graph the accumulation $F(x) = \int_{-3.14}^{x} f(t)dt$.

$F(x)$ has inflection points at $x = $ _____

and $x = $ _____. At those same two

input values, $f(t)$ has a _____

_____.

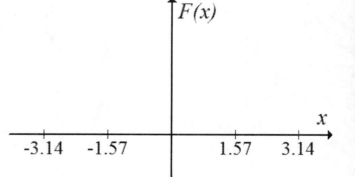

Example 3: Using Concavity to Refine the Sketch of an Accumulation Function

The circle to the right can be used as a quick indicator of the general shape that an accumulation function will take:

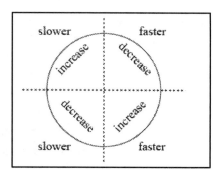

- An accumulation function showing slower increase will be shaped a bit like the upper-left arc of a circle. The accumulation function will be increasing and concave down.

- An accumulation function showing slower decrease will be shaped a bit like the lower-left arc of a circle. The accumulation function will be decreasing and concave up.

- An accumulation function showing faster decrease will be shaped a bit like the upper-right arc of a circle. The accumulation function will be decreasing and concave down.

- An accumulation function showing faster increase will be shaped a bit like the lower-right arc of a circle. The accumulation function will be increasing and concave up.

The graph of $F(x) = \int_{-3.14}^{x} f(t)dt$ is shown below. Add the functions $G(x) = \int_{-1.57}^{x} f(t)dt$

and $H(x) = \int_{0}^{x} f(t)dt$ to the graph.

x	-3.14	-1.57	0	1.57	3.14
$F(x) = \int_{-3.14}^{x} f(t)dt$	0	-1	-2	-1	0

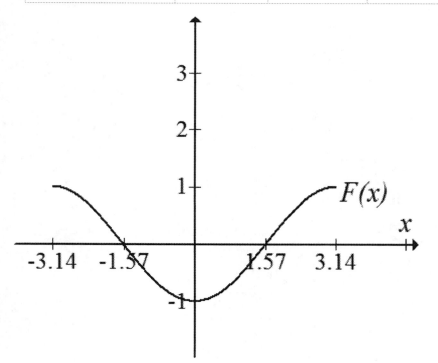

Summary:

Changing the a-value

required the graph of

$F(x)$ to be shifted

_____
(horizontally or vertically?)

until $(a, 0)$ is on the graph.

Example 4: Describing Accumulation Functions

The rate-of-change function for the equation that represents the number of states with PTAs from 1895 to 1931 is shown to the right.

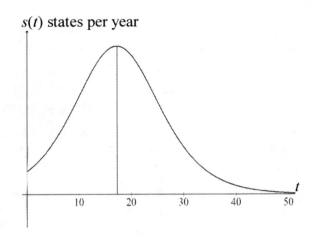

s(t) states per year

The rate-of-change function is positive (above the horizontal axis) for $t > 0$ and has a relative maximum point at $t \approx 18$.

Use the rate-of-change function to describe the accumulation function, $S(x) = \int_0^x s(t)\,dt$.

Use the following word bank.

increasing, decreasing, faster, slower, relative maximum, relative minimum, inflection point

a. $S(x)$ is _____ for $x > 0$.

b. $S(x)$ has a/an _____ at $x \approx 18$.

c. On the interval $0 < x < 18$, $S(x)$ is showing a _____ increase.

d. On the interval $x > 18$, $S(x)$ is showing a _____ increase.

e. Graph the accumulation function.

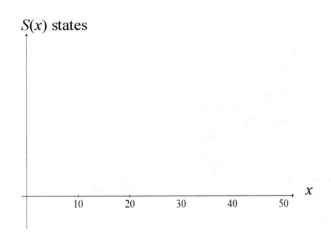

S(x) states

Example 5: Refining the Accumulation Graph

The graph of $f(t)$ is shown to the right.

$f(t)$ crosses the x-axis at $t = 0$ and $t = 6$.

$f(t)$ has a relative minimum at $t = 3$.

Use this information and the graph of $f(t)$ to determine the shape of the accumulation

$$A(x) = \int_a^x f(t)dt \,.$$

where a is the initial input value.

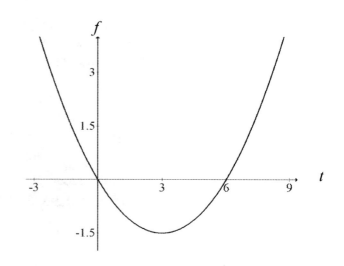

t	point on $f(t)$	point on $A(x)$	interval	$A(x)$ inc / dec	change in $A(x)$ is faster / slower	$A(x)$ is concave up/down
0	zero		$-3 < t < 0$			
3	relative minimum		$0 < t < 3$			
6	zero		$3 < t < 6$			
			$6 < t < 9$			

Sketch the graphs of $A(x) = \int_{-3}^x f(t)dt$ and $B(x) = \int_0^x f(t)dt$ on the axes below.

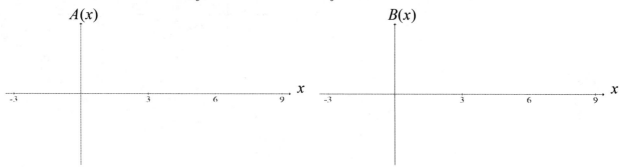

$A(x)$ $B(x)$

Example 6: Using Areas with Concavity to Sketch Accumulation Functions

The rate of change in the sales of organic coffee beans in the United States can be described by the graph of $c(t)$ where t is the number of years since 2004.

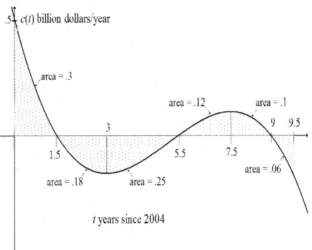

a. Were sales of organic coffee beans higher in 2006 than they were in 2010?

b. What was the change in the sales between the end of 2004 and the end of 2007?

c. Use the graph of the function c with input t years since 2004 to fill in the accumulation function values in the table below.

x	0	1.5	3	5.5	7.5	9	9.5
$C(x) = \int_0^x c(t)\,dt$							

d. Graph the accumulation function $\int_0^x c(t)\,dt$ for values of x between 0 and 9.5. Label units on both axes.

e. The accumulation function has a relative maximum of _____ at $x =$ _____ and another relative maximum of _____ at $x =$ _____ .

f. The accumulation function has a relative minimum of _____ at $x =$ _____ .

g. The accumulation function has inflection points at $x =$ _____ and at $x =$ _____ .

Example 7: Interpreting Critical Points on an Accumulation Function

The rate of change in the retail sales of running shoes in the United States can be described by the graph of $s(t)$ where t is the number of years since 2004.

$$S(x) = \int_0^x s(t)\,dt$$

Complete the table below using the following word bank:

relative maximum, relative minimum, inflection point

Point on $s(t)$	Related point on $S(x)$
1.3	
2.7	
4.6	
7.1	
8.8	

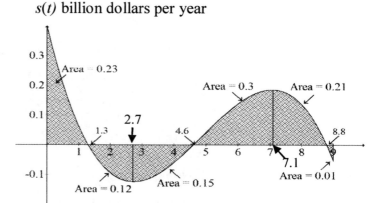

$s(t)$ billion dollars per year

t years since 2004

Use the graph of the function s with input t years since 2004 to fill in the table below.

x	0	1.3	2.7	4.6	7.1	8.8	9
$S(x) = \int_0^x s(t)\,dt$							
interval	$0 < x < 2.7$		$2.7 < x < 7.1$			$7.1 < x < 9$	
concavity							

a. Were retail sales of running shoes higher in 2011 than in 2004?

b. What was the difference (approximately)?

Section 5.4: The Fundamental Theorem

The Fundamental Theorem of Calculus states the connection between the two fundamental concepts of calculus, the derivative and the integral.

Example 1: Making Connections

a. The **function** graph and the **slope** function graph each cross the horizontal axis twice: near an input value of _____ and near an input value of _____.

b. The input values in part *a* give the locations of the

   relative _____ and the relative

   _____ of the **accumulation**

   function.

c. In the **function** graph, the input variable

   notation is _____ and the output notation is _____.

d. In the **slope** function graph,

   the input variable notation is _____ and

   the output notation is _____.

e. Other than the notation for the variables, the

   graphs of_____

   and the _____

   are identical.

f. The absolute minimum on the slope function

   corresponds to _____

   _____ on the accumulation function.

Function Graph

$f(t)$ billion dollars per year

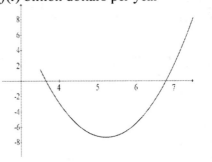

t years since 2000

Accumulation Function Graph

$F(x) = \int_{4}^{x} f(t)\,dt$ billion dollars

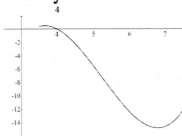

x years since 2000

Slope Function Graph

$$\frac{d}{dx}\left[\int_{4}^{x} f(t)\,dt\right] = f(x)$$

billion dollars per year

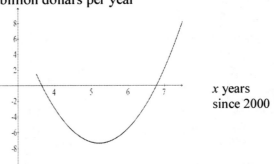

x years since 2000

The **Fundamental Theorem of Calculus** makes a connection between rates of change functions and accumulation functions (antiderivatives).

Fundamental Theorem of Calculus (Part 1)

For any continuous function f with input t,

the derivative of $\displaystyle\int_a^x f(t)dt$ is the function f **in terms of x**: $\dfrac{d}{dx}\left(\displaystyle\int_a^x f(t)dt\right) = f(x)$

Example 2: Notation and the Fundamental Theorem of Calculus

a. Given $g(r)$ is a continuous function, $\dfrac{d}{dx}\left(\displaystyle\int_6^x g(r)dr\right) =$

b. Given $f(x)$ is a continuous function, $\dfrac{d}{dp}\left(\displaystyle\int_{-4}^p f(x)dx\right) =$

c. $\dfrac{d}{dx}\left(\displaystyle\int_5^x \left(t^4 + 2t^2 + 7\right)dt\right) =$

d. $\dfrac{d}{dw}\left(\displaystyle\int_0^w \left(\sqrt[3]{x} + 1\right)dx\right) =$

Example 3: Antidifferentiation

Antidifferentiation is the process of starting with a known rate-of-change function and recovering the quantity function.

Find three functions whose derivative is $f(x) = 7$.

The process of finding an accumulation formula is the *reverse* of the process of finding a derivative. The function $A(x) = \int_a^x f(t)dt$ is called an **antiderivative** of the function f.

Rate of change function   **Quantity (antiderivative) functions**

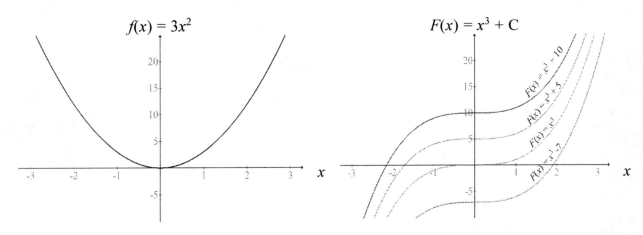

$f(x) = 3x^2$ $F(x) = x^3 + C$

Given the rate of change function $f(x) = 3x^2$, its *general antiderivative* is $F(x) = x^3 + C$.

If the value of C is known, for example, $C = 4$, then the *specific antiderivative* is $F(x) = x^3 + 4$;

If the value of C is 2π, then the *specific antiderivative* is $F(x) = x^3 + 2\pi$, etc.

Antiderivative

Let f be a function of x. A function F is called an antiderivative of f if

$$\frac{d}{dx}\left[F(x)\right] = f(x)$$

That is, F is an antiderivative of f if the derivative of F is f.

Antiderivative Rules

Simple Power Rule	$\int x^n dx = \dfrac{x^{n+1}}{n+1} + C$	for any $n \neq -1$
Constant Rule	$\int k\,dx = \int kx^0 dx = kx + C$	where k is a constant
Constant Multiplier Rule	$\int k \cdot f(x)\,dx = k\int f(x)\,dx$	where k is a constant
Sum and Difference Rule	$\int [f(x) + g(x)]\,dx = \int f(x)\,dx + \int g(x)\,dx$ $\int [f(x) - g(x)]\,dx = \int f(x)\,dx - \int g(x)\,dx$	

Example 4: Mixed Antiderivative Practice

Find the following general antiderivatives. Simplify exponents and coefficients when possible.

a. $\int x^3 dx =$

b. $\int (3x^6 - e^3)\,dx =$

c. $\int (5x^3 - 7x^2 + 9x - 6)\,dx =$

d. $\int (25 + \sqrt{x})\,dx =$

e. $\int \left(\dfrac{5}{x^6} - \pi\right)dx =$

f. $\int \dfrac{1}{2x^3}\,dx =$

g. $\int \left(\dfrac{6}{\sqrt[3]{x}} - \pi\right)dx =$

h. $\int x(x^2 + 1)\,dx =$

i. $\int \dfrac{x^2 - 5x}{x}\,dx =$

Example 5: Changes in Context

A certain country has an increasing population but a declining birth rate, (the number of babies born each year is increasing but at a slower rate). Over the next decade, the rate of change in the annual number of live births is estimated to follow the model $b(t) = -1.6t + 87$ thousand live births per year where t is measured in years and $t = 0$ at the end of last year. This year (Year 1) the number of live births is projected to be 1,272,000.

a. Write the general antiderivative for the function $b(t) = -1.6t + 87$.

   $B(t) =$

b. Write the specific antiderivative function for the annual number of live births.
    Use the fact that $B(1) = 1272$ to solve for C.

c. Write the specific antiderivative *model* for the annual number of live births.

> *A **model** is a statement that describes the relationship between an output variable and an input variable in context. It includes the following:*
> - *an equation*
> - *an output description, with units*
> - *an input description, with units*
> - *an input data range to describe the interval of data used to find the model*

d. Approximately _____ babies are predicted to be born in Year 10.

   Is it possible to find this amount using $b(t)$?

e. How many more babies will be born in year $t = 10$ than were born in year $t = 0$?

Show how to find this using $b(t)$.	Show how to find this using $B(t)$.

f. How quickly will the annual number of live births be changing in Year 10?

Show how to find this using $b(t)$.	Show how to find this using $B(t)$.

Example 6: Writing and Using a Specific Antiderivative

The rate of change in the number of people making online purchases from a company is given by $s(x) = 9x^2 + 16x + 21$ people per year, where x is the number of years since 2002.

a. Write the general antiderivative. Include units.

b. Write the specific antiderivative model if 255 people purchased online in 2005.

Example 7: Deriving and Verifying a Specific Antiderivative

The rate of change in the population of antelopes in a wildlife preserve is given by $a(x) = 3x^2 + 10x + 10$ antelopes per year, where x is the number of years since 2000.

a. Write the general antiderivative $A(x)$.

b. Given that at the end of 2011 there were 2400 antelopes in the preserve, write the specific antiderivative.

c. How many antelopes were in the preserve at the end of 2005?

d. Verify the change in the population using both $a(x)$ and $A(x)$. Show mathematical notation.

Example 8: Additional Practice with a Specific Antiderivative

The rate of change in the density of trees in a national forest is $m(x) = 15.5x^2 + 27x$ trees per acre per year, where x is the number of years since 2001.

a.   Write the general antiderivative $M(x)$.

a.   In 2010 there were 5133 trees per acre. Write the specific antiderivative model.

b.   Compute $M(6)$.

c.   Evaluate and interpret $M(9) - M(6)$.

d.   Use $m(x)$ to calculate the change in the number of trees between 2007 and 2010. Show the mathematical notation.

Section 5.5: Antiderivative Formulas for Exponential and Natural Log Functions

The rules for taking antiderivatives include the following:

x^{-1} Rule or $\dfrac{1}{x}$ Rule	$\int \dfrac{1}{x} dx = \ln|x| + C$ or $\int x^{-1} dx = \ln|x| + C$	
b^x Rule	$\int b^x dx = \dfrac{b^x}{\ln b} + C$	where $b > 0$
e^x Rule	$\int e^x dx = e^x + C$	
e^{kx} Rule	$\int e^{kx} dx = \dfrac{e^{kx}}{k} + C$	where k is a constant

Example 1: Writing Antiderivatives

a. $\int 4x^{-1} dx =$

b. $\int \dfrac{1}{2x} dx =$

c. $\int 2^x dx =$

d. $\int 2(1.5^x) dx =$

e. $\int 3e^x dx =$

f. $\int e^{6x} dx =$

g. $\int \dfrac{5}{e^x} dx$

h. $\int \left(e^{10x} + e^x + e^8 \right) dx =$

Example 2: Rate of Change of Average Walking Speed

The rate of change of the average walking speed in a city of population p persons can be modeled as $v'(p) = \dfrac{0.083}{p}$ meters per second per person where p is between 1,300 and 2,200,000 persons.

a. Write the general antiderivative for v with respect to p.

$$v(p) = \int \frac{0.083}{p}\,dp =$$

b. Write a model for average walking speed, given the population of a city. Use the fact that Karlsruhe, Germany, has a population of 268,309 and an average walking speed of 1.46 m/s.

Example 3: Using a Rate of Change Function to Estimate Future Employment:

From the end of 2004 through 2010, an internet sales company was hiring new employees at a rate of $f(x) = \dfrac{593}{x} + 138$ new employees per year, where x represents the number of years since the end of 2004. By the end of 2005, the company had hired 996 new employees.

a. Write the function that gives the number of employees hired x years since the end of 2004.

b. What are the restrictions on the input values for the function $F(x)$?

c. Calculate the total number of employees the company hired between the end of 2005 and the end of 2010.

Example 4: Writing an Equation from Rate of Change Data

The rates of change in vehicle traffic during peak hours at an intersection near a shopping center for years between 2007 and 2012 are shown in the table.

Year	2007	2008	2009	2010	2011	2012
Vehicles/hour per year	126	130	134	138	143	147

a. Align the input to years since 2000. Find an exponential model for the data in the table. Report the equation with values *rounded to three decimal places*.

b. Use the fact that the peak hourly traffic in 2007 was 3,980 vehicles to write a model for the hourly traffic during peak hours near the intersection.

c. In 2015, the peak hourly traffic at the intersection will be about _____ vehicles.

Example 5: Mixed Practice Finding General Antiderivatives

a. $\int 19.4(1.07^x)\,dx$

b. $\int 39e^{3.9x}\,dx$

c. $\int \left[6e^x + 4(2^x) \right] dx$

d. $\int \left(32x^3 + 3.28x - 15 \right) dx$

e. $\int \left(10^x + 6\sqrt{x} \right) dx$

f. $\int \left(0.5x + 0.5x^{-1} + (0.5)^x \right) dx$

Example 6: Finding General Antiderivatives with Units

a. $s(m) = 600(0.93^m)$ DVDs per month, m months after January.

b. $p(x) = 0.12x^2 - 0.5x + 1.4$ dollars per thousand cubic feet per year, x years after 2004.

c. $c(x) = \dfrac{0.8}{x} + 0.38(0.01^x)$ dollars per unit squared, when x units are produced

d. $p(t) = 1.034^t$ million people per year, t years after 1920.

Example 7: Finding Specific Antiderivatives

Write the specific antiderivative. If necessary, round C to 3 decimal places.

a. $f(t) = \dfrac{t^3}{3} + t^2;\ \ F(6) = 203$

b. $f(p) = \dfrac{4}{p} + p^2\ ;\ \ F(17) = 1582$

c. $f(t) = 10^t + e^{4t};\ \ F(1.1) = 30$

Section 5.6: The Definite Integral

The Fundamental Theorem of Calculus connects accumulation functions with derivatives.

Example 1: Two Ways to View Change

The *rate of change* of concentration in the bloodstream can be modeled as

$m(t) = 2(0.9^t) \dfrac{mg}{mL}$ per day, t days after the drug is first administered, $0 \le t \le 20$.

The **specific antiderivative** of $m(t)$ that gives the concentration of the drug in the bloodstream

t days after the first dose is $M(t) = \dfrac{2(0.9^t)}{\ln 0.9} + 20 \ \dfrac{mg}{mL}$.

The change described in this situation can be illustrated using either $m(t)$ or $M(t)$.

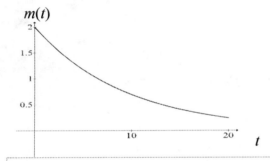

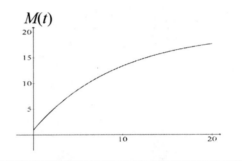

If possible, complete the following using $m(t)$.	If possible, complete the following using $M(t)$.
1. The concentration of the drug after 10 days was	1. The concentration of the drug after 10 days was
2. The concentration of the drug after 20 days was	2. The concentration of the drug after 20 days was
3. At 10 days, the concentration of the drug was changing at a rate of	3. At 10 days, the concentration of the drug was changing at a rate of
4. Between day 10 and day 20, the concentration changed by	4. Between day 10 and day 20, the concentration changed by
5. Illustrate the change on the graph.	5. Illustrate the change on the graph.

The Fundamental Theorem of Calculus (Part 2): Calculating the Definite Integral

If f is a continuous function from a to b and F is an antiderivative of f,

then $\int_a^b f(x)dx = F(b) - F(a)$ or $\int_a^b f(x)dx = F(x)\Big|_a^b$ is the definite integral of f from a to b.

Example 2: Evaluating a Definite Integral Algebraically

When asked to give the exact answer, all terms should be kept exact and no intermediate values should be rounded. Natural log and exponential terms (such as $\ln(2)$ *and* e^5*) as well as fractions (such as* $\frac{2}{3}$ *) should not be converted to their decimal approximations. Like terms should be combined when possible.*

a.   Evaluate $\int_{-1}^{3}\left(x^3 + 4x\right) dx$ algebraically. Give the exact answer.

Discussion: Why doesn't the +C have to be included in the antiderivative when evaluating a definite integral?

b. Evaluate $\displaystyle\int_2^8 5\left(0.37^x\right) dx$ algebraically. Give the exact answer.

c. Evaluate $\displaystyle\int_1^4 \left(\frac{3.6}{x} - e^{2.3x}\right) dx$ algebraically. Give the exact answer.

Example 3: Definite Integrals and Areas

For a function *f* that is *non-negative* on the interval from *a* to *b*,

$$\int_a^b f(x)dx = \text{the area of the region between } f$$

and the *x*-axis from *a* to *b*.

$$\int_1^9 f(x)dx =$$

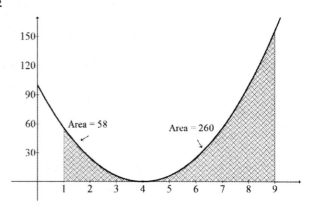

For a function *f* that is *negative* on the interval from *a* to *b*,

$$\int_a^b f(x)dx = \text{the } \textit{negative} \text{ of the area of the}$$

region between *f* and the *x*-axis from *a* to *b*.

$$\int_1^7 f(x)dx =$$

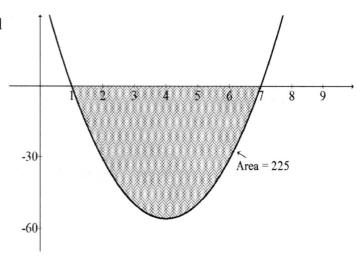

For a function *f* that *crosses the horizontal axis* on the interval from *a* to *b*,

$$\int_a^b f(x)dx = \text{the } \textit{sum of the signed areas} \text{ of the}$$

regions between *f* and the *x*-axis from *a* to *b*.

$$\int_1^8 f(x)dx =$$

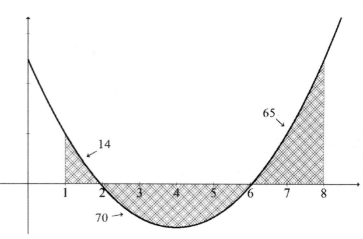

The Sum Property of Integrals: $\int_a^c f(x)dx = \int_a^b f(x)dx + \int_b^c f(x)dx$ where $a < b < c$

Example 4: Signed Area Compared With Total Area

For a general function f over an interval from a to b,

$\int_a^b f(x)dx =$ the sum of the signed areas of the regions between f and the x-axis from a to b.

(+ areas *above* the x-axis – areas *below* the x-axis.)

$\int_1^2 f(x)dx =$

$\int_2^6 f(x)dx =$

$\int_6^8 f(x)dx =$

$\int_1^8 f(x)dx =$

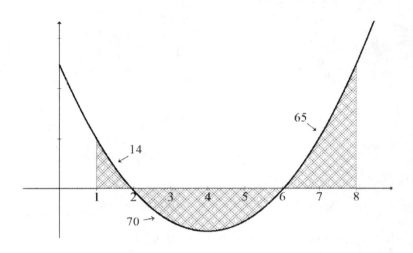

Which of the following expressions represents the total area between $f(x)$ and the x-axis between $x = 1$ and $x = 8$?

a. $\int_1^8 f(x)dx$

b. $\int_1^2 f(x)dx - \int_2^6 f(x)dx + \int_6^8 f(x)dx$

c. $\int_1^2 f(x)dx + \int_2^6 f(x)dx + \int_6^8 f(x)dx$

d. $\int_1^2 f(x)dx + \left| \int_2^6 f(x)dx \right| + \int_6^8 f(x)dx$

When asked to find the total area trapped between a function and the horizontal axis, the first thing to do is to determine if _____

_____which can be done by looking at the graph of the function.

Example 5: Calculating Total and Signed Areas

Consider the graph of $f(t) = t^2 + t - 6$.

Shade the region(s) that represent the area
trapped between the graph of $f(t)$ and the
t-axis on the interval $-4 \le t \le 4$.

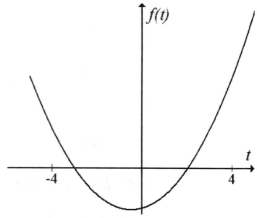

a.   Find the **total area.**

b.   Find the **signed area** (Verify the difference).

Example 6: Finding Zeros and Calculating Signed Areas

$f(x) = x^3 - 9x^2 + 18x + 2$

$f(-0.105) \approx 0, f(3.223) \approx 0,$ and $f(\quad) \approx 0.$

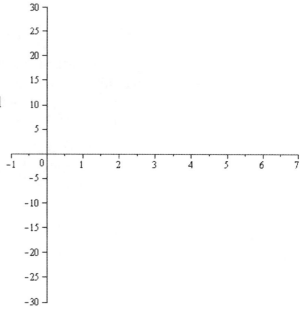

a.   Draw a graph of $f(x)$ on the grid to the right.

b.   Shade the region that represents the area trapped
     between of $f(x)$ and the x-axis on the interval
     $-1 \le x \le 7$.

c.   Write the expression that represents the
     sum of the signed areas trapped between
     $f(x)$ and the x-axis on the interval $-1 \le x \le 7$.

d.   Write the expression that represents the
     total area trapped between $f(x)$ and the
     x-axis on the interval $-1 \le x \le 7$.

217

Section 5.7: Differences of Accumulated Change

The difference of two accumulated changes is often expressed using the areas of regions between two curves.

<u>Area of a Region Between Two Curves</u>

If the graph of f lies above the graph of g from a to b, then the area of the region between the two curves from a to b is given by $\int_a^b [f(x) - g(x)]dx$.

<u>Example 1: Finding the Area Between Two Curves that Do Not Intersect</u>

Given: $f(x) = 0.17x^3 - 2.75x^2 + 9x + 30$ and $g(x) = 0.15x^2 - x + 3$, calculate the area of the region between $f(x)$ and $g(x)$ on the interval from $x=1$ to $x=9$.

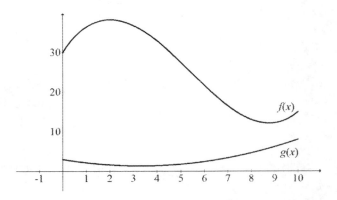

<u>Example 2: Interpreting the Area of a Region between Rate of Change Curves</u>

R' billion dollars per year is the rate of change in total revenue and C' billion dollars per year is the rate of change in total cost for a company in the first 8 years after the company began business.

Shade the area which represents the change in profit for the company between its second and 6th year. This area is 126. Interpret this value.

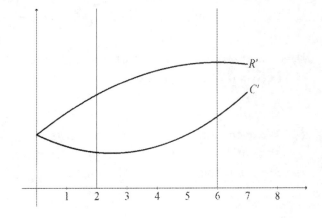

Example 3: Finding the Area between Two Curves That Do Intersect

Given: $f(x) = 3.7(1.194^x)$ and

$g(x) = 0.04x^3 - 0.54x^2 + 2.5x + 4.47.$

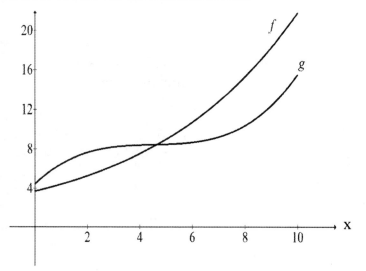

a. Shade the area(s) trapped between f and g on the interval $0 \le x \le 10.$

b. Find the input value at the point of intersection. Report this answer to 3 places.

c. Calculate the **total area** of the shaded regions.

d. Evaluate $\int_0^{10}\left[f(x) - g(x)\right] dx$ and $\int_0^{10}\left[g(x) - f(x)\right] dx$. How are these two related?

When calculating the **difference** between accumulated changes for two continuous rate of change functions that intersect, it is not necessary to split the interval of integration into subintervals.

Difference of Two Accumulated Changes

If f and g are two continuous rate of change functions, the difference between the accumulated change of f from a to b and the accumulated change of g from a to b is the accumulated change in the difference function $f - g$.

$$\int_a^b f(x)dx - \int_a^b g(x)dx = \int_a^b \left[f(x) - g(x)\right]dx$$

219

Example 4: Interpreting the Area of Regions between Rate of Change Curves

A small country in a state of civil war has a rapidly changing population due to the conflict.

$D(x)$ is the rate of change of the population due to migration from the country and deaths, $0 \leq x \leq 5$.

$I(x)$ is the rate of change of the population due to migration into the country and births, $0 \leq x \leq 5$.

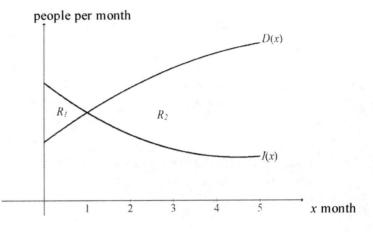

The area of $R_1 = 3690$ and the area of $R_2 = 9720$.

a. Interpret the area of Region R_1.

b. Interpret the area of Region R_2.

c. Calculate the change in the population over the five month period.

Example 5: Calculating and Interpreting the Area of Regions between Rate of Change Curves

The rate of change of the value of goods exported from the U.S. between 1990 and 2001 can be modeled as $E'(t) = -1.665t^2 + 16.475t + 7.632$ billion dollars per year and the rate of change of the value of goods imported into the U.S. during those years can be modeled as $I'(t) = 4.912t + 40.861$ billion dollars per year, where t is the number of years since 1990.

a. Calculate the difference between the increased value of exports and the increased value of imports from the end of 1990 through the end of 2001.

b. Sketch E' and I' on the axes below.
    Is the answer in part a equal to the area of the region(s) between the graphs?

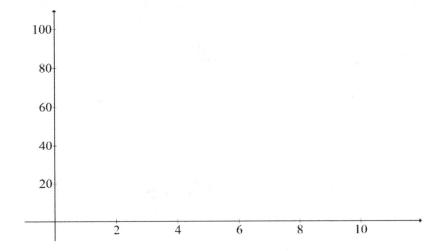

Example 6: Areas between Rate of Change of Revenue and Cost Curves

The figure shows the graphs of the rate of change of revenue $r(x)$ and the rate of change of costs $c(x)$ for a new company, which started in 2002. Profit = revenue – cost.

$r(x) = 0.125x^2 - 0.25x + 2$ million dollars per year and $c(x) = -0.3x^2 + 1.3x + 8$ million dollars per year, where x is the number of years since 2002. $r(6) = c(6)$.

million dollars per year

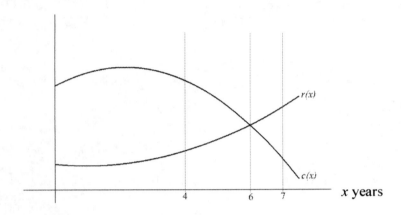

x years

a. In the first seven years, the company's costs increased by $_____million. Show the mathematical notation to find this value.

b. Using a single integral, write the mathematical notation that represents the *total change in profit* from 2006 to 2009. Evaluate the integral.

c. Why is it not possible to find the point where revenue equaled cost?

Section 5.8: Average Value and Average Rate of Change

Averaging is a balancing out of extreme values. Discrete data can be averaged by summing the values and dividing by the number of values.

Example 1: Finding the Average Value on an Interval by Averaging Discrete Data

Without a monitor, a person's heart rate could be measured every ten minutes. The average heart rate over the 50-minute period could be found by summing the six heart rates and dividing by six.

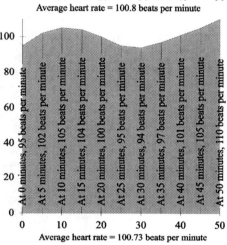

Average heart rate = 100.8 beats per minute

A more accurate average could be found when the heart rate is measured every five minutes.

Average heart rate = 100.73 beats per minute

The **average value of a continuous function** over an interval can be **graphically** represented as the signed height of a rectangle whose area equals the area between the function and the horizontal axis over the interval.

The **average value of a continuous function** over an interval is represented **algebraically** as the definite integral of a function over an interval divided by the length of that interval:

$$\left.\begin{array}{c}\text{Average value of}\\ f \text{ from } a \text{ to } b\end{array}\right\} = \frac{\displaystyle\int_a^b f(x)\,dx}{b-a}$$

223

$H(t)$ beats per minute is a continuous function that models the heart rate of an individual.

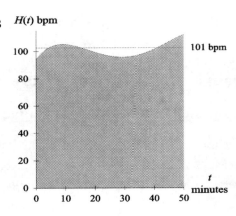

a. $\displaystyle\int_{0}^{50} H(t)dt \approx 5067$ beats represents

b. $\dfrac{\displaystyle\int_{0}^{50} H(t)dt}{50} \approx 101$ beats per minute represents

c. In the graph of $H(t)$, the horizontal line represents _____.

   and the shaded area represents _____.

Example 2: Finding and Graphing the Average Value of Sales

U.S. factory sales of electronic goods to dealers over a ten-year period can be modeled as
$s(t) = 0.0388t^3 - 0.495t^2 + 5.698t + 43.6$ billion dollars, $0 \le t \le 10$. (checkpoint: $s(3) \approx 57.2866$)

a. Calculate the average annual value of US factory sales of electronic sales to dealers over the ten year period.

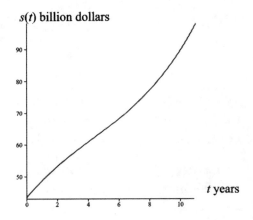

b. Graph the average annual value on the graph provided.

c. Calculate the average rate of change of US factory sales of electronic goods to dealers over the 10-year period.

224

Example 3: Average Population and Average Rate of Change in Population

The population of Mexico between 1921 and 2010 can be modeled as $p(t) = 8.028(1.025^t)$ million people, where t is the number of years since the end of 1900.

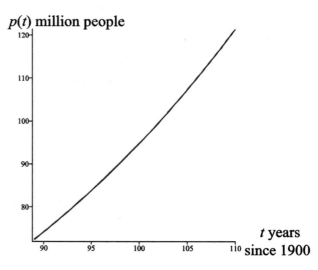

a. Find <u>and</u> interpret the average population of Mexico from the end of 1989 through the end of 2010.

b. Use a horizontal line to illustrate the average population on the graph.

c. Find <u>and</u> interpret the average rate of change in the population of Mexico from the end of 1989 through the end of 2010.

d. Illustrate the average rate of change in the population on the graph by drawing and labeling the slope of a secant line.

Example 4: Average Value of Sea Level Estimates since 1700:

Researchers have constructed a model for global sea

level over three-plus centuries as

$g(x) = 0.0046x^2 - 0.43x - 149.05$ mm,

where x is the number of years since 1700.

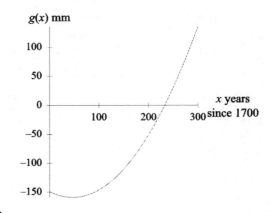

The global sea level was indexed at 0 mm in 1932.
(Source: S.Jevrejeva et al.)

a. Calculate the average sea level between 1700 and 2000.

b. Illustrate the answer to part a on the graph.

c. Use $g(x)$ to predict the global sea level in 2020.

If f is a continuous or piecewise continuous function describing a quantity from a to b:

The **average value** of the quantity from a to b is calculated as $\dfrac{\int_a^b f(x)dx}{b-a}$.

The **average rate of change** of the quantity can be calculated from the quantity function as $\dfrac{f(b)-f(a)}{b-a}$.

The **average rate of change** of the quantity *is the average value of the rate of change* and can also be calculated as $\dfrac{\int_a^b f'(x)dx}{b-a}$.

Example 5: Starting with the Antiderivative to Find Average Value and AROC

The growth rate of the population of South Carolina between 1790 and 2000 can be modeled as $p'(t) = 0.18t - 1.57$ thousand people per year where t is the number of years since 1790.
The population of South Carolina in 1940 was 1989.5 thousand people.

a. Find and interpret the average rate of change in population from 1995 to 2000.

b. What was the average size of the population from 1995 to 2000?

Example 6: Complete the Summary

Given ↓	Find the following on the interval from $x = a$ to $x = b$		
	Change in f	Average Value of f	Average rate of change of f
$f(x)$			
$f'(x)$			

Section 6.1: Perpetual Accumulation and Improper Integrals

Definite integrals have specific numbers for both the upper and lower limits of integration.

An integral for which one or both of the limits of integration are infinite is an **improper integral**. Improper integrals are seen in various areas including economics and statistics.

Examples of Improper Integrals: $\displaystyle\int_{a}^{\infty} f(x)\,dx \qquad \int_{-\infty}^{b} g(x)\,dx \qquad \int_{-\infty}^{\infty} h(x)\,dx$

Example 1: Evaluating an Improper Integral

The improper integral $\displaystyle\int_{1}^{\infty} 12e^{-0.02x}\,dx$

can be represented **graphically** as the area of the region between the graph of $f(x) = 12e^{-0.02x}$ and the x-axis starting at $x = 1$ and increasing without bound.

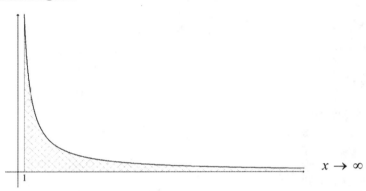

$x \to \infty$

Numerically, the area of the region can be estimated by finding the limit of the areas between the graph of f and the x-axis from $x = 1$ to increasingly large input values, N.

N	$\displaystyle\int_{1}^{N} 12e^{-0.02x}\,dx$
100	$\displaystyle\int_{1}^{100} 12e^{-0.02x}\,dx = 506.918$
200	$\displaystyle\int_{1}^{200} 12e^{-0.02x}\,dx = 577.130$
400	$\displaystyle\int_{1}^{400} 12e^{-0.02x}\,dx = 587.918$
800	$\displaystyle\int_{1}^{800} 12e^{-0.02x}\,dx$
1600	$\displaystyle\int_{1}^{1600} 12e^{-0.02x}\,dx$

Conclusion:

The improper integral can be evaluated **algebraically** as the limiting value of a definite integral as one endpoint increases or decreases without bound.

Step 1: Replace ∞ with the variable N and rewrite the improper integral as the limit of a definite integral involving N.	$\displaystyle\int_1^\infty 12e^{-0.02x}\,dx = \lim_{N\to\infty}\int_1^N 12e^{-0.02x}\,dx$
Step 2: Find the antiderivative. Keep the limit notation until the limit is taken.	$\displaystyle = \lim_{N\to\infty} \left.\frac{12e^{-.02x}}{-.02}\right|_1^N$
Step 3: Show the antiderivative separately for inputs N and for 1. Keep the limit notation until the limit is taken.	$\displaystyle = \left[\lim_{N\to\infty}\frac{12e^{-0.02N}}{-.02}\right] - \left[\lim_{N\to\infty}\frac{12e^{-0.02(1)}}{-.02}\right]$
Step 4: Find the limits.	$\displaystyle = [0] - \left[-600e^{-0.02}\right]$
Step 5: Simplify. Note the difference between the **exact** solution and the **decimal approximation** of this answer.	$\displaystyle = 600e^{-0.02}$ ≈ 588.119

Example 2: Algebraically Evaluating an Improper Integral

$\displaystyle\int_2^\infty \frac{3}{x^3}\,dx =$

Example 3: Algebraic Integration

Evaluate $\displaystyle\int_{-\infty}^{1} 8(1.08^x)\,dx$. Give the exact solution.

Example 4: Exponential Decay

Carbon-14 dating methods are sometimes used by archeologists to determine the age of an artifact. The rate at which 100 milligrams of ^{14}C is decaying can be modeled as:

$r(t) = -0.01209\left(0.999879^t\right)$ milligrams per year where t is the number of years since the sample began to decay. [Check: $r(3) = -.0120856119$].

a. Show the mathematical notation used to compute the amount of the sample that would decay between year 0 and year 1000.

      After 1000 years, _____ milligrams of the ^{14}C will decay.

b. Use the numerical method to determine how much of the sample should eventually decay.

      Eventually, _____ milligrams of the ^{14}C will decay.

Example 5: Convergence and Divergence

If the limit of an improper integral exists, the improper integral **converges**.

$$\int_{1}^{\infty} 12e^{-0.02x}\, dx \text{ \textbf{converges} to } 588.119$$

If the limit of an improper integral does <u>not</u> exist, the improper integral **diverges**.

$$\int_{1}^{\infty} \frac{1}{x}\, dx = \lim_{N \to \infty} \ln|x| \Big|_{1}^{N} = \left[\lim_{N \to \infty} \ln|N| \right] - \left[\lim_{N \to \infty} \ln|1| \right]$$

$$= [\infty] - [0]$$

$$= \infty$$

$$f(x) = \frac{1}{x} \qquad\qquad\qquad\qquad F(x) = \ln x$$

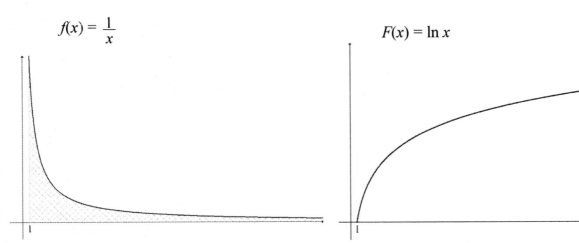

The function $\frac{1}{x}$ approaches the x axis as $x \to \infty$; $\lim\limits_{x \to \infty} \frac{1}{x} = 0$.

However, since the antiderivative, $\ln|x|$, increases without bound as $x \to \infty$, there is no limiting value for $\ln|N|$.

The area under the function $\frac{1}{x}$ continues to increase and $\int_{1}^{\infty} \frac{1}{x}\, dx$ <u>diverges</u>.

Example 6: Evaluating Improper Integrals

Evaluate each of the following algebraically. Determine whether the following integrals converge (to a specific value) or diverge.

a. $\displaystyle\int_{3}^{\infty} 36x^{-1.5}\,dx$ converges to _____ or diverges?

b. $\displaystyle\int_{5}^{\infty} 5(0.37^{x})\,dx$ converges to _____ or diverges?

c. $\displaystyle\int_{0.3}^{\infty} 6x^{-0.3}\,dx$ converges to _____ or diverges?

Example 7: Evaluating Improper Integrals on the interval $-\infty < x < +\infty$

If an improper integral is to be evaluated on the interval $-\infty < x < +\infty$, first split the interval at zero, then evaluate each part separately.

Evaluate $\displaystyle\int_{-\infty}^{\infty} xe^{-x^2}\,dx$

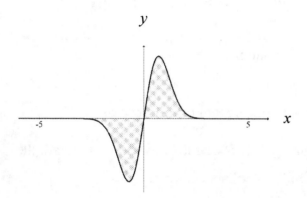

Section 6.2: Streams in Business

The income of large financial institutions and major corporations can be considered as being received continuously over time. Some companies receive payments throughout the month and at any time during the day or night. This flow of money is called a *continuous income stream.*

A *continuous income stream* is a regular flow of money that is generated by a business or investment. The *rate of flow* is a function R that varies according to time t. Some income streams flow at constant rates, but others have flow rates that vary as a function of time.

Example 1: Writing Equations for Constant, Linear, and Exponential Streams

Suppose a business posts an annual profit of $4.2 million and invests its profits as a continuous stream into investments. Complete the income stream equations.

a. Constant Flow: The *same amount* is invested each year.

   If the profits remain constant at $4.2 million per year, the stream is described as

   $R(t) =$ _____ million dollars per year. If only 5% of the profits are invested, the stream is described as $R(t) =$ _____ million dollars per year.

b. Linear Flow: The amount invested changes by the *same amount* each year.

   If the profits increase by $0.2 million each year, the stream is described as

   $R(t) =$ _____ million dollars per year.

   If the profits decrease by $0.3 million each year, the stream is described as

   $R(t) =$ _____ million dollars per year. If only half of these profits are invested, the stream is described as $R(t) =$ _____ million dollars per year.

c. Exponential Flow: The amount invested changes by the *same percentage* each year.

   If the profits increase by 7% each year, the stream is described as

   $R(t) =$ _____ million dollars per year.

   If the profits decrease by 5% each year, the stream is described as

   $R(t) =$_____ million dollars per year.

   If only 10% of these profits are invested, the stream is described as

   $R(t) =$ _____ million dollars per year.

An exponential function is expressed as $f(x) = ab^x$ where a is the starting value and b is the constant multiplier. A decreasing exponential function will have a b value between zero and one. An increasing exponential function will have a b value greater than one.

Example 2: Calculating Future Value, Amount Invested and Interest

Assume that $R(t) = 0.05(4.2 + 0.2t)$ thousand dollars per year is the flow rate of an income streaming into an account which pays 4% interest compounded continuously.

The **T-year future value** of a continuous stream is the total accumulated value of the income stream and its earned interest at some point in the future. If an income stream flows continuously into an interest-bearing account at the rate of $R(t)$ dollars per year, where t is measured in years and the account earns interest at $100r\%$ *compounded continuously*, the future value of the account at the end of T years is:

$$F_T = \int_0^T R(t) e^{r(T-t)} dt .$$

> Note: $R(t) e^{r(T-t)}$ is the rate of change of the T-year future value

a. The 10-year future value of $R(t)$ is $F_{10} = \int_0^{10} 0.05(4.2 + 0.2t) e^{.04(10-t)} dt = \$\underline{\hspace{2cm}}$

The **T-year principal** (the amount that the account holder actually invests over the T-year period) is calculated directly from the income stream as $\text{Principal}_T = \int_0^T R(t) dt$, where T is measured in years.

b. The 10-year principal for this account is $\text{Principal}_{10} = \int_0^{10} 0.05(4.2 + 0.2t) dt = \$\underline{\hspace{2cm}}$

The **interest earned** on the income stream over the first 10 years is the difference in the 10-year future value and the principal invested over 10 years, calculated as $\int_0^{10} \left[R(t) e^{r(T-t)} - R(t) \right] dt$.

c. Over the 10-year period, the interest earned is

$$\int_0^{10} \left[R(t) e^{r(T-t)} - R(t) \right] dt = F_{10} - \text{Principal}_{10} = \$\underline{\hspace{2cm}}$$

Example 3: Computing Flow Rates, Investments, and Future Value

A corporation offers merit-based college grants to children of its employees. To establish an annuity that will start awarding scholarships in twenty years, the corporation sets up an income stream that will deposit 3% of the corporation's profit into the fund, which bears 8% interest compounded continuously. Annual corporate profit is currently $2 billion, which is expected to decrease by 5% per year over the next 20 years.

a.   Write the flow rate equation for the income stream.

b.   How much will the corporation invest over the 20-year period into this fund?

c.   After 20 years the value of the annuity will be $_____.

d.   At the end of 20-years, how much interest will the investment have earned?

e.   How much will the college fund annuity be worth in twenty years?

Example 4: Present Value

The present value of a continuous stream is the amount P that would need to be invested at the present time at a known interest rate if there was to be only *one lump sum* invested.

Suppose that an income stream flows continuously into an interest-bearing account at the rate of $R(t)$ dollars per year, where t is measured in years. Interest is earned at a rate of $100r\%$ compounded continuously. The present value of the account is $P_T = \int_0^T R(t)e^{-rt}dt$.

When the future value is known, present value may also be computed as $P = \dfrac{\text{Future Value}}{e^{rT}}$.

A manufacturer regularly updates and replaces production machinery. If a portion of the profit is invested, the interest generated from the investment can be applied towards the cost of future capital improvements.

There are two strategies to fund capital improvements:

Plan A: The profit for the manufacturer last year was 32 million dollars. The manufacturer predicts that profits will increase by 5 million dollars each year for the next decade. 9% of the profit will be invested into an account paying 3.6% interest and compounded continuously for 10 years.

a.   Write the income stream flow rate equation. What will the manufacturer invest in 10 years?

b.   Compute the 10-year future value of this fund.

c.   Under this plan, the manufacturer will invest _____million dollars, and

the investment will yield _____ million dollars of interest.

Plan B: Invest a lump sum into an account bearing 3.6% interest for 10 years. How much would have to be invested so that Plan B would be worth the same amount as Plan A at the end of the 10-year period?

Example 5: Evaluating Assets Based on Present Value

Alpha Industries is attempting to negotiate a buyout of one of their suppliers, Beta Plastics. Currently, Alpha Industries makes an annual income of $1 million per year. Beta Plastics income is $1.1 million dollars per year. Analysts for Alpha Industries project that by owning Beta Plastics, Alpha could increase their income to an income starting at $1.6 million per year which would grow at a rate of 5% per year. Both companies can reinvest their income at 5.5%.

What is the 10-year present value of Alpha's projected income without the acquisition of Beta?	What is the 10-year present value of Beta's projected income?
What is the 10-year present value of Alpha's projected income with the acquisition of Beta?	
What is the added value to Alpha to own Beta?	
What is the *most* that Alpha will offer to obtain Beta Plastics?	What is the *least* that Beta would consider as a purchase price in the buyout?

Assuming that both companies make their decisions based upon the 10-year present values, will the buyout take place?

Example 6: Income Streams in Perpetuity

When there is no specific end date to an income stream, the stream is considered to flow in perpetuity. In the case of a perpetual income stream, the end time T is considered to be infinite. The present value of such a stream is calculated as the improper integral

$$\text{Present Value} = \int_0^\infty R(t)e^{-rt}\,dt$$

The Smithsonian Institution leased paintings to a private museum to be displayed permanently. The terms of the lease specify that the museum will pay the Smithsonian 1.8 thousand dollars per year. To fund the lease, the other museum will invest a lump sum into an account which pays 6% interest compounded continuously. What is the present value of this account?

Example 7: Lotteries

A lottery is established in which the winner and his heirs, who can inherit the prize, will receive 6 million dollars per year for life. This requires that the lottery be able to pay out the prize in perpetuity. An account will be established which will pay out the lottery winnings. This account will pay 4.6% interest, compounded continuously. How much money must be deposited into this account to be able to pay the winner(s) in perpetuity?

Example 8: Income Flow Streams, Future Value, and Present Value

For each of the following five scenarios, find the income flow stream and compute the indicated present and future values. Check answers using the alternate formula for future value.

a. Company A had a profit of $1.8 million last year. This company expects the profit to increase by 3% each year over the next 5 years and will reinvest the profits in an account earning 4.75% APR compounded continuously. Find the following:

Income Flow Stream:	5-year Future Value:
$R(t) = 1.8(1.03^t)$ million $/year	$F_5 = \int_0^5 R(t)e^{0.0475(5-t)}\,dt =$
5-year Present Value:	Verify 5-year Present Value:
$P_5 = \int_0^5 R(t)e^{-0.0475t}\,dt =$	$P = \dfrac{F_5}{e^{rT}} =$

b. Company B had a profit of $4 million last year. This company expects the profit to increase by 0.02 million dollars each year over the next 5 years and will reinvest the profits in an account earning 2.9% compounded continuously. Find the following:

Income Flow Stream:	5-year Future Value:
$R(t) =$	
5-year Present Value:	Verify 5-year Present Value:

c. Company C had a profit of $76 thousand last year. This company expects the profit to decrease by 7% each year over the next five years and will reinvest 4% of their profit in an account earning 4.7% compounded continuously. Find the following:

Income Flow Stream:	5-year Future Value:
5-year Present Value:	Verify 5-year Present Value:

d. Company D had a profit of $38 thousand last year. The company expects the profit to decrease by 0.04 thousand dollars each year over the next 3 years and will reinvest 2% of their profit in an account earning 3.25% compounded continuously. Find the following:

Income Flow Stream:	3-year Future Value:
3-year Present Value:	Verify 3-year Present Value:

e. Company E had a profit of $16 million last year. The company expects their profit to remain the same each year over the next 4 years and they will continually reinvest 20% of their profit in an account earning 4.7% compounded continuously. Find the following:

Income Flow Stream:	4-year Future Value:
4-year Present Value:	Verify 4-year Present Value:

Section 6.3: Calculus in Economics – Demand and Elasticity

Demand for a product is affected by several factors, including usefulness, necessity, the availability of substitutes and buyer income. However, when all other factors are held constant, the quantity demanded can be considered to be a function of market price.

A function giving the expected quantity of a commodity purchased at a specific market price is referred to as a **demand function** or demand schedule. The demand function D relates the input variable p (price per unit) with the output variable $q = D(p)$ (quantity).

The graph of a demand function is referred to as a demand curve.

All other factors being constant, **as the price of a commodity increases, the market will react by demanding less** and, **as the price of the commodity decreases, the market will react by demanding more**. This is the *Law of Demand*.

Example 1: Demand as a Function of the Price of a Commodity

As wholesale prices for potatoes increase, the quantity of potatoes demanded can be modeled as $D(p) = 461 + 47 \ln(17-p)$ million cwt (hundred pounds) where p is the wholesale price in dollars per cwt.

a. When potatoes are sold for $14 per cwt, how many potatoes are demanded?

b. When 480 million cwt potatoes are demanded, what is the market price per cwt?

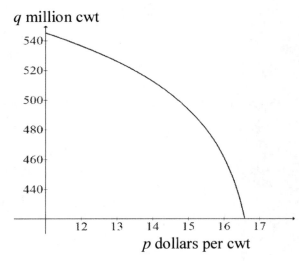

"Why does my economics text show demand as a function of quantity?"

In economic theory, many functions (including demand) are graphed with quantity on the horizontal axis. If quantity is considered to be the independent variable, the economics text is dealing with the *inverse demand function*. If price is the dependent variable, the economics text is simply drawing the demand function on a reversed set of axes to keep quantity on the horizontal axis.

Example 2: The Demand Curve

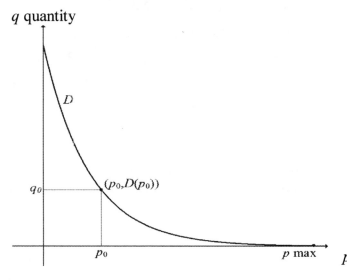

The graph to the right shows the quantity demanded at a certain price.

- $D(p)$ represents the quantity demanded.

- p_0 is the market price at which q_0 items are demanded.

- $q_0 = D(p_0)$.

- p_{max} is the price above which consumers will purchase none of the commodity.

Consumer Expenditure is the total amount spent on a commodity to purchase the quantity demanded at a set market price.

$$Consumer\ Expenditure = p_0 \cdot q_0$$

Consumer Willingness and Ability to Spend is the total amount of money consumers have available and are willing to pay to obtain a certain quantity of a commodity.

$$Consumer\ Willingness\ and\ Ability\ to\ Spend = p_0 \cdot q_0 + \int_{p_0}^{p_{max}} D(p)dp$$

Consumer Surplus is the amount that consumers have in excess from not having to spend as much as they are willing and able for a given quantity. The surplus is the difference between what consumers are willing and able to spend for a certain quantity of a commodity and the amount they actually spend on that quantity.

$$Consumer\ Surplus = \int_{p_0}^{p_{max}} D(p)dp$$

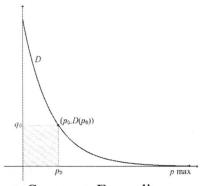

Consumer Expenditure

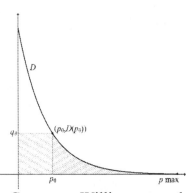

Consumer Willingness and
Ability to Spend

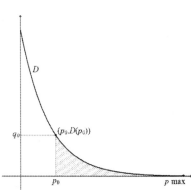

Consumer Surplus

Example 3: Demand in Context

The demand for tickets to a children's museum can be modeled as $D(p) = 0.03p^2 - 1.6p + 21$ thousand tickets when the market price is p dollars per ticket.

What is the price beyond which no tickets will be purchased? Calculate this amount and note this price as p_{max} on the graph.

a.   When the ticket price is set at $15.00 per ticket, how much will consumers spend for the tickets that will be purchased?

  CE =

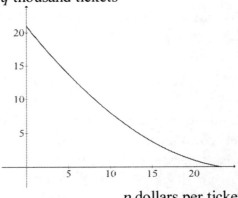

q thousand tickets

p dollars per ticket

Shade this area on the graph.

b.   When the ticket price is set at $15.00 per ticket, what is the consumer surplus?

  CS =

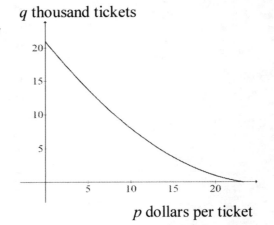

q thousand tickets

p dollars per ticket

Shade this area on the graph.

c.   When the ticket price is set at $15.00 per ticket, how much are consumers willing and able to spend for the tickets that will be purchased?

  CWAS =

q thousand tickets

p dollars per ticket

Shade this area on the graph.

Example 4: Demand at Any Price

The demand for a particular brand of toy hamster can be modeled as $D(p) = 37(0.94^p)$ million hamsters where p dollars per hamster is the market price.

a. What is the consumer expenditure when the toy hamsters are sold for the suggested retail price of $7.99? Shade the area representing consumer expenditure with vertical lines.

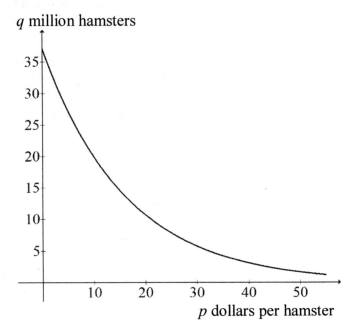

b. According to the model, is there a price at which consumers will no longer demand toy hamsters? If so, find the price. If not, explain.

c. Calculate the consumer surplus when the toy hamsters are sold for $7.99. Shade this area with horizontal lines.

d. Calculate the consumer willingness and ability to spend when the toy hamsters are sold for $7.99. Indicate this area on the graph by outlining the region.

Example 5: Finite Demand

The demand for a certain model of minivan in the United States can be modeled as

$D(p) = 14.12(0.933^p) - 0.25$ million minivans when the market price is p thousand dollars per minivan.

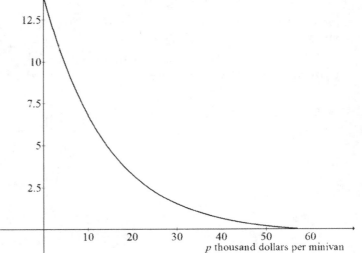

a. At what price will consumers purchase 2.5 million minivans? Label this price on the graph.

b. What is the consumer expenditure associated with this price and quantity of minivan sales? Shade the area representing consumer expenditure with vertical lines.

c. This model indicates a price above which consumers will purchase no minivans. Find this price and label it on the graph.

d. When 2.5 minivans are purchased, what is the consumer surplus? Shade the area representing consumer surplus with horizontal lines.

e. What is the total amount that consumers are willing and able to spend on 2.5 million minivans?

Elasticity of Demand

Elasticity is a measure of the responsiveness of a function's output to a change in its input variable. Because the measure of the quantities of output (demand) and input (market price) are normally very different, elasticity uses a ratio of percentage rates of change to compare the relative changes.

For a commodity with a differentiable demand function D and price per unit p, the price elasticity of demand is:

$$\eta = \frac{\text{percentage rate of change of } quantity}{\text{percentage rate of change of } price} = \frac{p \cdot D'(p)}{D(p)}$$

The **point of unit elasticity** is where $|\eta| = \left| \dfrac{p \cdot D'(p)}{D(p)} \right| = 1$

- For a given market price, when $|\eta| > 1$, a small change in the price results in a **relatively large** response in the level of demand. Demand is said to be *elastic* at that price.

- For a given market price, when $|\eta| < 1$, a small change in the price results in a **relatively small** response in the level of demand. Demand is said to be *inelastic* at that price.

Sellers of commodities use unit elasticity to set prices which permit them to maximize revenue without compromising demand.

Example 6: Determining Elasticity at a Point and the Intervals of Elasticity

The demand for kerosene in the United States is modeled by $D(p) = 1.5p^{-3} + 1.5$ million gallons where p is the price per gallon in dollars.

a. Is the demand for kerosene elastic or inelastic when kerosene is sold for $3.49 per gallon?

b. Determine the intervals of elasticity and inelasticity.

Example 7: Finding the Point of Unit Elasticity and the Intervals of Elasticity

In Example 5 the demand for a certain model of minivan in the United States was given by the function $D(p) = 14.12(0.933^p) - 0.25$ million minivans at a market price of p thousand dollars per minivan.

Suppose a dealer wishes to boost the demand for his product by having a sale. He is considering advertising a sale price of $13,000 per minivan.

Finding the point of unit elasticity would establish a rationale for a price that would both stimulate the demand for minivans and maximize his revenue at the same time.

Locate the point of unit elasticity for these minivans:

Let $Y_1 = 14.12(0.933^x) - 0.25$

Let $Y_2 = 14.12(0.933^x) \cdot \ln 0.933$

Let $Y_3 = \text{abs}\ (X \cdot Y_2/Y_1)$ or $\left| \dfrac{X \cdot Y_2}{Y_1} \right|$

Solver eqn: $0 = Y_3 - 1$

$$x = \underline{\hspace{3cm}}$$

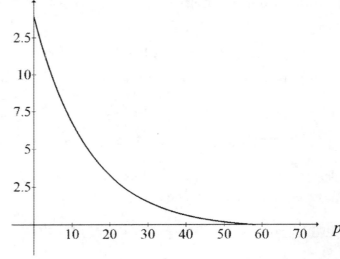

Find the interval of prices where the demand is inelastic.

Find the interval where the price causes the demand to be elastic.

Given your analysis, suggest an effective sale price for minivans: $\underline{\hspace{4cm}}$.

Example 8: Demand Review

Demand for marble sculptures is given by $D(p) = -1.002p^2 - 20.713p + 843.675$ marble sculptures, where p hundred dollars per sculpture is the market price.

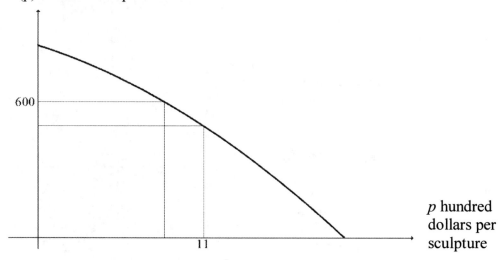

D(p) Marble Sculptures

600

11

p hundred dollars per sculpture

a. If the market price is \$1100, the associated level of demand is _____ sculptures. Round this answer to the nearest integer.

b. If the demand is 600 sculptures, the associated market price is \$_____._____. Round this answer to the nearest cent.

c. Find the point of unit elasticity.

The point of unit elasticity, rounded to the nearest dollar = \$ _____.

For prices less than this, the demand for sculptures is _____.

For prices more than this, the demand for sculptures is _____.

Section 6.4: Calculus in Economics – Supply and Equilibrium

A function giving the expected quantity of a commodity supplied at a specific market price is referred to as a **supply function** or *supply schedule*. The supply function S relates the input variable p (price per unit) with the output variable $q = S(p)$ (quantity).

The graph of a supply function is referred to as a **supply curve**.

Supply Terminology:

$S(p)$ represents the quantity supplied. It is generally represented as a piece-wise defined function.

The shutdown price, p_s, is the lowest market price that producers are willing and able to accept to supply any quantity of a certain commodity. The **shutdown point** is the point $(p_s, S(p_s))$ on the supply curve that marks the market price and quantity under which the production of a commodity will shut down.

p_0 is the market price at which q_0 items are supplied; $q_0 = S(p_0)$.

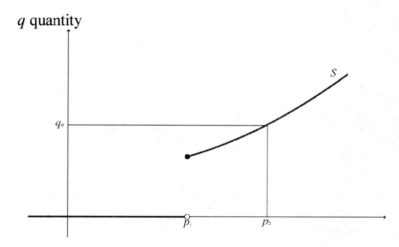

Producer Revenue is the total amount received from supplying a certain quantity of a commodity at a set market price.

$$Producer\ Revenue = p_0 \cdot q_0$$

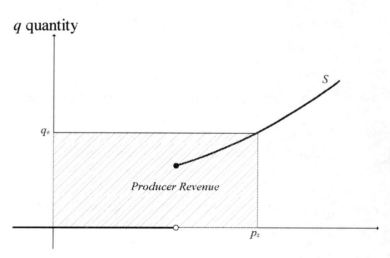

The **Producer Surplus** is the amount that producers receive in excess of the minimum amount they require to supply a certain quantity. The surplus is the difference between the revenue from supplying a certain quantity of a commodity and the amount producers must receive to be able to supply that quantity.

$$Producer\ Surplus = \int_{p_s}^{p_0} S(p)\,dp$$

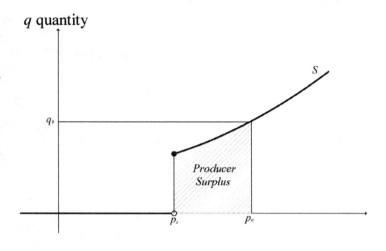

The **Producer Willingness and Ability to Receive** is the minimum amount of money producers need to receive in order to supply a certain quantity of a commodity.

Producer Willingness and Ability to

$$Receive = p_0 \cdot q_0 - \int_{p_s}^{p_0} S(p)\,dp$$

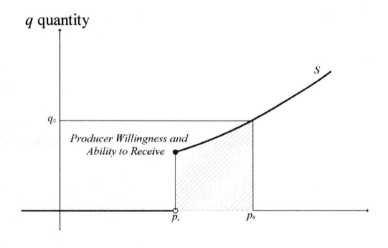

Example 1: Understanding the Supply Curve

The supply of a certain brand of disposable cellular phone can be modeled as

$$S(p) = \begin{cases} 0 & \text{when } p < 15 \\ 0.047p^2 + 9.38p + 150 & \text{when } p \geq 15 \end{cases} \text{ phones,}$$

where p is the market price in dollars per phone,

a.   What is the shutdown price?

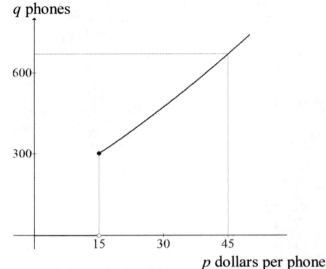

b.   What quantity of phones will producers be willing to sell at the price of $45?

c.   Compute the producer revenue corresponding to a market price of $45.

d.   At this price and quantity, what is the producer surplus? Shade and label this portion of the graph.

e.   At this price, what is the least amount that producers would be willing and able to receive to manufacture and sell the indicated quantity of phones? Shade and label this portion of the graph.

Example 2: Terminology of Supply and Demand

The point of **Market Equilibrium** occurs when the supply of a commodity is equal to the demand for that commodity.

The equilibrium point is denoted as (p^*, q^*).

$D(p^*) = S(p^*)$.

The **Total Social Gain** for a commodity is the sum of the producer surplus and the consumer surplus when the price is p^*.

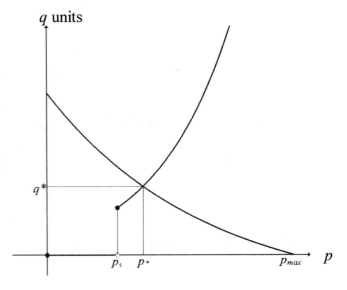

$$\begin{array}{c} \text{Producer Surplus} \\ + \text{Consumer Surplus} \\ \hline \text{Total Social Gain} \end{array}$$

$$\textit{Total Social Gain} \;=\; \int_{ps}^{p^*} S(p)\,dp + \int_{p^*}^{p_{max}} D(p)\,dp$$

The market equilibrium occurs when the supply of a good is _____ to its demand.

Shade the region on the graph which represents Total Social Gain.

Example 3: Market Equilibrium

A demand function and a supply function for the same commodity are given.

$$D(p) = 35 - 7\ln p$$

$$S(p) = \begin{cases} 0 & \text{when } p < 9 \\ 3(1.081^p) & \text{when } p \geq 9 \end{cases}$$

million units where $\$p$ is the price per unit.

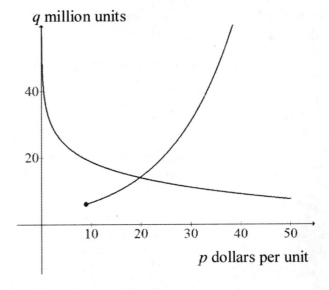

a. Locate the shutdown point. Write a sentence of interpretation for this point.

b. Find the point of market equilibrium. Write a sentence of interpretation for this point.

c. Shade the region that represents the total social gain at market equilibrium. Label all relevant values on the axes.

d. Find the total social gain at market equilibrium.

Example 4: Supply and Demand

The supply and demand for marble sculptures is shown below.

Demand and supply are given by:

$$D(p) = -1.002p^2 - 20.713p + 843.675 \text{ marble sculptures,}$$

$$S(p) = 0.312p^2 + 8.423p + 247.391 \text{ marble sculptures, when } p \geq 5.$$

where p hundred dollars per sculpture is the market price.

D(p) Marble Sculptures

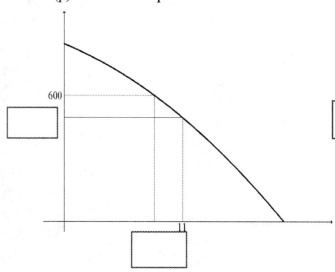

S(p) Marble Sculptures

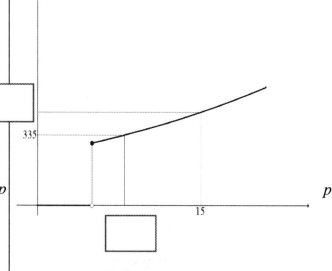

According to the demand curve above,

$D(11) =$ _____. This means that

the demand at $_____ per

sculpture equals _____ sculptures.

$D($ _____ $) = 600$.

The demand at $_____ equals 600

sculptures.

$P_{max} =$ _____. If the price of a

sculpture exceeds this price, no sculptures

will be demanded.

According to the supply curve above,

The lowest price that the manufacturer will

accept for a single sculpture is $_____.

At this price he will be willing to supply

_____ marble sculptures.

$S(15) =$ _____. If producers could

charge $_____ per sculpture, the

supply would be _____ sculptures.

$S($ _____ $) = 335$. If producers

could charge $_____ per sculpture,

335 marble sculptures would be supplied.

Example 5: Market Equilibrium

This example continues the context from Example 5 on the previous page. The figure below shows both the demand and the supply curves.

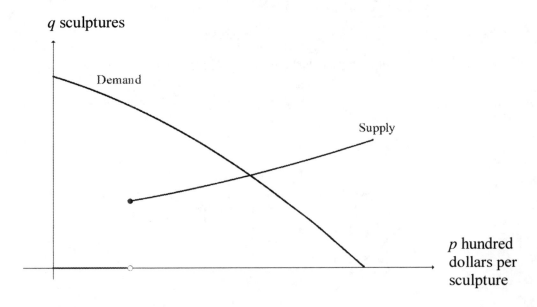

a. Find the point of equilibrium (where demand equals supply).

At equilibrium, price p^* = _____ and quantity q^* = _____.

Label the graph with these values.

b. At equilibrium, compute consumer expenditure.

c. At equilibrium, compute producer revenue.

Example 5: Market Equilibrium, Continued

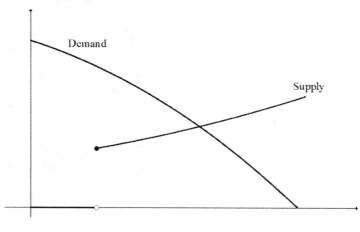

q sculptures

Demand

Supply

p hundred dollars per sculpture

Compute the following, showing mathematical notation.

d.   Producer Surplus

e.   Producer Willingness and Ability to Receive

f.   Consumer Surplus

g.   Consumer Willingness and Ability to Spend

h.   Total Social Gain

Section 6.5: Calculus in Probability (Part 1)

When all of the outcomes of a situation are considered, the pattern that indicates the amount of variability in the data is called the distribution of the quantity being studied. One way to illustrate the distribution is with a graph of rectangles called a **histogram**.

The scores of 1,518,859 students taking the mathematics portion of the SAT Reasoning Test in 2008 ranged between 200 and 800 points. The distribution of their scores is shown in the table below.

Math SAT I score x (points)	Number of students in score interval	Proportion of students in score interval
$200 \leq x < 400$	227,916	.15
$400 \leq x < 600$	911,450	
$600 \leq x \leq 800$	379,493	
	1,518,859	Sum =

When the sum of all the proportions equals ____, all possibilities have been considered.

A **histogram** is a graph composed of adjacent rectangles drawn so that the **area** of each rectangle is equal to the **proportion** of students in the corresponding interval.
The **width** of each rectangle is 200 points. Note that all widths must be equal.
The **area** of each rectangle is the proportion of the students scoring in the interval.
The **height** of each rectangle is found by dividing its area by the width.

Math SAT I	Width	Area	Height
$200 \leq x < 400$	200	0.15	0.00075
$400 \leq x < 600$	200		
$600 \leq x < 800$	200		

Calculate the height of the rectangles and the total area enclosed by the rectangles in the histogram.

Height

Score on Math Portion of the SAT

What proportion of scores is between 400 and 800?

258

A *continuous random variable* is one that can take on any real number value in a certain interval where those numerical values are determined by the results of an experiment involving chance.

The *probability* of an event is a measure of how likely it is to happen. The probability of an outcome is the proportion of times it occurs when an experiment involving chance is repeated under similar conditions a large number of times.

Probabilities are proportions, so they are real numbers between _____ and _____.

A *certain* or *sure event* is one that must happen; its probability is _____.

An *impossible* event is one that cannot happen, its probability is _____.

Probabilities for continuous random variables are associated *with intervals only*. That is, $P(x = a) = 0$ for a continuous random variable x and any real number a. Graphically, $P(x = a)$ is the area of the rectangle with width zero.

The following probabilities are equivalent:

$$P(a \leq x \leq b) = P(a < x \leq b) = P(a \leq x < b) = P(a < x < b)$$

When a histogram is drawn such that **the total area enclosed by all the rectangles is one** and the area of each rectangle equals the probability that the value of the random variable is in the interval that forms the base of the rectangle, the histogram is called a **probability histogram.**

Therefore, $P(a < x < b) =$ the sum of the areas of the rectangles whose bases are in the interval from a to b. Recalling the histogram from the previous page, the probability that a student taking the SAT exam scored between 200 and 600 on the math portion is P(200 < x < 600) = _____.

If there are many intervals in a histogram, it often simplifies matters to approximate the behavior of the random variable with a continuous function.

The continuous function that models the behavior of the probability histogram is called a *probability density function*. Probabilities are estimated by finding areas under the curve using *integral calculus*.

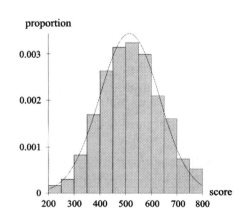

A **probability density function** (PDF) for a continuous random variable x is a continuous or piecewise-continuous function that satisfies the following two conditions:

- $f(x) \geq 0$ for each real number x (the graph must be on or above the x-axis)

- $\int_{-\infty}^{\infty} f(x)dx = 1$ (the trapped area must be equal to 1)

The probability that a value of x lies in an interval with endpoints a and b, where $a \leq b$, is given by $P(a \leq x \leq b) = \int_{a}^{b} f(x)dx$.

Example 1: A Probability Density Function

The proportion of patients who recover from mild dehydration x hours after receiving treatment is given by:

$$f(x) = \begin{cases} 12x^2 - 12x^3 & \text{when } 0 \leq x \leq 1 \\ 0 & \text{elsewhere} \end{cases}$$

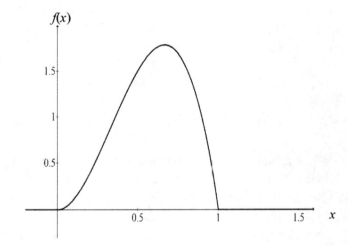

a. Verify that this is a probability density function:

Condition 1: Condition 2:

b. Calculate the probability that the recovery time is between 0.4 hours and 0.8 hours. Shade the relevant part of the graph. Show the <u>probability</u> and <u>integral</u> notation.

c. Calculate the probability that the recovery time is less than 30 minutes. Show the <u>probability</u> and <u>integral</u> notation.

Example 2: A Probability Density Function

The time t, in minutes, between successive arrivals at an emergency room of a certain city hospital on Saturday nights can be described by the function $A(t) = \begin{cases} 0.2e^{-0.2t} & \text{when } t \geq 0 \\ 0 & \text{otherwise} \end{cases}$.

a. Verify that $A(t)$ is a probability density function?

b. Calculate the probability that successive arrivals are between 20 and 30 minutes apart.

c. Calculate the probability that 10 minutes or less elapses between successive arrivals.

d. Calculate the probability that successive arrivals will be more than 15 minutes apart.

e. Write a sentence interpreting the answer to part d.

Mean, Variance, and Standard Deviation of a Probability Density Function

One important feature of a density function is its **central value**.

The mean is the arithmetic average of the data. The mode is the value that occurs most frequently and the median is the middle number in the data set (or the average of the two middles in a data set where the number of observations is even.) The mean or average is the primary estimate of central value.

The *mean* is denoted by the Greek letter μ (mu).

Distributions can have the same mean but a completely different spread, or variability, about that center. Two related measures of how closely the values of the distribution cluster about its mean are the **variance** and the **standard deviation**, denoted by the Greek letters σ^2 (sigma squared) and σ (sigma). If most of the values of the random variable are close to the mean, the variance and standard deviation are both *small*. If the values are widely scattered about the mean, the variance and the standard deviation are *large*.

In the graphs below, the mean for each distribution is 2. The variance and standard deviation for graph B is much larger than the variance for graph A.

Graph A   Graph B

Using integral calculus, it is simple to determine the mean, variance and standard deviation for any continuous probability density function, provided the integrals exist.

For the density function $y = f(x)$, with x defined on the interval of real numbers,

- Mean $= \mu = \displaystyle\int_{-\infty}^{\infty} x \cdot f(x)\,dx$

- Variance $= \sigma^2 = \displaystyle\int_{-\infty}^{\infty} (x-\mu)^2 f(x)\,dx$

- Standard deviation $= \sigma = \sqrt{\displaystyle\int_{-\infty}^{\infty} (x-\mu)^2 f(x)\,dx}$

The standard deviation is the square root of the variance.

Example 3: Finding the Mean, Variance, and Standard Deviation of a PDF

Buses that transport students from one location to another on a large campus arrive at the student parking lot every 15 minutes between 7:30 A.M. and 4:30 P.M. If x is the number of minutes before the next bus arrives at the lot, the distribution of waiting times is modeled by the density

function $f(x) = \begin{cases} \dfrac{1}{15} & \text{when } 0 \le x \le 15 \\ 0 & \text{elsewhere} \end{cases}$

a. Calculate the mean waiting time. Interpret the answer.

$$\mu = \int_{-\infty}^{\infty} x \cdot f(x)dx = \int_{0}^{15} x \cdot f(x)dx =$$

b. Calculate the variance of the waiting times.

$$\sigma^2 = \int_{-\infty}^{\infty} (x-\mu)^2 f(x)dx = \int_{0}^{15} (x - \underline{\quad\quad})^2 f(x)dx =$$

c. Calculate the standard deviation of the waiting times. Include units.

Example 4: Probability Density Function Parameters in Context

Let x represent the amount of frozen yogurt (in hundreds of gallons) sold by the G&T restaurant on any day during the summer. Storage limitations dictate that the maximum amount of frozen yogurt that can be kept on any given day is 250 gallons. Records of past sales indicate that the probability density function for x is approximated by $y(x) = 0.32x$ for $0 \leq x \leq 2.5$.

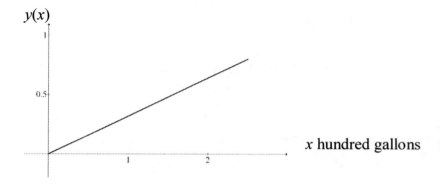

a. Verify that this is a probability density function.

b. Find the mean amount of frozen yogurt sold on a summer's day. Include units.

c. Find the standard deviation of the amount of frozen yogurt sold on a summer's day. Include units.

d. What is the probability that on some summer day G&T will sell less than 100 gallons of frozen yogurt? Show the probability and mathematical notation.

e. What is the probability that on some summer day G&T will sell between 100 and 150 gallons of frozen yogurt? Show the probability and mathematical notation.

Section 6.6: Calculus in Probability (Part 2)

This section addresses two commonly used probability density functions, the Uniform density function and the Normal density function

Example 1: The Uniform Density Function

The *uniform density function* provides a good model for random variables whose values are equally likely over an interval.

A function describing the likelihood that the random variable would take on any value, with equal likelihood, between *a* and *b*, where *a* and *b* are real numbers, is a *uniform density function*.

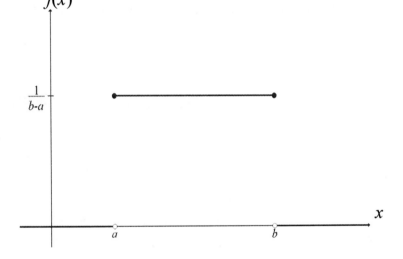

$$f(x) = \begin{cases} \dfrac{1}{b-a} & \text{when } a \le x \le b \\ 0 & \text{elsewhere} \end{cases}$$

The mean of the uniform distribution

is $\mu = a + \dfrac{b-a}{2}$

Verify that $f(x)$ is a valid probability density function.

Example 2: The Uniform Density Function

The amount of time it take for a student to complete a calculus quiz is uniformly distributed between 30 and 60 minutes.

a. Define and sketch this probability function.

b. What is the average completion time?

c. What is the probability that a particular student will require between 30 and 40 minutes to complete the quiz?

d. The professor would like to track (and possibly help) students who are in the longest ten percent of completion times. What completion time should she use?

e. What is the probability that it will take more than 43 minutes to complete the quiz?

The Normal Density Function

The normal density function is possibly the most well-known density function. The value of the mean determines the location of the midpoint of a normal curve, and the standard deviation of the normal curve determines the relative narrowness or width of the graph of the function.

The normal density function for the continuous random variable x with mean μ and standard deviation σ has the equation

$$f(x) = \frac{1}{\sigma\sqrt{2\pi}} e^{\frac{-(x-\mu)^2}{2\sigma^2}} \text{ where } -\infty < x < \infty$$

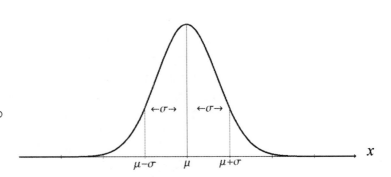

The figure above illustrates some important properties of any normal curve.

- The curve is bell-shaped, with the absolute maximum occurring at the mean μ.

- The curve is symmetrical about a vertical line through μ.

- As x approaches $\pm\infty$, $f(x)$ approaches zero.

- The inflection points occur at $\mu + \sigma$ and $\mu - \sigma$.

To enter the normal probability density function $f(x) = \frac{1}{\sigma\sqrt{2\pi}} e^{\frac{-(x-\mu)^2}{2\sigma^2}}$ in the calculator, use the calculator's built in normal probability density function which can be found under 2ND VARS (DISTRibutions) normalpdf.

To represent the normal probability density function when $\mu = 10$ and $\sigma = 2$, enter $Y_1 = normalpdf(X, 10, 2)$. That is, enter $Y_1 = normalpdf(X, \mu, \sigma)$ where the values of u and σ are specified.

Example 3: Using a Normal Density Function

A manufacturer of light bulbs advertises that the average life of these bulbs is 900 hours with a standard deviation of 100 hours. Suppose the distribution of the length of life of these light bulbs with a life span measured in hundreds of hours, is modeled by a normal density function.

a. Find the probability that a lightbulb lasts between 900 and 1000 hours.
    Shade and label the graph.

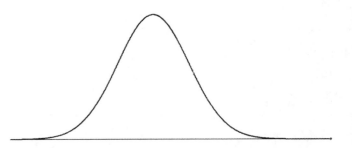

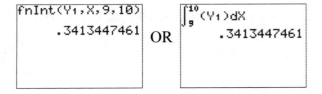

b. Find the probability that a lightbulb lasts more than 1100 hours. Shade and label the graph.

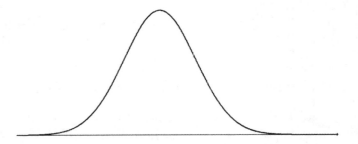

c. Find the probability that a lightbulb lasts less than 825 hours. Shade and label the graph.

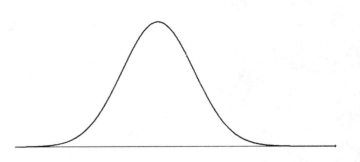

The Empirical Rule

For a density function that is symmetric and bell-shaped (in particular, for a normal distribution)

Approximately 68% of the values of the random variable lie between $\mu - \sigma$ and $\mu + \sigma$.

Approximately 95% of the values of the random variable lie between $\mu - 2\sigma$ and $\mu + 2\sigma$.

Approximately 99.7% of the values of the random variable lie between $\mu - 3\sigma$ and $\mu + 3\sigma$.

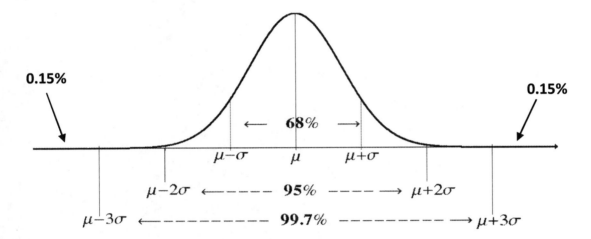

Example 5: Using the Empirical Rule

Recalling that the normal distribution is symmetric, what percentage of the values are:

a.   between μ and $\mu + \sigma$?

b.   less than $\mu - 2\sigma$?

c.   between $\mu + \sigma$ and $\mu + 2\sigma$?

Example 4: Using the Empirical Rule

The manufacturer in Example 6 has determined that the distribution of the length of life of his light bulbs, with a life span measured in hundreds of hours, is modeled by a normal density function with a mean of 950 hours and a standard deviation of 150 hours. Use the Empirical Rule to estimate the following probabilities. Include probability notation and a sketch.

a. A light bulb will last between 800 and 1100 hours.

b. A light bulb will last between 800 and 1250 hours.

c. A light bulb will last fewer than 650 hours.

d. A light bulb will last between 1250 and 1400 hours?

Example 4, Continued

The manufacturer in Example 6 has determined that the distribution of the length of life of his light bulbs, with a life span measured in hundreds of hours, is modeled by a normal density function with a mean of 950 hours and a standard deviation of 150 hours. Use the Empirical Rule to estimate the following probabilities. Include probability notation and a sketch.

Find that value that correctly completes the statements below.

e. Approximately 2.5% of the lightbulbs will last less than _____ hours.

f. Approximately 16% of the lightbulbs will last more than _____ hours.

Section 7.1: Multivariable Functions and Contour Graphs

A multivariable function is a function with a single output that depends on two or more input variables.

Example 1: Representing a Multivarible Function Algebraically:

The future value of a lump-sum investment: $F(P,r,n,t) = P\left(1 + \dfrac{r}{n}\right)^{nt}$ dollars gives the future

value of a lump-sum investment of P dollars after t years where n is the number of compounding periods per year and r is the nominal rate of interest.

a. Draw an input/output diagram for $F(P,r,n,t)$.

b. Calculate $F(10000, 0.05, 4, 17)$.

c. Complete the interpretation for the answer to part b.

The _____-year future value for an investment of _____ with

_____compounding at _____% interest is _____.

Silo capacity: $C(d,h) = 0.0041\, d^2 h^{1.4}$ tons gives the weight of a settled, unopened silo of corn with a moisture content of 68% when the silo has an inside diameter of d feet and the corn is h feet deep.

d. Calculate $C(40, 80)$.

e. Complete the interpretation for the answer to part d.

A _____ foot diameter silo filled to a depth of _____ feet with corn at a moisture

content of 68% has a weight of _____ tons.

Example 2: Viewing a Multivariable Function with Two Input Variables

Multivariable functions with **two** input variables are often illustrated using *contour curves.*

a. A **contour curve** for a 3-dimensional function is the collection of all points (x, y) for which $f(x, y) = K$. The graph to the right shows the contours for

   $f(x, y) =$ _____ , $f(x, y) =$ _____ , and $f(x, y) =$ _____ .

b. Estimate the following values:

   $f(1,5) =$ _____ , $f(3,4) =$ _____ , and $f(6.5,1.5) =$ _____ .

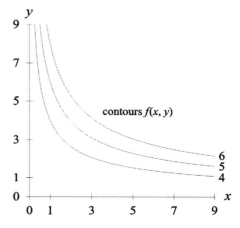

contours $f(x, y)$

Example 3: Interpreting a Contour Curve on a Data Table

The table gives the elevation of Missouri farmland, $E(e, n)$ feet above sea level with *contours* at elevations of 796, 797, 798, 799, 800, 801, and 802 feet.

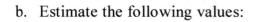

	0	0.1	0.2	0.3	0.4	0.5	0.6	0.7	0.8	0.9	1.0	1.1	1.2	1.3	1.4	1.5
0	802.2	801.0	800.2	799.7	799.4	799.3	799.3	799.4	799.5	799.5	799.5	799.2	798.7	797.0	796.7	795.1
0.1	802.4	801.2	800.4	799.9	799.6	799.5	799.5	799.6	799.7	799.8	799.7	799.4	798.9	798.1	796.9	795.3
0.2	802.6	801.4	800.6	800.1	799.8	799.7	799.7	799.8	799.9	799.9	799.9	799.6	799.1	798.3	797.1	795.5
0.3	802.7	801.5	800.7	800.2	799.9	799.8	799.8	799.9	800.0	800.1	800.0	799.7	799.2	798.4	797.2	795.6
0.4	802.8	801.6	800.8	800.3	800.0	799.9	799.0	800.0	800.1	800.1	800.1	799.8	799.3	798.5	797.3	795.7
0.5	802.8	801.6	800.8	800.3	800.0	799.9	799.9	800.0	800.1	800.2	800.1	799.8	799.3	798.5	797.3	795.7
0.6	802.8	801.6	800.8	800.3	800.0	799.9	799.9	800.0	800.1	800.1	800.1	799.8	799.3	798.5	797.3	795.7
0.7	802.7	801.5	800.7	800.2	799.9	799.8	799.8	799.9	800.0	800.1	800.0	799.7	799.2	798.4	797.2	795.6
0.8	802.6	801.4	800.6	800.1	799.8	799.7	799.7	799.8	799.9	799.9	799.9	799.6	799.1	798.3	797.1	795.5
0.9	802.4	801.2	800.4	799.9	799.6	799.5	799.5	799.6	799.7	799.8	799.7	799.4	798.9	798.1	796.9	795.3
1.0	802.2	801.0	800.2	799.7	799.4	799.3	799.3	799.4	799.5	799.5	799.5	799.2	798.7	797.9	796.7	795.1
1.1	801.9	800.7	799.9	799.4	799.1	799.0	799.0	799.1	799.2	799.3	799.2	798.9	798.4	797.6	796.4	794.8
1.2	801.6	800.4	799.6	799.1	798.8	798.7	798.7	798.8	798.9	798.9	798.9	798.6	798.1	797.3	796.1	794.5
1.3	801.2	800.0	799.2	798.7	798.4	798.3	798.4	798.5	798.5	798.6	798.5	798.2	797.7	796.9	795.7	794.1
1.4	800.8	799.6	798.8	798.3	798.0	797.9	797.9	798.0	798.1	798.1	798.1	798.8	797.3	796.5	795.3	793.7
1.5	800.3	799.1	798.3	797.8	797.5	797.4	797.5	797.6	797.6	797.7	797.6	797.3	797.8	796.0	794.8	793.2

800 799 798   797   796

a. $E(0.5, 0.9) =$

b. The point $E(0.5, 0.9)$ is located 0.5 miles (north, south, east, or west) of the western fence

   and 0.9 miles (north, south, east, or west) of the southern fence.

c. A person who starts at $(0.5, 0.9)$ and walks west is going (uphill, downhill).

d. The highest elevation shown on the graph is _____ feet above sea level.

Example 4: Tables May Be Shown from a Perspective that Differs from the Graph of the Data

Contour curves graphed on axes may look different from the related data table that has contour curves drawn on it.

a. How does the appearance of the curves of the contour graph shown to the right below differ from the contour curves drawn on the table?

e miles east of the western fence																
	0	0.1	0.2	0.3	0.4	0.5	0.6	0.7	0.8	0.9	1.0	1.1	1.2	1.3	1.4	1.5
0	802.2	801.0	800.2	799.7	799.4	799.3	799.3	799.4	799.5	799.5	799.5	799.2	798.7	797.0	796.7	795.1
0.1	802.4	801.2	800.4	799.9	799.6	799.5	799.5	799.6	799.7	799.8	799.7	799.4	798.9	798.1	796.9	795.3
0.2	802.6	801.4	800.6	800.1	799.8	799.7	799.7	799.8	799.9	799.9	799.9	799.6	799.1	798.3	797.1	795.5
0.3	802.7	801.5	800.7	800.2	799.9	799.8	799.8	799.9	800.0	800.1	800.0	799.7	799.2	798.4	797.2	795.6
0.4	802.8	801.6	800.8	800.3	800.0	799.9	799.0	800.0	800.1	800.1	800.1	799.8	799.3	798.5	797.3	795.7
0.5	802.8	801.6	800.8	800.3	800.0	799.9	799.9	800.0	800.1	800.2	800.1	799.8	799.3	798.5	797.3	795.7
0.6	802.8	801.6	800.8	800.3	800.0	799.9	799.9	800.0	800.1	800.1	800.1	799.8	799.3	798.5	797.3	795.7
0.7	802.7	801.5	800.7	800.2	799.9	799.8	799.8	799.9	800.0	800.1	800.0	799.7	799.2	798.4	797.2	795.6
0.8	802.6	801.4	800.6	800.1	799.8	799.7	799.7	799.8	799.9	799.9	799.9	799.6	799.1	798.3	797.1	795.5
0.9	802.4	801.2	800.4	799.9	799.6	799.5	799.5	799.6	799.7	799.8	799.7	799.4	798.9	798.1	796.9	795.3
1.0	802.2	801.0	800.2	799.7	799.4	799.3	799.3	799.4	799.5	799.5	799.5	799.2	798.7	797.9	796.7	795.1
1.1	801.9	800.7	799.9	799.4	799.1	799.0	799.0	799.1	799.2	799.3	799.2	798.9	798.4	797.6	796.4	794.8
1.2	801.6	800.4	799.6	799.1	798.8	798.7	798.7	798.8	798.9	798.9	798.9	798.6	798.1	797.3	796.1	794.5
1.3	801.2	800.0	799.2	798.7	798.4	798.3	798.4	798.5	798.5	798.6	798.5	798.2	797.7	796.9	795.7	794.1
1.4	800.8	799.6	798.8	798.3	798.0	797.9	797.9	798.0	798.1	798.1	798.1	797.8	797.3	796.5	795.3	793.7
1.5	800.3	799.1	798.3	797.8	797.5	797.4	797.5	797.6	797.6	797.7	797.6	797.3	797.8	796.0	794.8	793.2

(n miles north of the southern fence)

800   799   798   797   796

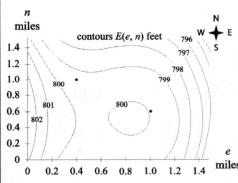

b. How does the appearance of the 520-contour curve drawn on the table shown to the left below differ from the contour curves shown in the graph?

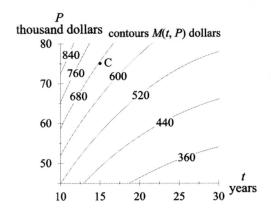

Face value, P (thousand dollars)	Term, t (years)								
	10	12.5	15	17.5	20	22.5	25	27.5	30
5	58.05	50.11	44.94	41.36	38.76	36.82	35.34	34.18	33.27
10	116.11	100.22	89.88	82.72	77.53	73.65	70.68	68.36	66.53
15	174.16	150.32	134.82	124.08	116.29	110.47	106.02	102.54	99.80
20	232.22	200.43	179.77	165.44	155.06	147.30	141.36	136.72	133.06
25	290.27	250.54	224.71	206.80	193.82	184.12	176.69	170.90	166.33
30	348.33	300.65	269.65	248.16	232.59	220.95	212.03	205.08	199.59
35	406.38	350.76	314.59	289.52	271.35	257.77	247.37	239.27	232.86
40	464.43	400.86	359.53	330.88	310.12	294.60	282.71	273.45	266.12
45	522.49	450.97	404.47	372.24	248.88	331.42	318.05	307.63	299.39
50	580.54	501.08	449.41	413.60	387.65	368.25	353.39	341.81	332.65
55	638.60	551.19	494.36	454.96	426.41	405.07	388.73	375.99	365.92
60	696.65	601.30	539.30	496.32	465.18	441.90	424.07	410.17	399.18
65	754.71	651.40	584.24	537.68	503.94	478.72	459.41	444.35	432.45
70	812.76	701.51	629.18	579.04	542.71	515.54	494.75	478.53	465.71
75	870.81	751.62	674.12	620.40	581.47	552.37	530.08	512.71	498.98
80	928.87	801.73	719.06	661.76	620.24	589.19	565.42	546.89	532.24

Example 5: Estimating Output Values from a 3-D Graphical Representation

To estimate the input values of a point on a 3-D graphical representation, follow the surface of the graph (using lines that are parallel to each of the input axes).

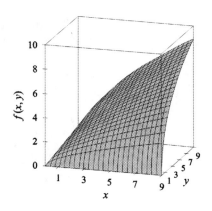

Estimating an output value on a 3-D graph is less accurate than estimation using a contour graph.

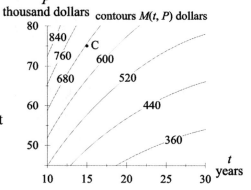

Estimating the input values on a contour graph is similar to estimating point coordinates on any 2-D graph. To estimate the output value, compare the location of the point to the nearest contour curves.

The point C on the contour graph above has input and output

values of $t =$ _____ , $P =$ _____ , and $M \approx$ _____ .

> When the constants K used for the K-contour curves are *equally spaced*, the steepness of the three-dimensional graph at different points (or in different directions) can be compared by noting the closeness (or frequency) of the contour curves. If the contour curves are close together near a point, the surface is **steeper** in that region than in a portion of the graph where the contour curves are spaced farther apart.

Example 6: Estimating Steepness from Contour Curves

The contour graph to the right gives the elevation of a tract measured e miles east of the western fence and n miles north of the southern fence.

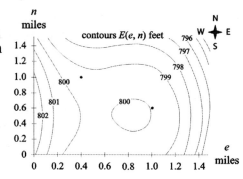

a. From (0.4, 1.0), a hiker walks (*downhill/uphill*) if he walks 0.4 miles north.

b. From (1.0, 0.6), does east 0.4 mile or north 0.4 mile have a steeper descent?

Example 7: Finding the Change and Percentage Change between Two Points

Recall from MATH 1020 the concepts of change and percentage change. For any two specific input points for the function f,

Change (from p_1 to p_2) = $$f(p_2) - f(p_1)$$	**Percentage change** (from p_1 to p_2) = $$\frac{f(p_2) - f(p_1)}{f(p_1)} \cdot 100\%$$

The figure to the right shows a contour graph of the function M giving the monthly payment necessary to pay off a mortgage of P thousand dollars over t years at nominal interest of 7%.

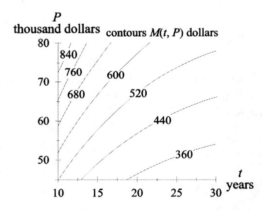

a. Estimate and interpret $M(22.5, 70)$.

b. From the point (22.5, 70), does $M(t, P)$ decrease when t decreases or when P decreases?

c. Find the following output values: $M(15, 55) \approx$ _____ . $M(25, 55) \approx$ _____ .

d. What is the change in the monthly payment on a $55,000 mortgage when the length of the mortgage is increased from 15 years to 25 years?

e. What is the percentage change in the monthly payment on a $55,000 mortgage when the length of the mortgage is increased from 15 years to 25 years?

Example 8: Sketching a Contour Curve on a Table

Data tables do not show every possible value for the input and output values of a multivariable function. When sketching contour curves on tables, assume the multivariable function is *continuous* over the entire input intervals and that ***the curve will be continuous and relatively smooth.***

- *Find two output values so that one value is greater than the desired contour and one value is less than the desired contour. Start a 'path' at that point.*
- *Work through the table so that the given-path is always between a value greater than the desired contour and a value less than the desired contour.*
- *Extend the path to the edges of the table or form a closed curve.*
- *It is not necessary to start on the edge of the table.*
- *Consider that there may be more than one path.*
- *Once the path is identified, sketch in the contour curve(s). The curve(s) should be drawn as smoothly and with as few changes in concavity as possible.*

a. Sketch the 2000 kg-calories contour curve on the table showing Body Heat Loss in $H(v,t)$ (kg-calories/ square meter of body surface area per hour) as a function of air temperature and wind speed.

Air temp, t	Wind speed, v (meters per second)					
	0	5	10	15	20	25
-20	554	1474	1700	1812	1864	1879
-25	606	1613	1860	1982	2040	2056
-30	658	1752	2021	2153	2216	2233
-35	711	1891	2181	2324	2392	2411
-40	763	2030	2341	2495	2568	2588

b. Sketch the 1700 kg-calories contour curve on the table.

Example 9: Sketching a Contour Curve from an Equation

$H(v,t) = \left(10.45 + 10\sqrt{v} - v\right)\left(33 - t\right)$ kg-calories gives the heat loss where wind speed is v mps (meters per second) and air temperature is $t\,°C$. Plot at least four points on the 2000 kg-calorie contour curve and sketch the curve. [Check: $H(2,20) \approx 293.698$]

v	t
5	
10	
15	
20	
25	

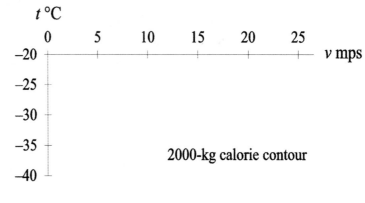

277

TI 7.1.1 Evaluating a multivariable function.

- **Y=** Enter F in Y_1
  **ALPHA 8 (1 + ALPHA X /
  ALPHA LOG) ^ (ALPHA
  LOG APLHA 4)**
- **MATH 0** (0: Solver) The equation
  eqn: must contain Y1
- **ENTER** returns the screen
  beginning Y1 =... all variables
  should be listed
- ▼ Enter the values of
  P, R, N and T
- **2ND MODE** to return to the
  homescreen
- **VARS ▶ 1 1**
- **ENTER**

Note: There is not a way to clear the stored values on the calculator. If you wish to see the current value of any variable, type the variable name on the homescreen using the ALPHA key and press ENTER. When dealing with single variable functions, the functions were stored in Y_1 as a function of x. With multivariable functions, the solver is used to store multiple variable values so that entering Y_1 on the will give evaluate the function at the given values.

TI 7.1.2 Solving a multivariable function to find the value of one of the input variables

- **Y=** Enter H in Y_1
- **MATH 0** (0: Solver)
  On the EQUATION SOLVER
  SCREEN, complete eqn:0= **Y1 - 2000**
- ▼ Store the value of $V = 5$
- ▼ With the cursor in the T = row, **ALPHA
  ENTER** returns the value of T so that
  $H(5,T) = 2000$;
  Repeat to solve for T as V changes
  to 10, 15, 20 and 25.

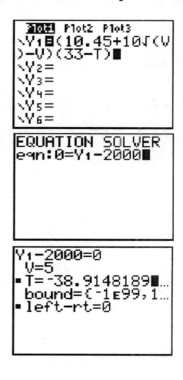

Section 7.2: Cross-Sectional Models and Rates of Changes

A **cross section** of a multivariable function is a relation with one less dimension (variable) than the original multivariable function.

Example 1: Three Representations of Cross Sectional Models

For a function with two input variables, a cross section is represented **graphically** as the curve that results when a three-dimensional graph of the function is intersected by a plane.

The three-dimensional representation with x held constant at 7 is shown to the right.

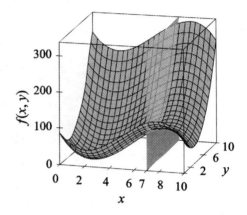

A simple cross section is represented **numerically** on a table of data by one row or column of the data.

The table shows the yield of Iowa corn crops in bushels per acre as a function of temperature. The highlighted column gives the yield when 17 mm of rain falls each month.

r mm $t\ {}^{0}$ F	16	16.5	17	17.5	18	18.5
64	96	92	87	83	80	76
67	114	109	105	100	95	91
70	134	130	125	121	117	113
73	158	154	150	147	144	139
76	187	183	179	175	170	166

When a multivariable function is represented **algebraically** by an equation, a simple cross section of the function is written by replacing one input variable with a constant and then rewriting the equation.

a. Find the cross-section of $f(x,y) = (3x^2 + 2x)(y+5)$ when $x = 4$.

b. Find the cross-section of $f(x,y) = (3x^2 + 2x)(y+5)$ when $y = 2$.

Example 2: Modeling Cross-sectional Data for Uninsured Americans

When data is given in a table with two input variables and one output variable, modeling the data in one row (or one column) results in a cross-sectional model. A cross-sectional model is a model of a subset of multivariable data obtained by holding all but one input variable constant and modeling the output variable with respect to the one input variable.

The table below gives the number of million people in a particular age-range in the United States who had no form of health insurance during an entire year.

$w(g,t)$ million people without health insurance

		Year, t					
		2002	2003	2004	2005	2006	2007
Age, g, years	<18	8.53	8.37	8.27	8.05	8.66	8.15
	18 to 24	8.13	8.41	8.77	8.20	8.32	7.99
	25 to 34	9.77	10.35	10.18	10.16	10.71	10.33
	35 to 44	7.78	7.89	8.11	7.90	8.02	7.72
	45 to 64	9.11	9.66	10.20	10.05	10.74	10.79
	≥ 65	0.26	0.29	0.30	0.45	0.54	0.69

Use the table to identify the input and output data that will be used to find the model. The data is taken from **parallel** rows *or* columns. The **input** data always comes from the **left column** or **top row**.

The **output** data comes from the fixed input level (the variable that is being held constant). Use all available output data at the fixed input level. The input and output lists must have the same length.

Write the model for the number of people 65 years of age or older who were without health insurance as a function of the number of years since 2001.

$w(\geq 65, t) =$

Recall a MODEL requires the following:
- An equation
- A description of the output with units
- A description of the input with units
- A domain or input interval

Example 3: Finding Cross-Sectional Models from a Data Table

The table below gives the yield of Iowa corn crops ($y(r,t)$ bushels per acre) with respect to the average monthly surface temperature (t degrees Fahrenheit) and average monthly rainfall (r mm).

		Rainfall, r (millimeters)					
		16	16.5	17	17.5	18	18.5
Temp, t (°F)	64	96	92	87	83	80	76
	67	114	109	105	100	95	91
	70	134	130	125	121	117	113
	73	158	154	150	147	144	139
	76	187	183	179	175	170	166

a. Find an exponential cross-sectional **model** that can be used to estimate the yield of Iowa corn crops when the average monthly rainfall is 17 mm.

b. Find the yield when the average monthly rainfall is 17 mm and the average monthly surface temperature is 72 °F.

c. Determine the rate of change of yield with respect to temperature when the average monthly rainfall is 17 mm and the average monthly surface temperature is $72°F$. Interpret your answer.

Example 3, Continued.

Rainfall, r (millimeters)							
		16	16.5	17	17.5	18	18.5
Temp, t (°F)	64	96	92	87	83	80	76
	67	114	109	105	100	95	91
	70	134	130	125	121	117	113
	73	158	154	150	147	144	139
	76	187	183	179	175	170	166

d. Find a linear cross-sectional **model** that can be used to determine the yield when the average monthly surface temperature is 73 °F and the average monthly rainfall is 18.25 mm.

Find the yield if $t = 73$ and $r = 18.25$.

e. Find and interpret the rate of change of yield with respect to the average monthly rainfall when the average monthly rainfall is 18.25 mm and the average monthly surface temperature is 73°F.

Example 4: Using Data to Calculate Monthly Payments for a Loan

The table to the right shows monthly payments on a $1000 loan at different interest rates over different loan periods.

a. Is it possible to find a cross-sectional model for the monthly payments for a 42-month loan?

Monthly Payments (dollars) on a $1000 Loan

Monthly Interest %	Term (months)				
		24	36	42	48	60
5	43.87	29.97	26.00	23.03	18.87
6	44.32	30.42	26.46	23.49	19.33
7	44.77	30.88	26.91	23.95	19.80
8	45.23	31.34	27.38	24.41	20.28
9	45.68	31.80	27.84	24.89	20.76
10	46.14	32.27	28.32	25.36	21.25
11	46.61	32.74	28.79	25.85	21.74
12	47.07	33.21	29.28	26.33	22.24

b. If so, this cross section would be represented by a row or a column of the table?

c. Is it possible to find a cross-sectional model for monthly payments for a loan at 10.5%?

d. If so, would this cross section be represented by a *row/column* (circle one) of the table?

Monthly Payments (dollars) on a $1000 Loan

		Term (months)				
		24	36	42	48	60
Monthly Interest %	5	43.87	29.97	26.00	23.03	18.87
	6	44.32	30.42	26.46	23.49	19.33
	7	44.77	30.88	26.91	23.95	19.80
	8	45.23	31.34	27.38	24.41	20.28
	9	45.68	31.80	27.84	24.89	20.76
	10	46.14	32.27	28.32	25.36	21.25
	11	46.61	32.74	28.79	25.85	21.74
	12	47.07	33.21	29.28	26.33	22.24

e. Find the appropriate cross-sectional **model** (either part a or part c).

f. Use the model to estimate the monthly payments for a 42-month loan at 10.5%.

Example 5: Apparent Temperature by Dew Point and Air Temperature

The table below shows how it feels (the apparent temperature in degrees F) for certain air temperatures and dew points. The dew point is the temperature to which the air needs to be cooled in order to achieve a relative humidity of 100%. The higher the dew point, the muggier it feels.

		Dew point (°F)							
		50	55	60	65	70	75	80	85
Air Temperature (°F)	65	62.7	63.8	65.0	66.6				
	70	67.8	68.7	69.8	71.1	72.6			
	75	73.1	73.9	74.8	75.9	79.2	80.7		
	80	79.8	80.6	81.6	82.8	84.4	86.9	90.9	
	85	83.5	84.7	86.1	88.0	90.5	94.0	99.0	106.6
	90	87.9	89.4	91.2	93.6	96.9	101.2	107.2	115.6
	95	92.9	94.5	96.7	99.6	103.4	108.4	115.2	124.3
	100	98.1	99.9	102.4	105.6	109.8	115.3	122.7	132.3
	105	103.4	105.4	108.1	111.6	116.1	122.0	129.7	139.7
	110	108.7	110.9	113.8	117.5	122.3	128.4	136.3	146.5

(Source: National Oceanic and Atmospheric Administration.)

a. In order to model the apparent temperature as a function of the air temperature when the dew point is 70°F, the _____ variable must be held constant

b. The cross section in part *a* is represented by a *row/column* (circle one) of the table.

c. Find a cross-sectional model for the apparent temperature as a function of the air temperature when the dew point is 70°F.

Calculator Example (Using a TI-84 Plus)

TI 7.2.1 Finding a cross-sectional equation from a data set (CC5e p. 543)
(*includes choosing between two models based on fit*)

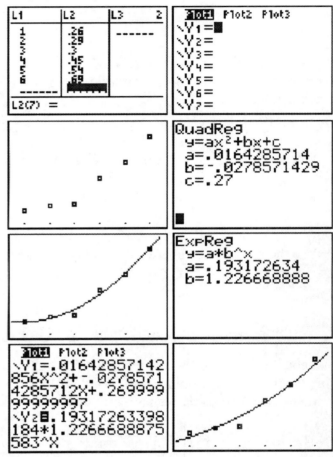

- **STAT** **1** Enter data into L1 & L2
- **Y=**
  Confirm that Plot1 is turned on
- **ZOOM** **0** returns the scatter plot
- **2ND** **MODE** returns to the Homescreen
- **STAT** ▶ **5** (QuadReg) **VARS** ▶
  1 **1** **ENTER** returns the quadratic
  equation in Y1
- **GRAPH** shows the equation over
  the scatter plot
- **2ND** **MODE** returns to the Homescreen
- **STAT** ▶ **0** (ExpReg) **VARS** ▶
  1 **2** **ENTER** returns an exponential
  model in Y2
- **Y=** Move cursor over the = next to Y₁
  ENTER turns off Y₁
- **GRAPH**

Section 7.3: Partial Rates of Change

Before discussing partial rates of change of multi-variable functions, recall the derivative rules for a single variable function:

Derivative Rule	$f(x)$	$f'(x)$
Constant Rule	$f(x) = 5$	$f'(x) =$
Power Rule	$f(x) = x^5$	$f'(x) =$
Exponential Rule	$f(x) = 5^x$	$f'(x) =$
e^x Rule	$f(x) = e^x$	$f'(x) =$
e^{kx} Rule	$f(x) = e^{5x}$	$f'(x) =$
Natural Log Rule	$f(x) = \ln x$	$f'(x) =$
Constant Multiplier Rule	$f(x) = 6x^5$	$f'(x) = 6(5x^4) =$
Sum and Difference Rule	$f(x) = e^{3x} + 4\ln x - \pi^5$	$f'(x) =$

Derivatives of a multivariable function are called **partial derivatives** because they describe change in only one input direction, so they give only a *partial* picture of change.

The function $f(x, y)$ has two partial derivatives:

- The partial derivative of f with respect to x is found by treating x as the variable and all input variables other than x as constants. f_x ("f sub x") and $\frac{\partial f}{\partial x}$ ("del f del x")

- The partial derivative of f with respect to y is found by treating y as the variable and all input variables other than y as constants. f_y ("f sub y") and $\frac{\partial f}{\partial y}$ ("del f del y")

Example 1: Finding Partial Derivatives

Given $f(x,y) = 3x + x^2 y + 5y^2$, find

- f_x

- f_y

Given $g(x,y) = x^5 y^9 + 3^y \cdot e^{2x}$, find

- $\dfrac{\partial g}{\partial x}$

- $\dfrac{\partial g}{\partial y}$

Example 2: Partial Derivative Notation at a Point

$g(h,s)$ is the expected college grade point average of a typical freshman college student who had a GPA of h in high school and has a combined score of s on the SAT.

a. Write the notation for the rate of change of the expected college GPA with respect to the combined SAT score when the high school GPA is 3.5 and the combined SAT score is 1200.

b. Write the notation for the rate of change of the expected college GPA with respect to the high school GPA when the high school GPA is 2.8 and the combined SAT score is 1020.

Example 3: Finding and Interpreting the Partial Derivative at a Point

The daily sales of Coke products from a vending machine is modeled by
$S(c, p) = 196.42p - 50.2c^2 + 9.6c + 66.4 - 1.04cp$ cans when Coke products are sold for $\$c$ and Pepsi products are sold for $\$p$.

a.   Find $S(0.75, 1)$.

b.   Find $S_c(1, 1.25)$ algebraically.

c.   Find $S_c(1, 1.25)$ on the calculator.

Note: When finding derivatives <u>at a point</u> using the calculator, it is necessary to store the point into Solver <u>before</u> evaluating nDeriv.

d.   Interpret $S_c(1, 1.25)$.

Example 4: Finding and Interpreting Partial Derivatives at a Point

The future value of a lump-sum investment of P dollars over t years at 6% nominal interest compounded quarterly is $F(P,t) = P(1.0614^t)$ dollars.

a.   Calculate and interpret $\left. \dfrac{\partial F}{\partial P} \right|_{(7500,10)}$

b.   Given $F(7500,10) \approx \$13,610$ approximate $F(7525,10)$.

Example 5: Writing Second Partial Derivatives

A partial derivative of a partial-derivative is called a **second partial derivative**. The multivariable function $f(x,y)$ has four second partial derivatives.

$f_{xx} = \dfrac{\partial^2 f}{\partial x^2}$ = the second partial derivative of f_x with respect to x

$f_{xy} = \dfrac{\partial}{\partial y}\left(\dfrac{\partial f}{\partial x}\right) = \dfrac{\partial^2 f}{\partial y \partial x}$ = the mixed partial derivative of f_x with respect to y

$f_{yx} = \dfrac{\partial}{\partial x}\left(\dfrac{\partial f}{\partial y}\right) = \dfrac{\partial^2 f}{\partial x \partial y}$ = the mixed partial derivative of f_y with respect to x

$f_{yy} = \dfrac{\partial^2 f}{\partial y^2}$ = the second partial derivative of f_y with respect to y

As with second derivatives of single-variable functions, second partial derivatives measure **how quickly rates of change are changing** and **indicate concavity**.

Recall that the first partial derivatives of $f(x,y) = 3x + x^2 y + 5y^2$ are

$$f_x = 3 + 2xy \qquad \text{and} \qquad f_y = x^2 + 10y$$

Write the equations of the second partial derivatives.

The matrix of second partial derivatives will be used in Chapter 8 to classify the optimal points of a multivariable function. The second partials matrix of $f(x,y)$ is $\begin{bmatrix} f_{xx} & f_{xy} \\ f_{yx} & f_{yy} \end{bmatrix}$. Therefore the

matrix of second partial derivatives of $f(x,y) = 3x + x^2 y + 5y^2$ is: $\begin{bmatrix} 2y & 2x \\ 2x & 10 \end{bmatrix}$.

Example 6:   Finding Second Partial Derivatives

Given $g(x,y) = x^5 y^9 + 3^y \cdot e^{2x}$, find the second partial derivatives. (function from Example 1)

Recall: $\dfrac{\partial g}{\partial x} = g_x = 5x^4 y^9 + 3^y \left(2e^{2x} \right)$ and $\dfrac{\partial g}{\partial y} = g_y = 9x^5 y^8 + \left(\ln 3 \right)\left(3^y \right)\left(e^{2x} \right)$

Example 7:   Finding the Matrix of Second Partial Derivatives

Given $f(x,y) = y^2 \ln x$, find the matrix of second partial derivatives.

Example 8: Partial Derivatives of a Function with Three Input Variables

A measure of the adhesiveness of cheese spread can be modeled as a function of the percentage of the glycerol, salt, and lactose used in preparation:

$$A(g,s,l) = 5600 - 3400s + 1600s^2 + 400l - 1800g + 140g^2 + 1200sl - 500s^2l + 200sg \text{ AU (adhesive units)}$$

where g is the % of glycerol, s is the %of salt, and l is the % of lactose.

a. Write the three first partial derivatives of A. Include units.

$A_g =$

$A_s =$

$A_l =$

---

b. Write the following second partial derivatives. No units are necessary.

$A_{sl} =$ $A_{gl} =$ $A_{gs} =$

$A_{ss} =$ $A_{ll} =$ $A_{gg} =$

$A_{ls} =$ $A_{lg} =$ $A_{sg} =$

Calculator Example (Using a TI-84 Plus)

TI 7.3.1 Evaluating a partial derivative at a point

- **Y=** Enter F in Y_1
- **MATH 0** (0: Solver)
- ▲ Confirm that Y_1 is referenced in the equation 0 =
- ▼ Enter the values of P and T
- **2ND MODE** returns to the Homescreen
- **MATH 8** (8: nDeriv)
- Complete the expression nDeriv(**Y1, P, 7500**)
- **ENTER**

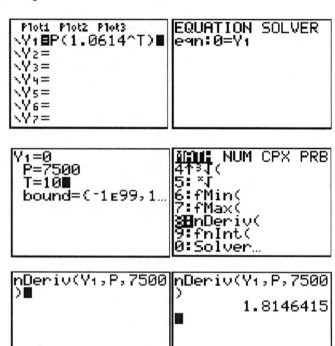

Section 7.4: Compensating for Change

For a multivariable function which must maintain a constant level of output, a change in one variable may be compensated for by a change in the other variable. This change can be found using the slope of a tangent line drawn to the contour curve.

Example 1: Estimation with a Tangent Line Drawn to a Contour

When the output of a function depends on two input variables and must remain fixed at some constant level, a change in one of the input variables must be *compensated* for by a change in the other input variable. The **slope of a tangent line drawn to a contour curve** is used to estimate this change.

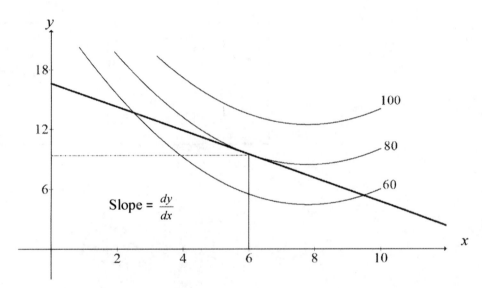

Example 2: Using a Graph to Compensate for Change

If a multivariable function has *two* input variables, it is possible to find the rate of change of *one input variable* with respect to *the other* input variable. The rate of change of one input variable with respect to the other is represented graphically as the slope of the line tangent to a contour.

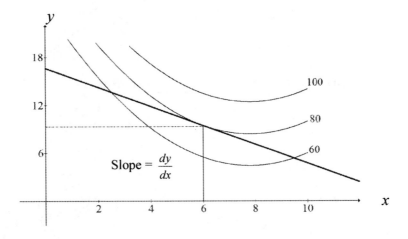

The graph shown above has a line drawn at the point $(6, 9.3, 80)$ tangent to the 80-contour

curve. In order to compensate for a decrease in the *x*-value from 6 to 4 while remaining on the

80-contour curve, the *y*-value must _____ to approximately _____.

The Slope of a Line Tangent to a Contour Curve
When the output of a function *f* with two input variables, *x* and *y,* is held constant at a value *c*, the slope at any point on the contour curve $f(x, y) = c$ is calculated as $\dfrac{dy}{dx} = \dfrac{-f_x}{f_y}$, $f_y \neq 0$.

Linear approximation is the process of using points along a tangent line to approximate points on a curve. When *y* can be considered as a function of *x* and *x* changes by a small amount Δx, the corresponding change Δy can be approximated as: $\Delta y \approx \dfrac{dy}{dx} \Delta x$. Note: $\dfrac{\Delta y}{\Delta x} \approx \dfrac{dy}{dx}$.

Example 3: Finding the Formula for the Slope of a Contour Curve

Given $f(x, y) = x^2 + 4y^2 + 1$,

a. Calculate $\dfrac{dy}{dx} = \dfrac{-f_x}{f_y} =$

b. Calculate $\dfrac{dx}{dy} =$

Example 4: Using the Formulas to find the Slope at a Point

a. $f(4,5) =$

b. $\dfrac{dy}{dx}\bigg|_{(4,5)} =$

c. $\dfrac{dx}{dy}\bigg|_{(4,5)} =$

d. $\dfrac{dy}{dx}\bigg|_{(4,5)} \times \dfrac{dx}{dy}\bigg|_{(4,5)} =$ _____ , so these two values are _____ of each other.

e. When x increases from 4 to 4.1, how must y change in order to remain on the $f = 117$ contour curve?

$f(4.1, \underline{\hspace{1cm}}) \approx 117$

f. When y decreases from 5 to 4.9, how must x change in order to remain on the $f = 117$ contour curve?

$f(\underline{\hspace{1.5cm}}, 4.9) \approx 117$

Example 5: Approximating Change on a Contour Curve

$C(s, p)$ gives a salesman's commission (in hundred dollars) when he sells s standard and p premium car insurance policies each month.

a. Complete the following interpretations for the given notation.

    When the salesman sells _____ standard policies and _____ premium policies...

    $C(21,16) = 15$: ...his commission is

    $C_p(21,16) = 0.8$: ...his commission is

    $C_s(21,16) = 0.4$: ...his commission is

b. Suppose this month the salesman is unable sell 16 premium policies. He still hopes to make \$1500 of commission by selling more standard policies.

    Find the slope of the 15 (hundred dollar) contour curve at $(21,16)$ using the partial derivatives given in part *a*.

$$\left.\frac{ds}{dp}\right|_{(21,16)} = \left.\frac{-C_p}{C_s}\right|_{(21,16)} =$$

    If the salesman sells only 12 premium policies this represents a change of $\Delta p = -4$.

    Use this to find the change in s, the number of standard policies which must be sold to compensate for the change in p (the number of premium policies) for the commission to remain approximately \$1500.

$$\frac{\Delta s}{\Delta p} = \frac{ds}{dp} \text{ so, } \Delta s \approx \frac{ds}{dp}\Delta p$$

    The salesman must sell _____ more standard policies.

Example 6: Calculate the Slope of a Production Contour Curve

$Q(x, y) = 0.3x^{0.6}y^{0.4}$ thousand mattresses is the monthly production function for a plant where the inputs to production are x thousand labor hours and y thousand dollars of investment.

A plant can manufacture 3.96 thousand mattresses monthly with 10 thousand labor hours and 20 thousand dollars of investment.

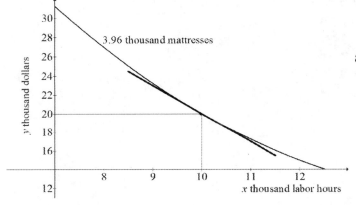

a. Calculate $\dfrac{dy}{dx}$ at the point $Q(10, 20)$ on the 3.96 thousand level contour curve. Include units.

Note: When finding derivatives <u>at a point</u> using the calculator, it is necessary to store the point into Solver <u>before</u> evaluating nDeriv.

b. Use the slope from above to estimate the **change** in capital needed if the plant **increases** the monthly labor force by 500 labor hours while keeping production constant at 3.96 thousand mattresses.

c. Amount of capital needed ≈ $_____ thousand.

d. If the plant intends to use $23,000 in capital investment, estimate how many labor hours will be required to produce 3.96 thousand mattresses.

    Amount of labor hours needed ≈ _____ thousand.

Example 7: Using Slope to Compensate for Change

The apparent temperature can be modeled as $A(h,t) = 2.70 + 0.885t - 78.7h + 1.20th$ F for an air temperature of t degrees Fahrenheit and a relative humidity of $100h$ %.

a. How hot does it feel when the relative humidity is 85% and the air temperature is 90 °F ?

b. Write a formula for $\dfrac{dh}{dt}$. Include units.

c. Use $\dfrac{dh}{dt}$ to approximate the change in the relative humidity that will compensate for a 2 °F increase in temperature if the apparent temperature is to remain constant.

d. Approximate the change in the temperature needed to compensate for a 2% decrease in humidity if the apparent temperature is to remain constant.

Example 8: Compensating for Change in Production Cost

The cost of having t-shirts printed depends on the number of colors in the design and the number of t-shirts ordered. A function giving the average cost per t-shirt when c colors are used and n t-shirts are ordered is

$$A(c,n) = \left(-.02c^2 + 0.35c + 0.99\right)\left(0.99897^n\right) + 0.46c + 2.57 \text{ dollars.} \qquad \text{Check: } A(2,200) = 4.800$$

a. Calculate the average cost per t-shirt when 250 shirts with 6 colors are ordered.

b. When 250 t-shirts with 6 colors are printed, how quickly is the average cost changing when more t-shirts are printed?

c. When 250 t-shirts with 6 colors are printed, how quickly is the average cost changing when more colors are used in the design?

d. Suppose the customer wanted to use 7 colors. If 250 t-shirts were ordered, what would be the average cost per shirt?

e. Suppose the customer wanted to use 7 colors, but wanted to keep the average cost per shirt about the same as the 6 color shirt in part a. How many more t-shirts would have to be ordered? Verify the answer.

Calculator Examples (Using a TI-84 Plus)

TI 7.4.1 Evaluating the slope of a tangent line at a point

- **Y=** Enter Q in Y_1

- **MATH 0** or **B** (Solver)

- ▲ Confirm that Y_1 is referenced in the equation 0 =

- ▼ Enter the values of X and Y

- **2ND MODE** to return to the homescreen

- Enter $\left.\dfrac{-Q_x}{Q_y}\right|_{(10,20)}$ using **MATH 8** (8: nDeriv)

- **ENTER** returns the slope of the tangent

Section 8.1: Extreme Points and Saddle Points

Single-variable functions can contain relative maxima and minima. Some multivariable functions contain similar points – relative maxima, relative minima, and saddle points.

Example 1: 3-Dimensional Graphs with Extrema or a Saddle Point

The output value of a point on a three-dimensional graph is a **relative minimum** if it is smaller than all of the output values around it and a **relative maximum** if it is larger than all of the output values around it.

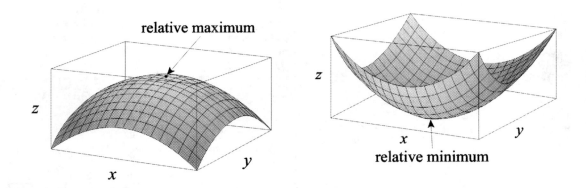

A **saddle** point is a point that corresponds to a relative maximum of a cross section in one direction (possibly diagonal to the input axes) and to a relative minimum of a cross section in another (possibly diagonal) direction.

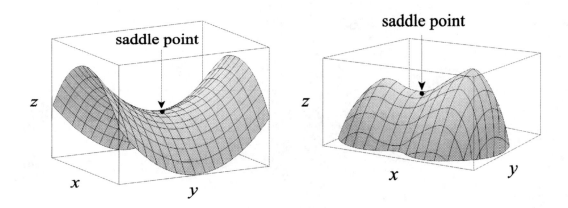

Example 2: Relative Extrema and Saddle Points on Contour Graphs

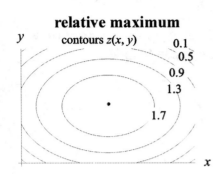

relative maximum

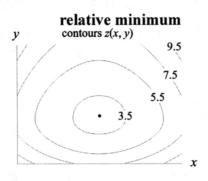

relative minimum

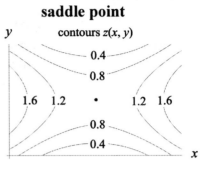

saddle point

Maximum value = _____   Minimum value = _____   Saddle Point value = _____

Example 3: Classifying Extrema and Saddle Points on a Contour Graph

The contour graph to the right has two relative extremes and a saddle point. Find and label the points A, B and C. classify the points.

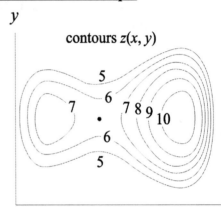

Point A is a _____

Point B is a _____

Point C is a _____

Note: Each relative extreme point and saddle point should be identified with two input values and the corresponding output value. There are two ways to notate this: function notation $f(x, y) = m$ or ordered triple notation $(x, y, f(x, y))$.

Example 4: Finding Input and Output Values for Relative Extrema and Saddle Points on a Contour Graph

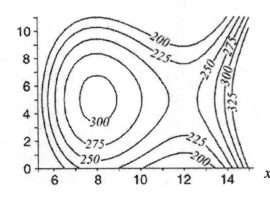

a. A relative _____ is located

at (_____ , _____ , _____).

b.. A saddle point is located at

$f(\underline{\hspace{1cm}} , \underline{\hspace{1cm}}) = \underline{\hspace{1cm}}$.

Example 5: Locating Relative Extrema and Saddle Points on a Table

On a table, an entry that is higher (or lower) than all eight of its neighboring entries is a **relative maximum** or **relative minimum**. **Contour curves** sketched on the table can help identify relative extreme points and saddle points.

Absolute extrema can be located *only within concentric closed contour curves* or *on terminal edges of a table or graph.*

Locating relative extrema on a table:

Sketch contour curves if they are not given.
Locate any candidates on terminal edges, if any terminal edges exist, and consider end behavior beyond nonterminal edges (could there be another column or row?)
Compare relative extrema, candidates on terminal edges, and limits of end behavior beyond nonterminal edges.

The table below gives the volume of a rectangular package that conforms to the maximum allowable measurements for printed material to receive the special bound printed-matter rate at the United States Postal Service. The depth of the box is fixed at 36 inches. What combination of height and width would give the largest shipping volume?

a. Sketch contours on the table at volumes of 8000, 10000, and 11000 cubic inches.

b. Locate the relative extreme point: The dimensions of the package with maximum volume

   has height_____ inches, width_____ inches, and volume_____ inches.

Height (inches)								
	3	6	9	12	15	18	21	24	27
3	864	1620	2268	2808	3240	3564	3780	3888	3888
6	1620	3024	4212	5184	5940	6480	6804	6912	6804
9	2268	4212	5832	7128	8100	8748	9072	9072	8748
12	2808	5184	7128	8640	9720	10,368	10,584	10,368	9720
15	3240	5940	8100	9720	10,800	11,340	11,340	10,800	9720
18	3564	6480	8748	10,368	11,340	11,664	11,340	10,368	8748
21	3780	6804	9072	10,584	11,340	11,340	10,584	9072	6804
24	3888	6912	9072	10,368	10,800	10,368	9072	6912	3888
27	3888	6804	8748	9720	9720	8748	6804	3888	0

Width (inches) (row axis label)

Example 6: Locating Extreme Points and Saddle Points on a Table with Contours and Terminal Edges

The table below shows a measure for the consistency of cheese spread as a function of the percentage of salt and the percentage of glycerol used in processing. All of the relative extreme points and saddle points lie within the region represented by the table.

Salt (%) \ Glycerol (%)	0	1	2	3	4	5	6	7	8	9	10
0.0	8028	6412	5078	4026	3256	2768	2562	2638	2996	3636	4558
0.3	9153	7593	6315	5319	4604	4172	4022	4154	4568	5263	6241
0.6	9953	8448	7226	6286	5627	5251	5156	5344	5814	6565	7599
1.0	10513	9083	7935	7069	6485	6183	6163	6425	6969	7795	8903
1.3	10553	9179	8087	7276	6748	6502	6538	6856	7455	8337	9501
1.6	10268	8950	7913	7159	6686	6496	6588	6961	7617	8554	9774
2.0	9382	8138	7176	6496	6098	5982	6148	6596	7326	8338	9632
2.3	8338	7150	6243	5619	5277	5217	5439	5942	6728	7796	9146
2.6	6968	5836	4985	4417	4131	4126	4404	4963	5805	6929	8334
3.0	4636	3578	2802	2308	2096	2166	2518	3152	4068	5266	6746
3.3	2507	1505	785	347	191	316	724	1414	2386	3640	5175

a. Mark and identify the saddle point in the table:

   % glycerol =_____, % salt =_____, measure for consistency =_____

This table has terminal edges of 0% glycerol and 0% salt.

b. Mark and classify the extreme point on the 0% glycerol terminal edge.

   % glycerol =_____, % salt =_____, measure for consistency =_____,

   The extreme point on the 0% glycerol terminal edge is a _____.

c. Mark and classify the extreme point on the 0% salt terminal edge.

   % glycerol =_____, % salt =_____, measure for consistency =_____,

   The extreme point on the 0% salt terminal edge is a _____.

Section 8.2: Multivariable Optimization

Relative extreme points on the graph of a continuous, differentiable, single-variable function occur at points where the tangent line is horizontal. The **first derivative** is used to locate relative extreme points and the **second derivative** is used to classify them as maxima or minima.

For functions with two input variables, critical points (relative extrema and saddle points) occur at points where the two first partial derivatives are equal to zero.

The y_0 cross-section: For f to have a relative maximum point at (x_0, y_0), the y_0 cross-sectional function must have a *relative maximum point* at x_0.
The slope of the line tangent to the cross-sectional function at the maximum is 0.

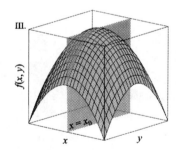
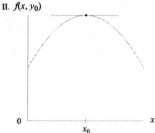

The x_0 cross-section: For f to have a relative maximum point at (x_0, y_0), the x_0 cross-sectional function must have a *relative maximum point* at y_0. The slope of the line tangent to the cross-sectional function at the maximum is 0.

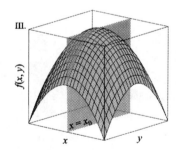
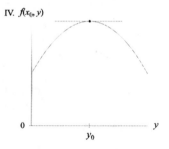

Similar illustrations indicate that for relative minima and saddle points, both partial derivatives are zero.

For a continuous function, f, with input variables x and y, a **critical point** of f occurs where the partial derivatives of f equal zero or fail to exist. For our purposes we will only consider functions for which first partial derivatives exist.

Example 1: Locating a Critical Point Algebraically

Locate the critical point of $f(x, y) = x^2 + 4xy + 3y^2 + 3x + 7y$ using algebra.

How to find the Critical Point of $f(x, y)$ Using Matrices

Matrices can be used if the first partial derivatives are linear.
An equation is linear if no variable has a power higher than 1 and there are no xy terms
For Example 1, the system of equations is

$\begin{aligned} 2x+4y &= -3 \\ 4x+6y &= -7 \end{aligned}$ which is equivalent to $\begin{bmatrix} 2 & 4 \\ 4 & 6 \end{bmatrix}\begin{bmatrix} x \\ y \end{bmatrix} = \begin{bmatrix} -3 \\ -7 \end{bmatrix}$

To Solve, $\begin{bmatrix} x \\ y \end{bmatrix} = \begin{bmatrix} 2 & 4 \\ 4 & 6 \end{bmatrix}^{-1}\begin{bmatrix} -3 \\ -7 \end{bmatrix} = \begin{bmatrix} \quad \end{bmatrix}$

Note # 1: it is possible to obtain the same solution when the order of the equations is reversed.

$\begin{aligned} 4x+6y &= -7 \\ 2x+4y &= -3 \end{aligned}$ which is equivalent to $\begin{bmatrix} 4 & 6 \\ 2 & 4 \end{bmatrix}\begin{bmatrix} x \\ y \end{bmatrix} = \begin{bmatrix} -7 \\ -3 \end{bmatrix}$

To Solve, $\begin{bmatrix} x \\ y \end{bmatrix} = \begin{bmatrix} 4 & 6 \\ 2 & 4 \end{bmatrix}^{-1}\begin{bmatrix} -7 \\ -3 \end{bmatrix} = \begin{bmatrix} \quad \end{bmatrix}$

Note # 2: it is also possible to obtain the same solution when the order of the x and y terms are reversed.

$\begin{aligned} 4y+2x &= -3 \\ 6y+4x &= -7 \end{aligned}$ which is equivalent to $\begin{bmatrix} 4 & 2 \\ 6 & 4 \end{bmatrix}\begin{bmatrix} y \\ x \end{bmatrix} = \begin{bmatrix} -3 \\ -7 \end{bmatrix}$

To Solve, $\begin{bmatrix} y \\ x \end{bmatrix} = \begin{bmatrix} 4 & 2 \\ 6 & 4 \end{bmatrix}^{-1}\begin{bmatrix} -3 \\ -7 \end{bmatrix} = \begin{bmatrix} \quad \end{bmatrix}$

Example 2: Locating a Critical Point in Context

At an assembly plant, the percentage of product that is flawed can be modeled as
$f(x,y) = 0.3x^2 - 1.8x + 0.1y^2 - 1.2y + 0.03xy + 6.5$ percent, where x is the average number of workers assigned concurrently to one assembly station and y is the average number of hours each worker spends on task during a shift, $1 \le x \le 5$ and $1 \le y \le 8$.   *Check:* $f(3,4) = .96$

a. Write the two partial derivatives of f.

   $f_x =$

   $f_y =$

b. Find the number of workers and the shift length will optimize quality.
    Step 1: Set up the system of equations to be solved.

   $f_x = 0$:

   $f_y = 0$:

   Step 2: Solve the system of equations using matrices.

c. What percentage of product will be flawed when quality is optimized?

Example 3: Verifying the Nature of the Critical Point in Example 2

In Example 2, the context suggested that the optimal point would minimize flawed product. Use the Determinant Test to classify the optimal point.

The Determinant Test: The **second partials matrix** is a square matrix formed by labeling the rows and the columns with the input variables (in the same order) and writing the second partial derivatives found by taking the derivative of the function with respect to the row variable and then the column variable.

Let $f(x, y)$ be a continuous multivariable function. Let (a,b) be the input for a point at which the first partial derivatives of f are both 0. The determinant of the second partials matrix evaluated at the input (a,b) is

$$D(a,b) = \begin{vmatrix} f_{xx} & f_{xy} \\ f_{yx} & f_{yy} \end{vmatrix}_{(a,b)} = \left[f_{xx}f_{yy} - f_{xy}f_{yx} \right]_{(a,b)}$$

If $D(a,b) > 0$ and $f_{xx}(a,b) < 0$, then f has a relative maximum at (a,b).

If $D(a,b) > 0$ and $f_{xx}(a,b) > 0$, then f has a relative minimum at (a,b).

If $D(a,b) < 0$, f has a saddle point at (a,b).

If $D(a,b) = 0$, the test does not given any information about (a,b).

---

a. Use the information in the box to complete the following:
   If $D(a,b)$ is zero, then the point is _____ ;
   If $D(a,b)$ is negative, then the point is _____ ;
   If $D(a,b)$ is positive, then the point is _____ ;
   If $D(a,b)$ is positive and $f_{xx}(a,b)$ is positive, then the point is _____ ;
   If $D(a,b)$ is positive and $f_{xx}(a,b)$ is negative, then the point is _____ .

b. Classify the critical point found in Example 2. Be specific.
   The first partial derivatives were: $f_x = 0.6x + 0.03y - 1.8$ and $f_y = 0.03x + 0.2y - 1.2$

   Find the second partials matrix (ORDER IS IMPORTANT)

   Find the determinant of the second partials matrix at the critical point. Then classify this point. Use specific values in your justification.

   The critical point is a _____ because:

   • _____ and (if necessary)

   • _____ .

Example 4: Classifying a Point when the Partials are Not Linear

The function $f(x,y) = 3x^2 - x^3 + 12y^2 - 8y^3 + 60$ has four critical points.

One of them is (0, 1, 64). Classify this point. Use specific values in your justification.

The critical point is a _____ because:

(1)_____ and (if necessary) (2) _____

The three remaining critical points are $(0,0,60)$, (2, 1, 68) and (2, 0, 64). Classify these points.

Example 5: Maximizing Cake Volume

The volume index of a cake provides a measure of how much the cake rises. An index of 100 corresponds to the volume of the batter.

The index can be modeled as $V(r,m) = -3.1r^2 + 22.4r - 0.1m^2 + 5.3m$ percent when r grams of leavening are used and the cake is baked at 177°C for m minutes. *Check:* $V(5,20) = 100.5$

a. Write the two partial derivatives of V .

b. Show the system of equations that must be solved to find the critical point.

c. Find the maximum volume possible and the conditions needed to achieve that volume.

d. Use the determinant test to verify that the point found in part c is in fact a maximum.

e. Complete the sentence of interpretation of the relative maximum of V .

The _____ volume index of _____ % can be obtained by using _____ grams

of leavening in the cake batter and baking the cake for _____ minutes at a temperature of

177°C.

Example 6: Online Marketing

$R(t, p) = 12,000 - t^2 - 2pt - 2p^2 + 200t + 260p$ dollars gives the revenue of an internet site where p is the number of pop-up advertisements that appear during a 30-minute online session and t is the number of months the site has been in operation. *Check: $R(6,5) = 14354$*

a. Write the system of equations that can be used to find the critical point.

b. Find the critical point.

c. Find the 2nd partials matrix at the critical point and find the determinant.

d. Classify the critical point using the determinant test.

e. Interpret the critical point:

The revenue of an internet site which has been operational for _____ months is

_____ at $ _____ when _____ pop-up advertisements appear

during a 30-minute on-line session.

Calculator Example (Using a TI-84 Plus)

TI 8.2.1 Solving a system of linear equations using matrices

Step 1: Arrange the terms so that variables and constants appear in the same order in each equation and the right side of the equation = 0

$$f_x = 0.6x - 1.8 + 0.03y = 0 \qquad 0.6x + 0.03y = 1.8$$
$$f_y = 0.2y - 1.2 + 0.03x = 0 \qquad 0.03x + 0.2y = 1.2$$

Step 2: Set up the system of matrices $[A][X] = [B]$ where

$$[A] = \begin{bmatrix} 0.6 & 0.03 \\ 0.03 & 0.2 \end{bmatrix}, \ [X] = \begin{bmatrix} x \\ y \end{bmatrix}, \text{ and } [B] = \begin{bmatrix} 1.8 \\ 1.2 \end{bmatrix}$$

Step 3: Solve: $[X] = [A]^{-1}[B]$

- **2ND X⁻¹** (MATRIX) ▶ ▶ (Edit) **ENTER** ([A])
- Enter the dimensions of the matrix **2** (rows) ▶ **2** (columns)
- **.6 ENTER .03 ENTER .03 ENTER .2 ENTER**
- **2ND X⁻¹** (MATRIX) ▶ ▶ (Edit) ▼ ([B]) **ENTER**
- **2** (rows) ▶ **1** (columns)

- **1.8 1.2**

- **2ND MODE** [QUIT]

- **2ND X⁻¹ 1** ([A]) **X⁻¹ 2ND X⁻¹ 2** ([B])

- **ENTER** returns the solution

  ➢ $x = 2.720, y = 5.592$

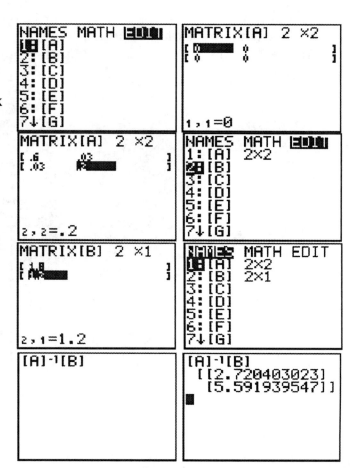

Alternate method using reduced row echelon form

Step 1: Arrange the terms so that variables and constants appear in the same order in each equation and the right side of the equation = 0

$$f_x = 0.6x - 1.8 + 0.03y = 0 \quad\quad 0.6x + 0.03y = 1.8$$
$$\quad\quad\quad\quad\quad\quad\quad\quad\quad\quad\quad\rightarrow$$
$$f_y = 0.2y - 1.2 + 0.03x = 0 \quad\quad 0.03x + 0.2y = 1.2$$

Step 2: Matrix [A] is written as $\begin{bmatrix} 0.6 & 0.03 & 1.8 \\ 0.03 & 0.2 & 1.2 \end{bmatrix}$

Step 3: The system is solved as rref[A]

- **2ND X⁻¹** (MATRIX) ▶ ▶ (Edit) **ENTER** ([A])
- Enter the dimensions of the matrix **2** (rows) ▶ **3** (columns)
- Enter the values

- **2ND MODE** [QUIT]
- **2ND X⁻¹** (MATRIX) ▶ (MATH) ▼ to **B** (rref())
- **ENTER**

- **2ND X⁻¹** (MATRIX) **1** [A]
- **ENTER)**

- **ENTER** returns the solution

  ➢ $x = 2.720, y = 5.592$

Section 8.3: Optimization under a Constraint

Constrained optimization is the process of determining the maximum (or minimum) output value of a multivariable function when there are restrictions placed on the input values that can be used. As an example, a manufacturer trying to optimize revenue from the sales of a product, may be constrained by production capability.

The 3-dimensional view of Graph I function f with input variables x and y shown below has an unconstrained maximum occurring at $f(3,7) = 100$. Graph II shows a constraint function $g(x,y) = x - y = 3$. The highest contour that the constraint touches is between 60 and 80.

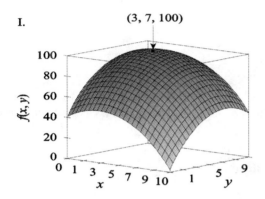
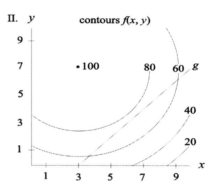

If the only input points allowed are those where $g(x,y) = 3$, as in Graph II, shown to the *right*, the original critical point is no longer feasible.

Under the constraint, f will have a different optimum, referred to as the *constrained optimum*. The constrained optimum is estimated by drawing an additional curve tangent to g *and* estimating the x, y, and f values at the constrained optimum point. *The point (x,y) must satisfy the g constraint.*

Example 1: Finding and Classifying a Constrained Optimal Point.

Refer to Graph II above. Estimate the values of x, y and f at the optimal point. Classify the point. Explain how this classification was determined.

Example 2: Locating an Optimal Point with a Constraint (graphically)

The function $f(x,y)$ has an optimal point of 100. A constraint, $g(x,y) = x + 1.5y = 8.5$ is shown. *Under the constraint*, the maximum obtainable value is on the 22 contour.

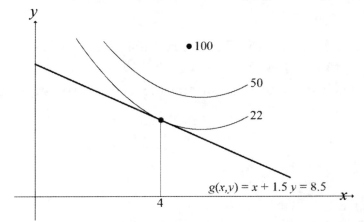

Given that $x = 4$, use the constraint to find the y – value. The point MUST be on the constraint.

Evaluate f at this point: $f(4, \_\_\_\_\_) = \_\_\_\_$ is a constrained _____.

The **optimal point** $f(x, y)$ subject to the constraint $g(x, y) = c$, is the point on the contour graph of f where the constraint curve $g(x, y) = c$ is tangent to the contour curve $f(x, y) = m$. The constant m is the optimal output subject to the constraint.

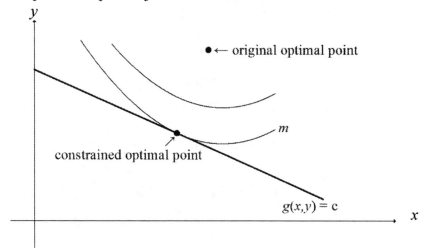

The slope of the tangent line at a constrained optimal point can be calculated using either the function f or the constraint function g.

For a function $f(x, y)$ and constraint function $g(x, y)$, the slope of the tangent line at the optimal point can be calculated as either $\dfrac{dy}{dx} = \dfrac{-g_x}{g_y}$ or $\dfrac{dy}{dx} = \dfrac{-f_x}{f_y}$.

Rearranging the equation $\dfrac{-f_x}{f_y} = \dfrac{-g_x}{g_y}$ gives the Lagrange Multiplier: $\dfrac{f_x}{g_x} = \dfrac{f_y}{g_y} = \lambda$.

The Lagrange Multiplier is used to estimate the change in the output of the function that would result from a small change in the constraint.

To find the constrained optimal point, set up and solve the system of three equations and three unknowns which will solve for x, y and λ at the constrained optimal point.

$$f_x = \lambda g_x$$
$$f_y = \lambda g_y$$
$$g(x, y) = c$$

Example 3: Solving for a Constrained Optimal Solution

In Example 6 of Section 8.2, the following function was optimized:

$$f(x, y) = 12,000 - x^2 - 2xy - 2y^2 + 200x + 260y.$$

The system of equations used to solve the problem was

$$P_x = -2x - 2y + 200 = 0 \qquad -2x - 2y = -200$$
$$P_y = -2x - 4y + 260 = 0 \qquad \rightarrow \qquad -2x - 4y = -260$$

The matrices used in the solution of this system of equations are:

$$\begin{bmatrix} x \\ y \end{bmatrix} = \begin{bmatrix} -2 & -2 \\ -2 & -4 \end{bmatrix}^{-1} \begin{bmatrix} -200 \\ -260 \end{bmatrix} = \begin{bmatrix} 70 \\ 30 \end{bmatrix}$$

The optimal solution is $x = 70$, $y = 30$, $f(x,y) = 22,900$.

Now consider the constraint $g(x, y) = 2x + 3y = 190$. Find the optimal point of $f(x, y)$ subject to the constraint $g(x, y)$.

a. Find the following partial derivatives:

$f_x =$ $g_x =$

$f_y =$ $g_y =$

b. To solve the constrained system of equations, the following three equations must be satisfied.

$$f_x = \lambda g_x$$
$$f_y = \lambda g_y$$
$$g(x, y) = c$$

The solution of the constrained system is $x =$ _____, $y =$ _____, $\lambda =$ _____ $f(x,y) =$ _____.

Example 4: Classifying a Constrained Optimal Point

Not every solution to this system is guaranteed to be an optimal point of the constrained system. Once a solution is found, it is necessary to verify the type of point found graphically or numerically.

Numerically verify that the solution found in Example 3 is a constrained maximum. Use the constraint function $g(x, y) = 2x + 3y = 190$ to determine the corresponding y-values.

3 points:	x values, *choose the close points*	y values, *solve the constraint to find the y-values at the close points*	$f(x, y)$
Close point in one direction	61.5		
Optimal point	62	22	22,580
Close point in the opposite direction	63		

Conclusion: (62, 22, 22580) is a _____ .

Example 5: Interpreting Lambda (λ)

λ is the rate of change of the extreme value with respect to the constraint level c: $\lambda = \dfrac{dm}{dc}$.

If the constraint level c is increased by one unit, the extreme value m of the function changes by approximately λ units.

The **units** for lambda are the output units of the function being optimized per output unit of the constraint.

When the level of the constraint changes by a small amount, Δc, the extreme value m changes by $\Delta m = \Delta c \left(\dfrac{dm}{dc} \right) = \Delta c(\lambda)$.

The value of lambda for the above constrained optimization problem is 16.

Complete the following:

If the constraint is increased by 1, then the optimal value will increase by _____ to _____ .

If the constraint is decreased by 0.5, then the optimal value will decrease by _____ to _____ .

Example 6: Optimization of Production

A monthly production function for a certain mattress-manufacturing plant is $f(x, y) = 0.3x^{0.6}y^{0.4}$ thousand mattresses where x is thousand hours worked and y is the amount of money invested, in thousands of dollars. The budget constraint equation is $g(x, y) = 18x + y = 200$.

The solution to the Lagrange system is $x = 6\frac{2}{3}$, $y = 80$, and $\lambda \approx 0.03$.

Complete the table to classify the critical point.

3 points:	x values, *solve the constraint to find the x-values*	y -values, *choose close points*	$g(x, y)$	$f(x, y)$
Close point 1		79.5		
Optimal point	6.67	80		
Close point 2		80.5		

Conclusion: ($6^2/_3$, 80 _____) is a _____.

The value of lambda for the above constrained optimization is approximately 0.03 thousand mattresses per thousand dollars.

Complete the following:

a. If the budget is increased from $200,000 to $201,000, then the optimal value will change

by _____ to _____.

b. If the budget is decreased from $200,000 to $199,000, then the optimal value will change

by _____ to _____.

c. If the budget is increased from $200,000 to $205,000, then the optimal value will change

by _____ to _____.

d. If the budget is decreased from $200,000 to $197,000, then the optimal value will change

by _____ to _____.

Example 7: Constrained Optimization in Context

$P(h,s) = 2s^2 + 8s - h^2 + 2h - 8hs + 1000$ gives the daily production cost in dollars at a plant where s is the number of hours Robot S works and h is the number of hours that Robot H works.

The owner of the plant has decided that Robot H and Robot S are allowed to work only a combined total of 12 hours.

a. Write the constraint function $g\,(h,\ s)$ that represents this limitation.

b. Find the four partial derivatives of $P\,(h,\ s)$ and $g\,(h,\ s)$.

   $P_h =$ $g_h =$

   $P_s =$ $g_s =$

c. Find the constrained optimal point.

d. Classify the optimal point as a maximum or minimum. *Remember the test points must satisfy the constraint $h + s = 12$.*

close-point method	h	s	$P(h,s)$
test point			
optimal point			
test point			

Conclusion:

e. What is λ? What are the units on λ?

f. Write a sentence of interpretation for λ.

g. If there is only enough money in the budget for the robots to work a combined total of 11.5 hours instead of 12 hours a day, estimate how much the optimal cost would change. Estimate the new optimal cost as a result of this change.

Calculator Example (Using a TI-84 Plus)

TI 8.3.1 Solving a system of linear equations using matrices

Step 1: The system of equations $\begin{cases} y+1=\lambda(1) \\ x+2=\lambda(1.5) \\ x+1.5y=8.5 \end{cases}$ is rewritten as $\begin{cases} 0x+1y-1\lambda=-1 \\ 1x+0y-1.5\lambda=-2 \\ x+1.5y+0\lambda=8.5 \end{cases}$

Step 2: The matrices $[A][X]=[B]$ are written as $\begin{bmatrix} 0 & 1 & -1 \\ 1 & 0 & -1.5 \\ 1 & 1.5 & 0 \end{bmatrix}\begin{bmatrix} x \\ y \\ \lambda \end{bmatrix}=\begin{bmatrix} -1 \\ -2 \\ 8.5 \end{bmatrix}$

Step 3: The system is solved as $[X]=[A]^{-1}[B]$

- 2ND X^{-1} (MATRIX) ▶ ▶ (Edit)
  ENTER ([A])
- Enter the dimensions of the matrix **3** (rows) ▶ **3** (columns)
- Enter the values
- 2ND X^{-1} (MATRIX) ▶ ▶ (Edit)
  ▼ ([B]) **ENTER**
- **3** (rows) ▶ **1** (column)
- Enter the values
- **2ND** **MODE** [QUIT]
- **2ND** **X⁻¹** **1** ([A]) **X⁻¹** **2ND** **X⁻¹** **2** ([B])
- **ENTER**

```
NAMES  MATH  EDIT
1■[A]
2:[B]
3:[C]
4:[D]
5:[E]
6:[F]
7↓[G]
```

```
MATRIX[A]  3 ×3
[ 0      1      -1    ]
[ 1      0      -1.5  ]
[ 1      1.5    0     ]


3,3=0
```

```
NAMES  MATH  EDIT
1: [A]  3×3
2■[B]  2×1
3: [C]
4: [D]
5: [E]
6: [F]
7↓[G]
```

```
MATRIX[B]  3 ×1
[ -1  ]
[ -2  ]
[ 8.5 ]


3,1=8.5
```

```
[A]⁻¹[B]
```

```
[A]⁻¹[B]
          [[4]
           [3]
           [4]]
```

Alternate method using reduced row echelon form

Step 1: The system of equations $\begin{cases} y+1=\lambda(1) \\ x+2=\lambda(1.5) \\ x+1.5y=8.5 \end{cases}$ is rewritten as $\begin{cases} 0x+1y-1\lambda=-1 \\ 1x+0y-1.5\lambda=-2 \\ x+1.5y+0\lambda=8.5 \end{cases}$

Step 2: Matrix [A] is written as $\begin{bmatrix} 0 & 1 & -1 & -1 \\ 1 & 0 & -1.5 & -2 \\ 1 & 1.5 & 0 & 8.5 \end{bmatrix}$

Step 3: The system is solved as rref[A]

- **2ᴺᴰ X⁻¹** (MATRIX) ▶ ▶ (Edit) **ENTER** ([A])
- Enter the dimensions of the matrix **3** (rows) ▶ **4** (columns)
- Enter the values

- **2ND MODE** [QUIT]
- **2ND X⁻¹** (MATRIX) ▶ (MATH) ▼ to **B** (rref())

- **ENTER**
- **2ND X⁻¹** (MATRIX) **1** [A]

- **ENTER)**
- **ENTER**

```
NAMES MATH EDIT
1▮[A]
2:[B]
3:[C]
4:[D]
5:[E]
6:[F]
7↓[G]
```

```
MATRIX[A] 3 ×4
[ 0    1    -1    ]
[ 1    0    -1.5  ]
[ 1    1.5   0    ]
```

```
MATRIX[A] 3 ×4
[ .5    -1    -1    ]
[ 0    -1.5   -2    ]
[-1.5    0    8.5   ]

1,2=1
```

```
NAMES MATH EDIT
6↑randM(
7:augment(
8:Matr▶list(
9:List▶matr(
0:cumSum(
A:ref(
B▮rref(
```

```
rref(
```

```
NAMES MATH EDIT
1▮[A]  3×4
2:[B]
3:[C]
4:[D]
5:[E]
6:[F]
7↓[G]
```

```
rref([A])
```

```
rref([A])
    [[1 0 0 4]
     [0 1 0 3]
     [0 0 1 4]]
```

TI 8.3.2 Determining the nature of the solution to the Lagrange system

- In Y1, enter **.3^X Y^.4**
- ▼ In Y2, enter **18X +Y -200**
- Go to the EQUATION SOLVER (**MATH 0**) verify that Y1 is the equation

- **ENTER** (or ▼)changes screens so that the values X = **6.666** and Y = **80** are stored in the calculator
- Return to the Homescreen, **Y1** **ENTER** returns the optimum value
- ➤ $f(6.666, 80) \approx 5.4038$ is a critical point
- Go back to the EQUATION SOLVER, use ▲ to return to the page shown to the right and change the equation to 0 = **Y2**

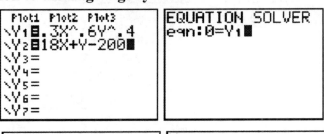

```
Plot1 Plot2 Plot3
\Y1◼.3X^.6Y^.4
\Y2◼18X+Y-200◼
\Y3=
\Y4=
\Y5=
\Y6=
\Y7=
```

```
EQUATION SOLVER
eqn:0=Y1◼
```

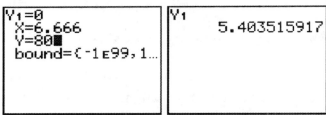

```
Y1=0
X=6.666
Y=80◼
bound={-1ᴇ99,1...
```

```
Y1
        5.403515917
```

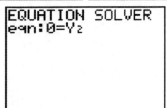

```
EQUATION SOLVER
eqn:0=Y2
```

- **ENTER** (or ▾) changes screens so that the close value for *y*: Y = **79.5** can be stored in the calculator
- ▴ ENTER solves the constraint equation for *x*, given that *y* = 79.5

- Return to the Homescreen, **Y1 ENTER** returns the close value, $f(79.5) \approx 5.403769693$
- Repeat the previous 4 bulleted steps to evaluate $f(80.5) \approx 5.403769889$

➤ The constrained optimal point, $f(x, y) = f(6.666, 80) \approx 5.4038$ is verified to be a constrained maximum because close points on either side of the optimal point have lower output values.